MECHANIX ILLUSTRATED
HOW-TO-DO-IT
ENCYCLOPEDIA

Edited by the Combined Staffs of MECHANIX ILLUSTRATED
FAWCETT BOOKS and ELECTRONICS ILLUSTRATED

IN SIXTEEN VOLUMES

COMPLETE CONTENTS
AND INDEX IN VOLUME 16

VOLUME 10

No part of the text or illustrations in this encyclopedia may be used without the written permission of Fawcett Publications, Inc. All rights reserved under Pan-American Copyright Convention and the International Copyright Convention.

COPYRIGHT 1961 FAWCETT PUBLICATIONS, INC.

Well-known reader services of Mechanix Illustrated are extended to readers of this encyclopedia to the extent of blueprint and plan offerings as indicated throughout the various volumes. Inquiries relating to such services and communications regarding the editorial material in this encyclopedia should be directed to Fawcett Publications, Inc., Encyclopedia Service, 67 West 44th Street, New York 36, N. Y. Printed in the United States of America.

GOLDEN PRESS • NEW YORK

HOUSE PLANTS

Let There Be Light

Aage Moller

Use foliage plants in windows that receive little or no direct sunshine. Shown are aralia, ivy, etc.

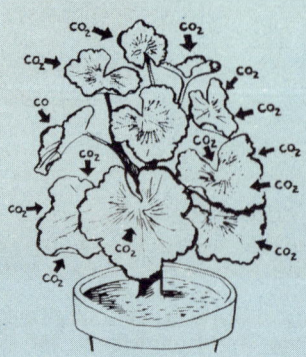

Cutaway shows complex roots which take in water.

Each leaf draws carbon dioxide (CO_2) from the air.

ALL house plants require light, but not all need the same amount. Ferns, bromeliads, palms, philodendrons, sansevierias, rex begonias, and indeed most foliage plants get along perfectly well in subdued light and usually respond unfavorably to strong sunshine. A few highly colored foliage plants such as crotons and coleus, as well as most gray-leaved plants, need full sun. Sun-lovers, too, are most cactuses and succulent and many flowering plants such as geraniums, abutilons, agapanthuses and wax begonias. Between the extremes of the cactus that needs full sun and the maranta that thrives better without any direct sunshine are a variety of plants from which kinds can be chosen for all intermediate conditions.

When considering light requirements for your plants, bear in mind the following points. Many that need shade in summer prefer full sun in winter. Light in cities is often more subdued than country light because of smoke and dust particles in the air. Light indoors is much less intense than outdoors and rapidly diminishes as one retreats from the window. Curtains and drapes cut down light very markedly.

South facing windows afford plants the maximum amount of light, north facing windows the least. This holds true, of course, only if the light is unimpeded. A south window with a tree growing outside

Palms, philodendrons, dumb-canes, prayer plants will survive in a room which gets very little sun.
Roy F. Wilcox Co.

HOUSE PLANTS
Irving Kaufman Studios
Only foliage plants may be used in dark corners like this and even they will need replacement.

it or with a nearby wall facing it may let in less light than an unshadowed east, west, or north window. East and west windows are sunny enough for a great variety of plants.

Bay windows and corner windows are usually particularly good locations for plants because they receive light from more than one side. Sun rooms and sun porches, too, are lighter than ordinary rooms and hence are well suited for plant growth. The most difficult places in which to persuade plants to grow are locations away from windows in comparatively dark areas of the room, on mantel shelves for example. Only the toughest subjects such as snake plants, aspidistras, fatshederas, and English ivy can be expected to live with so little light and even they may not succeed indefinitely. It may be necessary to discard and replace them from time to time or to arrange a rotation system whereby they stay two, three, or four weeks in the dark location and then are removed to a window where they remain for a like period.

Of one thing you must be careful: never move a plant from a dark location to a bright, sunny place directly. If you do it will react much as a person does who has been much indoors and then is exposed to strong sunshine. It will suffer from sunburn. In plants this manifests itself either by scalded areas (which dry, turn brown and die) appearing on the leaves whereever the maximum sun strikes them, or by an all-over yellowing of the foliage except where it is shaded by other leaves. To avoid this, shade the plants moved from dark locations to sunny ones by throwing a layer or two of cheesecloth over them or use some other way wherever the sun is bright. Do this for a week or two after making the move.

To a certain extent natural light can, with advantage, be supplemented by artificial illumination. Some plants, notably African violets, geraniums, and begonias

Every green leaf manufactures sugar from hydrogen in water and carbon in the carbon dioxide.

respond well to light from either incandescent or fluorescent light bulbs. So complete is this response in the case of African violets that it is possible to grow good specimens entirely by electric illumination without the aid of daylight at all, and this is probably true of certain other plants. However, not all kinds show improvement

1731

HOUSE PLANTS

Irving Kaufman Studios

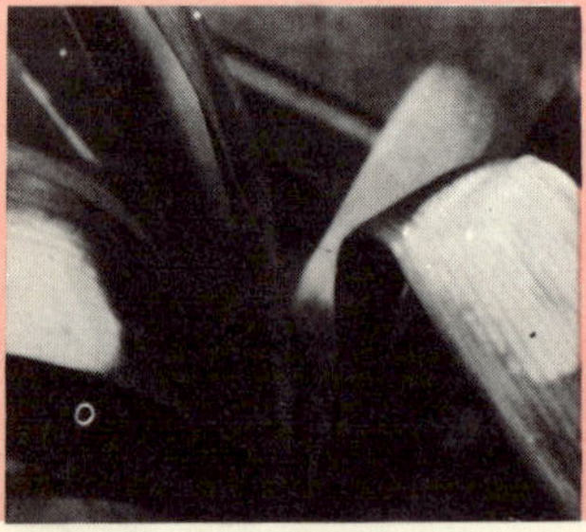

Upper left photo shows philodendron and sedum under a lamp. This helps growth.

Sugar formation or photosynthesis takes place only in light (see drawing above).

Sugar, changed to protein, fat, starch, etc., makes possible growth of the plant at right.

Many plants are harmed by too much sun. Leaves at left and below are scorched.

when subjected to artificial illumination. Some respond better to fluorescent light than to light from Mazda bulbs; others the reverse.

The use of electric light to supplement daylight is really a matter for experiment. Try it by all means and draw your own conclusions from the tests you make. Be careful not to put your plants so near the source of the light that they suffer from too high temperatures or from excessive dryness of the air. Remember, too, that if you lengthen the day by providing illumination during hours of natural darkness you may play tricks with the flowering habits of your plants. Some kinds (here belong poinsettias and chrysanthemums) must have a comparatively long period of darkness each night to produce flower buds, other kinds need long days and short nights to bloom satisfactorily, the flowering periods of yet other house plants seem to be unaffected by the length of the day provided. You may, then, use artificial illumination to provide additional light on dull days during daylight hours or to increase the length of the day by providing light at night, or both. This affords a fascinating field for experiment by the indoor gardener.

Plants that do not get enough light usually proclaim the fact by producing pale, anemic-looking leaves, that are smaller than normal. Their leaf stalks and stems become weak and stretch toward the light. The distances between leaves on the stem increases and the whole plant takes on a lankier appearance. Plants that become "drawn" in this way are much more likely to become diseased than are sturdier specimens grown with ample illumination. This is particularly true of young seedlings. Damping-off disease can wipe out great numbers of these in the space of a very few hours. Weakening and "drawing" of the seedlings because of poor light is one of the commonest predisposing conditions to damping-off infections. •

HOUSE PLANTS

The leaves of this maranta curl because the light is too strong.

When plants get light from one direction their stems are apt to bend to that side.

Ageratum stems are "drawn" by too little light.

Too much sun has made this clivia, at right, droop.

PLANTS FOR SUNNY PLACES

These plants need plenty of sunshine. They grow best in southern exposures but may be cultivated in east- or west-facing windows provided they receive a few hours' direct sunshine daily.

For Cool Conditions: agathaea, ageratum, babiana, bleeding heart, cactuses and succulents in variety, calendula, calla lily, Campanula isophylla, cape-cowslip, Christmas cherry, chrysanthemums, cineraria, crocuses, cyclamen, daffodils, Easter lily, flowering-maple, flowering tobacco, forget-me-not, freesia, geraniums, heather, heliotrope, hyacinths, hydrangeas, ixia, Jasminum primulinum, kumquats, lemons, lily-of-the-Nile, lily-of-the-valley, marigold, Martha Washington geranium, narcissuses, nasturtium, oranges, oxalis, Paris daisy, primroses, spiraeas, star of Bethlehem, sweet alyssum, torenia, tulips, and veltheimia.

For Warm Conditions: amaryllis, artillery plant, black-eyed Susan vine, bloodleaf, cactuses and succulents in variety, chenille plant, coleus, crabs eye vine, croton, crown of thorns, hibiscus, kalanchoe, lantana, poinsettia, rouge plant, shrimp plant, tibouchina, velvet plant and wax begonia.

PLANTS FOR PARTIAL SHADE

These plants need some sunshine. Give them all possible from November to February inclusive, and early morning or late afternoon sun at other seasons. Shade them from very strong sun. They are well adapted for east windows and for west windows if they are curtained or otherwise lightly shaded against strong early afternoon sun.

For Cool Conditions: achimenes, asparagus ferns, aucuba, Australian silk-oak, azalea, babys-tears, camellia, clivia, coprosma, crinum-lilies, daphne, English ivy, fuchsia, German-ivy, ground-ivy, kangaroo vine, Kenilworth-ivy, leopard plant, lily turf, Norfolk Island pine, pick-a-back plant, pittosporum, podocarpus, serissa, skimmia, spider plant, strawberry begonia, sweet laurel, sweet olive, Osmanthus Delavayi and vinca.

For Warm Conditions: African violets, Amazon-lily, amorphophallus, anthurium, ardisia, begonias, bromeliads, caladiums, gloxinias, hydrosme, jacobinia, marica, patience plant, rosary vine, twelve apostles, wandering Jew, and wax plant.

PLANTS FOR SHADY PLACES

These plants will grow without any direct sunshine. They do need good light for their best development and are not harmed by weak sunshine. Those marked with an asterisk withstand poor light conditions best.

For Cool Conditions: *Aucuba, *creeping fig, *English ivy, ferns in variety, *lily turf, pick-a-back plant, *skimmia, strawberry begonia, sweet laurel, sweet bay, and vinca.

For Warm Conditions: *aglaeonema, *Chinese evergreen, dracaenas, *dumb-canes, ferns in variety, *fiddle leaf fig, fittonia, grape ivy, *India rubber, *maranta, *palms, pandanus, peperomia, *philodendrons, *schismatoglottis, *scindapsus, *snake plant, watermelon pilea.

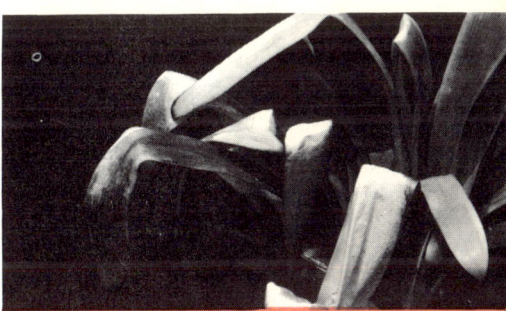

Plants shown above and below vary in their sunshine requirements (see chart at left). You can make hyacinths taller by shading in early stages.

HOUSE PLANTS

Heat versus Cold

The lower leaves of this dumb-cane are drooping because it has been exposed to low temperatures. Plant will die if not moved to warmer location.

PLANTS vary in their temperature requirements. Some like it hot, others need cooler conditions. The same plant may require different temperatures at different stages of its growth as do, for example, daffodils, hyacinths, and tulips which thrive best if kept cool until plenty of roots have grown from their bulbs, then respond to more heat.

Excessive temperatures produced artificially do more harm than the same temperatures resulting from sun heat. This is because artificial heating lowers the relative humidity of the air to where it is often quite difficult to compensate for, and because at the time of the year when the furnace is running, days are shorter and light intensities are lower than during the warmer season. Under these conditions plants naturally need to be kept cooler than during the summer.

To illustrate what I mean, consider camellias. In summertime, out of doors they thrive where day temperatures of eighty degrees and higher are fairly common and where night temperatures do not drop much below daytime levels. Yet it is fatal to attempt to grow them in winter in a living room where the thermometer registers seventy or seventy-two degrees. The air is too dry and, for that time of the year, the temperature is too high. In winter indoor camellias need the shelter only of a light porch or similar place where the temperature is kept between forty and fifty degrees and where the air is normally moist.

This matter of seasonal variation in the temperature needs of plants you must take into account. It varies with different kinds. Those that are natives of low elevations in the tropics such as dumb-canes, snake plants, philodendrons and the like get along perfectly well with no marked change from season to season but plants that have their natural homes in more northerly or more southerly latitudes or that come from high elevations in the tropics ordinarily need comparatively low temperatures during our fall and winter. Here belong azaleas, Norfolk Island pine, Kenilworth ivy, English ivy, leopard plant, and asparagus ferns.

The above mentioned plants are all evergreen. There are others that lose their leaves during a part of each year—some including gloxinias, tuberous begonias, and amaryllis in winter—others such as poinsettias and calla lilies in summer. When they are without foliage these plants rest; while resting they need to be kept fairly cool. Too high temperatures during the dormant season may cause shrivelling of the bulbs, may excite premature growth, and may prevent the plants from blooming the following season.

All plants grow better when nights are cooler than days. That is how it is in na-

1734

HOUSE PLANTS

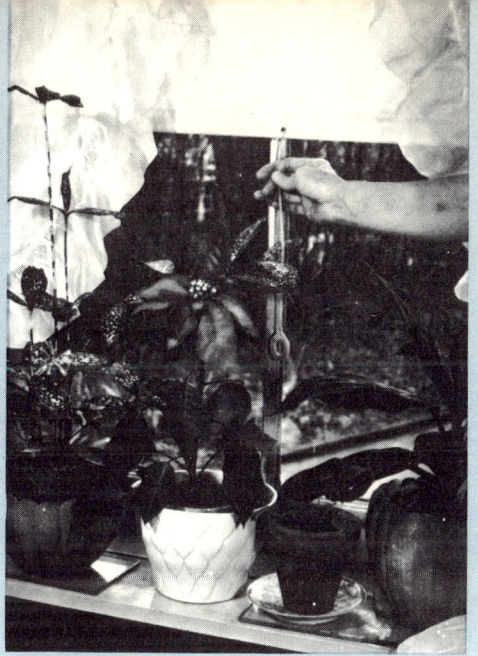

Temperature close to a window may drop quite low during the winter. Pulling down the shade will afford considerable protection for your plants.

On very cold nights or during cold spells, add a few sheets of newspaper or cardboard as insulation between window and plants. Check thermometer.

ture; that is how it works best with cultivated specimens. A good general rule is to have the temperature at night five to ten degrees below that of normal days. On very sunny days a rise of five or ten degrees above normal is permissible for plants growing in direct sunshine.

Greenhouse men carefully adjust their day and night temperatures to suit the needs of their plants. In the home it is not easy to do this. We heat our houses to suit our own needs and comfort, the requirements of plants take second place. Yet much can be done.

In the first place study the different locations in the home. Some rooms are certainly cooler than others and, equally important, locations in the same room may vary tremendously in the matter of temperature. Positions close to radiators and other sources of dry heat are particularly distressing to plants.

But excessive heat is not all that you must guard against. Cold can be quite as harmful. Do not fool yourself because a thermometer hanging on an inside wall indicates a comfortable seventy degrees that a plant close to a window in the same room is living in that temperature. When it is cold outdoors the indoor temperature near the glass may be twenty degrees or more lower than in other parts of the room. The only sure way of learning just what temperatures prevail where your plants are or where you consider placing them is to put a thermometer there and watch it at different times of the day and night over a period. The results may surprise you.

No house plants suffer from cold if the temperature doesn't drop below sixty. A few, such as African violets, poinsettias, and florists' gardenias, show ill effects then, but a great many others grow better between fifty and sixty degrees than at higher temperatures. For most plants our homes are apt to be too warm rather than too cold except in locations near windows in very cold weather. To prevent danger from this cause on cold nights, pull down the window shades and if necessary supplement this protection by slipping a few sheets of brown paper or newspaper between the glass and the plants. Alternatively move the plants away from the window to a warmer part of the room. Careful watering, pruning, and soil care are wasted if cold kills your plants.

Excessive heat, especially if accompanied by too much shade, causes plants to become spindly and weak, makes their stems lengthen unduly, and makes the distances between the leaves on the stems become longer than usual. Low temperatures check growth, often cause a yellowing (or in the case of red-leaved plants, a blueing) of the foliage followed by dropping of the leaves beginning with those lower-most on the stems. •

HOUSE PLANTS

Cactuses and succulents will stand dry air better than other plants. Blinds must be raised for sun.

Only tough plants will live in a fireplace. Close the flue to protect plants from chimney drafts.

Atmosphere is Important

Give your plants air—but in right amounts. They can suffer more from sudden drafts and dryness than from lack of air in a terrarium.

PLANTS need air to live but they do not need considerable volumes of fresh air as do animals and humans. It is not necessary that the air in which they grow be changed frequently. Plants will thrive for years in a nearly air-tight terrarium or even in a large bottle. Do not open windows or otherwise ventilate merely to give your plants fresh air. Do so on mild days, if you want to reduce the indoor temperature or to create sufficient circulation to dry soil or foilage that seems to remain wet too long after watering.

Plants resent drafts. Those with large, soft leaves such as cinerarias, poinsettias and geraniums quickly show ill effects by their foliage drooping, dropping off or yellowing, but even such tough subjects as aspidistras and snake plants are harmed by being constantly exposed to air currents although they may show no immediate effects. If long exposed they deteriorate and may eventually die. When choosing locations for your plants consider carefully whether or not they will be subject to drafts. Situations between doors or windows where cross currents are likely to occur are usually bad; so, too, are locations in empty fireplaces unless care is taken to close the flue while the plants are in position.

Of great importance is the relative humidity of the air. About this it is important to remember that relative humidity varies with changing temperatures. It works like this: A volume of air—a roomful for instance—contains a certain amount of water vapor, enough, let us say, so when the temperature is fifty degrees the relative humidity is sixty per cent (a satisfactory level for many plants). Now if the temperature is raised to seventy degrees, the roomful of air contains exactly the same *amount* of water vapor as before but its relative humidity is reduced to less than thirty per cent, a level far too low for the well being of all except desert plants. The only way to bring the relative humidity back to its previous level is to add water vapor to the air or to reduce the temperature.

During that period of the year when our homes are heated we constantly draw in outside air, and raise its temperature. Consequently we lower its relative humidity. That is one of the chief reasons why it is difficult to grow plants in houses. That is why many house plants thrive all summer and then drop leaves and otherwise fail after the heat is turned on. That is why plants are more difficult to keep in good condition in overheated rooms than where more moderate temperatures are maintained.

Fortunately steps can be taken to humidify the indoor air at least to a modest extent, if not throughout the entire room then at least in the vicinity of the plants. Let's see what can be done.

HOUSE PLANTS

The artificial heat used in winter makes the air very dry and plants, above left, lose moisture.

Plants continually give off water vapor, spraying an invisible fountain into the air all the time.

Primula, upper right, may have had recent water but leaves wilt if air is still excessively dry.

A base of gravel, sand, or moss kept always moist, right, can be helpful in humidifying plants' air.

First, foliage as well as damp soil and pots gives off moisture, therefore if plants are grown together in groups—many in a window rather than a single specimen for instance—the air in their immediate vicinity is likely to be moister. A little local climate, more humid than that of the rest of the room, is created. This condition can be accentuated by spraying the foliage on suitable occasions with a fine mist of clear water, wetting it quite thoroughly but not drenching it.

Just which are suitable occasions? That depends somewhat on the plant. A few hairy leaved kinds such as African violets, gloxinias and gesnerias resent having their leaves wetted. There are really no suitable occasions for spraying them. Other hairy-leaved and soft-leaved plants such as primroses, begonias and the pick-a-back plant may be sprayed once or twice a day whenever you expect that the moisture applied will dry within an hour or two. This means on the mornings and early afternoons of bright days when air circulation is good. It does not mean on dull days or so late in the day that it will be dark before the leaves are dry.

When spraying plants such as primroses and pick-a-backs that have their leaves all arising from near the ground, be careful not to get too much water into the centers of the plants—otherwise rotting may result.

Plants with hard leathery foliage such as palms, screw-palms, bromeliads, aspidistras and dracaenas as well as aroids and most other smooth-leaved plants, may be sprayed more freely and more frequently.

Two or three applications a day will ordinarily be beneficial but even these plants will be better without spraying if the leaves are likely to remain wet for several hours at a time.

An excellent method of adding to the moisture content of the air in the vicinity of your plants is to stand them on broad shallow trays filled with moss, gravel, cinders or sand that is kept always wet. Evaporation from the trays will effectively moisten the air. Make the trays of zinc, copper, wood, plastic or other suitable material. It is sufficient if they are about two inches deep and of any suitable length and width.

Terrariums are splendid devices. They make it possible to provide plants with atmospheres that have adequate relative humidity. Terrariums are containers—usually somewhat box-like—built largely of glass or transparent plastic. In effect they are little greenhouses that retain moist air about the plants grown in them. They are provided with adjustable means of ventilation so that the humidity can be controlled. Plants in them are grown either in pots or in a bed of soil or other rooting medium placed in the bottom of the terrarium.

HOUSE PLANTS

These are means by which you can increase the atmospheric humidity about your plants. In addition, more general and decidedly beneficial humidification can be achieved by placing evaporating pans on all radiators and keeping them filled with water, and by making sure that humidifying devices attached to hot air furnaces are always operating satisfactorily. A reasonably humid air results in benefits to you as well as to your plants. You save heat because you feel comfortably warm at lower temperatures than you would in an arid atmosphere. And you probably will be less subject to at least some respiratory ailments.

One more point, don't overlook the fact that in almost every habitation there are rooms and positions in rooms that are naturally moister, and other rooms and positions in rooms that are naturally drier. The kitchen, because of its steaming kettles, pans, and pots, and the bathroom for equally obvious reasons are likely to be somewhat humid; locations near radiators and other sources of dry heat are disastrously arid. Consider these factors carefully when locating your plants.

Pollution of the air may cause distress to house plants. One of the commonest causes of pollution is escaped illuminating gas. Traces in the atmosphere much too minute for you to smell may seriously harm plants. Remember that it is *escaped* gas that causes trouble not *consumed* gas.

Heating and cooking by gas are not harmful provided there are no leaks. Be sure that stoves and furnaces are in good order. Ignite jets immediately after they are turned on and be careful that pilot lights do not blow out. Be sure that flues are adequate to carry off incompletely burnt gases.

Common effects of gas poisoning are a rather rapid yellowing or dropping of foliage and a general unhappy appearance within a few hours of exposure. When gas is present African violets do not bloom and Christmas cherries drop their fruits (these happenings can, of course, be due also to other causes).

Two plants most sensitive to gas are tomatoes and carnations. Young plants of the former bend their leaves down sharply after being twenty-four hours or less in air containing extremely dilute proportions. Carnations, freshly cut and placed in water curl their petals inward and "go to sleep" within a few hours. If you suspect gas poisoning set some carnations or potted tomato plants in your rooms as a test. Natural gas is much less harmful than

Curing the dry winter air of your home will be beneficial for both you and your plants. Hang humidifiers full of water on radiators, let cooking steam escape, or under severe conditions put plants in terrarium.

To make a simple bell-jar terrarium, tie kerosene-soaked string around cider jug bottom. Light it.

After string has burned around bottom of gallon bottle, plunge in water and bottom will break off.

gas manufactured from coal or oil. In any house where gas is burnt, be sure to ventilate the rooms as freely as possible consistent with maintaining comfortable temperatures but above all have cooking and heating equipment checked occasionally to make sure that there are no leaks.

Plants suggested by Montague Free and other authorities as being able to withstand small amounts of gas without noticeable harm are: bromeliads, cactuses and succulents, begonia heracleifolia, ardisia, wandering Jew (tradescantia and zebrina), philodendron, scindapsus, patience plant, Podocarpus neriifolia, pick-a-back plant, lantana, screw-pine, Selaginella brownii, wax plant, large leaved English ivy, holly fern, anthurium, Dracaena sanderiana, Dracaena godseffiana, arrowroot, Campanula isophylla, Nephthytis Afzelii, rubber plant, amaryllis, clivia, gardenia, marica and poinsettia.

Pollution of the atmosphere near industrial plants and in cities is not uncommon. Damage to plants may be caused by the presence of small amounts of sulphur dioxide, hydrogen fluoride, hydrogen chloride, hydrogen sulphide, ammonia, chlorine, mercury vapor, and other gases, as well as by the presence of smog—that curious smoke or smoke-fog combination that is familiar to residents of the Los Angeles area and of some other parts of the country. Pollutions of these kinds may result in retarded growth, leaf drop, yellowing or bleaching of the foliage to an ivory color in patches at the tips or near the margins (or in some kinds the changing of similar patches to a brown or red coloring). If you live in a constantly polluted area you may find by experiment and by observation which plants succeed with your neighbors, kinds that are most tolerant to your particular atmosphere. If you are in an area that suffers from pollution only occasionally, as for instance when an unusual change of wind brings the fumes of an industrial plant in your direction or when an occasional smog lies heavy around you, be careful not to overwater, not to wet foliage at such times and to keep temperatures as low was reasonably possible during the periods of affliction to minimize the effects on your plants.

It is chiefly gases in the air that cause damage to plants, but accumulations of dust and grime on foliage may cause some harm, particularly by cutting down the amount of light the leaves receive. To remove grime sponge smooth-leaf kinds such as rubber plants and dracaenas with a soap sudsy water and rinse immediately with clear water. Most plants that cannot be conveniently sponged may be freed of dirt by washing them thoroughly with a fairly forceful jet of water from a hose or syringe. Plants that are injured by washing or syringing (as African violets may be) are unsuited for cultivation in places where the air contains much dirt. Dust may be removed from them by brushing each leaf with a soft-bristle brush. •

Finished bell jar covers newly planted runner of a strawberry begonia plant.

A glass jar with top tilted to let in a little air keeps moist a newly potted pick-a-back plant so that it will root.

Daily spray moistens air around plant. Don't spray plants with hairy foliage.

HOUSE PLANTS

When to Water

Plants must be watered only when they need it, not at fixed intervals. Too much water will make roots rot.

When watering newly potted plants from the top use a fine spray. A stream of water will dislodge the surface soil.

HOW often shall I water my plant? No question is asked of me more often. None is less susceptible of a stock answer. The great American horticulturist, Dr. Liberty Hyde Bailey emphasized that plants should be watered only when they *need* it, not whenever they will stand it. This is first class advice. The trick is to know when they need watering.

First put aside all thoughts that plants should be watered at *regular* intervals, in the way that a dog is fed once, or a husband thrice a day. Plants are not like that. They do not drink at stated times. They absorb moisture continuously.

Therefore, the soil should be always moist (except during the resting seasons of those plants that go completely dormant as do gloxinias, tuberous begonias, and amaryllis). But it should not be constantly saturated (the soils of aquatic and bog plants such as the umbrella-palm are exceptions to this rule). The soil for most plants should be always moist throughout, but not so wet that if it were squeezed water would run from it. When as wet as that it contains insufficient air for the well being of the roots and they rot. The soil is soured. To keep the soil of pot plants sufficiently moist requires that they be watered at intervals. The length of time between waterings depends upon a great many factors such as the kind of plant, its stage of growth, its size in relation to its pot, the character of its soil, the condition of its roots, and such variable environmental factors as light and temperature.

Obviously soil in a pot filled with healthy roots, all absorbing moisture, dries more rapidly than that of a newly potted specimen that has not yet filled its container with roots. Clearly when the temperature is high, the sun strong, and the atmospheric humidity low, drying will be more rapid than in cool, dull, and moist weather. The frequency with which water should be given varies then, according to conditions.

A leafy hydrangea, primula or cineraria

HOUSE PLANTS

One method of watering is to fill saucers which hold pots. Empty saucers when soil becomes moist.

Leaves of plant at left are wilting because soil is too dry. Plant at right was properly watered.

An effective method of watering is to plunge pot to half its depth in water. As soon as the surface soil is wet, remove pot from water and let drain.

in a pot well filled with roots may require soaking two or three times a day in sunny, warm weather, whereas a pruned-back geranium, a newly potted amaryllis, or a succulent cactus may not need such attention more often than once a week, particularly if the weather is dull.

To judge whether or not the soil of a plant has reached the stage where water is needed examine its surface. If it looks moist and feels moist it is likely wet enough although if previous waterings have been skimpy it is possible that the surface is wet and the soil beneath dry. If you suspect this turn the plant out of its pot and inspect its soil ball. You can easily judge by its appearance whether the earth is dry or wet. The weight of the pot and its contents is often a good indication of the degree of moistness of the soil. Wet earth is heavier than dry. With a little practice you will be able to judge by lifting the pot just how wet its contents are. Another time honored test is to rap the pot with a thick wooden stick or small wooden mallet. A dull heavy sound indicates wetness, a clear ringing sound dryness. If the leaves wilt, suspect dryness. Remember, however, that wilting can be caused also by excessive sunshine, drafts, stem injuries, damage to the roots caused by transplanting, overstrong fertilizers, or even by excessive watering. Make quite sure that the wilting is caused by dryness before you attempt to remedy it by applying water. Actually you should never permit plants to get so dry that their leaves droop unless you are purposely drying them off in preparation for a period of rest. Wilting is harmful to growing plants.

One watering rule is inviolable: when a plant needs water give it plenty, enough to saturate its entire body of soil, not a

1741

HOUSE PLANTS

Don't leave plants standing in saucers of water for very long since this will make roots rot.

Many plants are sold in containers which have no drainage holes. Never overwater.

Plants growing in glazed pots need much less water than in ordinary clay flower pots.

WATER SPARINGLY

Newly potted plants which have few roots.

Plants with foliage which has been heavily pruned.

Cactuses, succulents with no leaves or fleshy ones.

Plants going to rest after their season of growth.

WATER FREELY

Pot-bound plants having containers filled with roots.

Specimens that have large amounts of healthy leaves.

Plants with large leaves like cinerarias, primroses.

Plants in height of growing season like this calla lily.

1742

WATER SPARINGLY

Plants just starting growth after lying dormant a while.

When it is raining or dull and very humid weather.

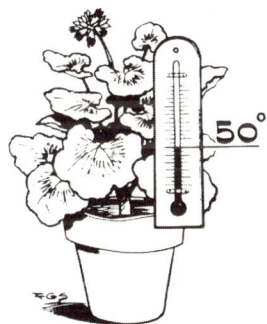

In winter when the temperature is comparatively low.

Plants growing in containers with no drainage holes.

WATER FREELY

Plants in full growth and leaves like an amaryllis.

When weather is sunny and dry or when windy.

In summer when the mercury becomes quite high.

Plants in containers with holes in bottom as shown.

HOUSE PLANTS

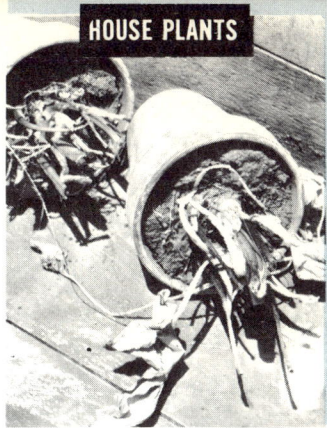

Certain plants that need time of complete dormancy are kept dry for that rest period.

Many florists display plants in glazed pottery ducks, etc. Don't overwater these.

Dish garden below, also, must be watered with care so that soil is not saturated.

1743

parsimonious dribble that wets only the surface. This applies whether you are dealing with a bog plant or a desert cactus, a newly planted seedling or an old established and pot-bound specimen. A good way to be sure that you saturate the soil is to immerse the pot to half its depth in water and keep it there until moisture seeping from below wets the surface soil. Do not leave it immersed for long after the soil is thoroughly wet. Most plants are harmed if they are left standing in water for lengthy periods. This immersion method is particularly useful for seedlings and newly planted specimens where disturbance of the surface soil may result from top watering. I recommend it, too, for plants that have filled their containers with a tight mass of roots and that are difficult to water thoroughly from above. It is excellent for any plant that is not too heavy to lift in and out of water.

Popular opinion to the contrary, there are no plants that *must* be watered from below (that is, by the immersion method). It is just a sure means of soaking the soil completely and a method that does not wet the foliage, as careless surface watering may, of plants that need to have their leaves kept dry.

Surface watering, properly done, is just as effective as watering from beneath. Properly done simply means that the soil is soaked through and that foliage is not wet if not desirable.

Ordinarily the surface soil of a potted plant is some little distance below the rim of its container. Under the best circumstances the space that is left will hold sufficient water to soak the soil beneath. When this is so, watering consists of filling this space once with water. However, due to growth of roots or other causes, the space above the soil is sometimes not sufficient to hold water enough to soak the whole ball of earth. In such cases it is necessary to fill it two, three, or more times at each watering—as many as are needed to make sure that all the soil is saturated and that surplus water runs out of the hole in the bottom of the pot. When, as sometimes happens with plants that have occupied the same containers for a long time and with plants that have been very dry, the soil ball shrinks from the pot leaving a space between the pot and its contents, the fact that water runs out through the bottom of the container does not necessarily indicate that the soil mass is soaked through. In such cases make doubly sure that soaking is accomplished.

Semiautomatic watering by the use of wicks of glass fiber is possible. It is most successful with plants in pots from four to seven inches in diameter, and in the case of fine rooted kinds, such as African violets, begonias, and pick-a-back plants. It is less satisfactory for specimens in quite small or quite large pots and for coarse rooted subjects such as palms and snake plants. The glass wick is inserted through the hole in the bottom of the pot, the upper end is unravelled and spread and is brought into intimate contact with the soil, the lower end is immersed in a container of water. The wick is put into position when the plant is potted. No drainage material is used in the pot.

Keeping the soil in a constantly saturated condition has rotted roots of this rhizomatous begonia.

The leaves of this African violet are wilted and drooping because roots rotted from overwatering.

HOUSE PLANTS

Unless you use good sense in watering you will not be successful with your house plants. If you follow the suggestions I have made and see that the soil is thoroughly saturated when it is watered and then is not wet again until it verges on dryness but is not yet completely dry you will go far to becoming a good waterer. But there are refinements to the practice that you should know if you are to do best by your plants. First you must understand that when gardeners speak of this plant needing a lot of water and that plant requiring little they do not refer to the *amount* of water that should be given at each application. This must always be sufficient to saturate the soil. They refer rather to the degree of dryness the soil shall be allowed to attain before water is applied. Plants that need little water, such as fat cactuses and other succulents, are not watered until their soil is *almost completely* dry. Plants that need a lot of water such as spiraea, hydrangeas in full leaf and pot-bound cinerarias are watered as soon as the soil *begins to be dry.* In their needs for water the great majority of house plants fall between these extremes.

Plants need more water when they are growing actively and are developing new leaves than they do when they are semi-dormant. Specimens that have ample foliage in comparison to the size of the pot they occupy need more water than those that are sparser of leaf. For this reason individuals that have been pruned back or have had their foliage seriously damaged by insects, disease, frost damage or other cause should be kept "on the dry side."

Plants that have filled their containers with healthy roots need more water than newly transplanted and freshly potted specimens the roots of which have not yet permeated the available soil. Plants in very porous soils need more water than those in more retentive earths and those accommodated in porous clay pots need more than those in glazed or other non-porous containers.

If you have a window garden with a variety of flowers, you may find it helpful to plan a check list for each plant's needs. Too often a novice home gardener will water all plants at once with the same amount, cactuses and ferns alike. On the same chart you might list ailments to check for—see "Bugs and Blights."

In dull weather do whatever watering is needed early in the day if you can. Despite this rule, if a plant is evidently suffering from lack of moisture apply it at any time. Avoid using water that is excessively cold. Room temperature is best. If you have a hard alkaline water, it will bring death to azaleas, heather, camellias, gardenias, and other acid-soil plants. Use rain water or at least non-alkaline water for such kinds. Rain water as a matter of fact is excellent for all plants.

When plants growing in porous clay pots dry out too quickly, thus necessitating very frequent watering, relief may be had by sinking the pot to its rim in a larger pot or other container and packing the space between with peat moss, sand, fine cinders, or sphagnum moss and keeping this constantly moist. This is much to be preferred to watering every few hours. •

Never stand plants on hot radiators, even for a short time. The heat will kill them very quickly.

Any plant can be watered from the top if enough water is used to moisten the whole body of soil.

HOUSE PLANTS

Irving Kaufman Studios

Assemble these basic ingredients for your potting soil mixture: top soil, peat moss, sand, charcoal, bone meal. Leaf mold or humus may be substituted for peat moss. Add fertilizer for some plants. Then moisten slightly and mix ingredients very thoroughly.

Start With The Soil

The right soil provides the right food and foundation for your plants. Choose and mix it to meet your plants' nutritional needs.

HOUSE PLANTS

Good top soil is essential as the foundation for all potting mixtures. Do not sift or screen the soil; keep a fairly coarse-textured consistency.

Organic matter in the form of leaf mold, humus, or peat moss is added to the top soil. Leaf mold should be flaky; peat moss broken into fine bits.

Coarse sand ensures that the finished potting mixture will be porous. Seashore sand must be well washed to free it from all traces of salt before use.

Next add cow manure to mixture, as shown in these New York Botanical Garden photos. The proportion should usually be one-tenth to one eighth by bulk.

WHILE it is true that plants can be grown without soil, it is certain that the vast majority will be cultivated in it, at least in the forseeable future. Soil serves as an anchorage for roots; from it plants obtain water and nutrients.

When you prepare soil for house plants remember that its physical state is even more important than its chemical composition. Very few plants (the exceptions are bog and aquatic kinds) will grow in waterlogged soil. Their roots need air. In order to assure a constant supply, the soil must be well drained and should consist of fairly coarse particles.

Earth that is perfectly satisfactory for outdoor gardening may be quite unsuitable for indoor use. Plants growing in containers exist under artificial conditions. Their soil is usually more firmly packed than is that of the open garden, it is watered oftener, it quickly becomes drained of nutrients and sooner filled with roots. Because of this it should be specially compounded.

Fortunately, any good garden soil can be made suitable for house plants quite easily. It is merely a matter of adding various ingredients to improve its texture or physical condition, to increase its fertility, and, more rarely, to change its

1747

HOUSE PLANTS

Bone meal at the rate of one pint to each bushel can be added. It is a safe fertilizer that can benefit all plants and seems harmful to none.

In addition to the bone meal, mix in some complete fertilizer. This is usually measured at the rate of from one-half to one pint per bushel of soil.

acidity-alkalinity reaction. To increase fertility a wide variety of manures and fertilizers are employed. Ordinarily those that have fairly long-lasting effects such as dried cow manure, pulverized sheep manure, cotton seed meal, bone meal, superphosphate and wood ashes are preferred. Quick-acting fertilizers such as sulphate of ammonia, nitrate of soda, muriate of potash and sulphate of potash are reserved for feeding plants after they have filled their pots with roots. Don't mix them with the soil before potting or planting. Complete commercial fertilizers (those that carry on the package a formula of three numbers such as 5-10-5) may be used with advantage provided the nitrogen they contain (represented by the first number) is of organic origin. If it is not then the fertilizer containing it should be used for supplemental feeding rather than for adding to the soil before planting.

Two types of materials are added to soil to improve its physical condition. Inorganic substances such as sand, cinders, and broken brick that do this and nothing more, and organic materials such as peat moss, leaf mold, and humus that both change the physical character of the soil and supply greater or lesser amounts of plant nutrients. Lime is sometimes added to correct over-acidity and, more rarely, aluminum sulphate or sulphur to increase acidity.

Although plants vary as to the types of soil they thrive best in, it is by no means necessary to prepare a special formula for each species and variety. In their needs they fall into a few groups—those, such as cacti and other succulents that require a coarse, gritty, medium that contains a comparatively small amount of organic material and through which water passes with great ease; those such as ferns, begonias, and African violets that give of their best only when grown in a soil that is extremely rich in decayed organic matter and that revel in the evenly moist root conditions that such a soil provides; those that succeed best in a fairly heavy (moderately clayey) soil such as geraniums and chrysanthemums; those such as gardenias and camellias that prefer acid soil conditions; and those such as Martha Washington geraniums that respond best in a decidedly sweet soil. Some plants have a wider range of tolerance for soils than others. Many will grow in any reasonably good earth provided it is well drained—others are more finicky, you must give them a soil pretty much to their liking. This is particularly true of plants that favor acid soil conditions.

THE INGREDIENTS

As a house plant grower, stock the following soil mixture components.

1. LOAM

Let this be the best quality topsoil you can obtain. For preference cut grass sods four to five inches thick from a lush meadow or field and pile them (with a three inch layer of manure between eight to ten inch layers of sod) grass side down out of doors for six months or so, until the grass is dead, but not until its fibrous roots have completely decayed. Then chop it with a spade or break it with the fingers *but do not remove* the fiberous portion. This gives "life" to the soil. Good loam prepared in this way should be pleasant to handle, slightly springy, and have a delightfully sweet earthy smell. If you lack

HOUSE PLANTS

Mix these ingredients thoroughly. Your result will be a soil mixture for a great variety of pot plants such as geraniums, chrysanthemums, dracaenas.

Once you have prepared your basic potting mixture you may adapt it for special purposes. Here some additional leaf mold starts a more woodsy mixture.

turf soil prepared in this way, use for your loam topsoil taken from a rich vegetable garden or cultivated field. Soil that has grown good corn is excellent.

2. SAND

This must be coarse and free of all fine silty particles. That from a river or sand bank is usually better than sea sand although the latter may be used provided it is coarse and provided it has been well washed to free it of all traces of salt. To do this leave it outdoors exposed to normal rains for a few months, or alternatively, stick the end of a hose into the bottom of a pail or barrel, fill the pail or barrel with sand and run water through the hose. Let the water overflow for ten minutes or so. Strain off the surplus water and let the sand dry.

3. BROKEN CROCK, BROKEN BRICK, CINDERS

Use these when you want your soil to be especially porous and gritty, when mixing soil for cactuses, for example. You have special need for such material if your loam is heavy and consists of all fine particles. Crocks are simply pieces of common unglazed earthen flower pots. Break them to sizes ranging from that of a pin head to that of a pea. Broken brick is an adequate substitute for broken crock. Smash it to the same sizes. Use old, soft, porous bricks rather than hard burned or vitrified samples. Coal cinders that have been outdoors for several months until all soluble injurious compounds have been leached from them are also good for the purpose. By cinders I mean the gritty cokey particles of burned coal, not fine ash. This latter is harmful rather than helpful when added to potting soil mixture.

4. LEAF MOLD

Leaf mold is compost that results from the decay of leaves without the addition of soil or other substances. The best is made from the leaves on non-evergreen trees and shrubs. Oak and beech leaves produce particularly good grades. Leaf mold may be made by piling leaves outdoors in a shaded, sheltered place for a year or two, turning them occasionally to hasten uniform decay, or by stacking them in one of the several types of bins or pits that gardeners use for making compost. If you search woodland areas you will usually find accumulations of natural leaf mold in hollows and other locations where leaves gather. Scrape away the undecayed surface layer and gather the partially decayed material beneath. Leaf mold should be decomposed to such an extent that it is easy to rub it through a sieve having a half-inch or three-quarter inch mesh but not rotted so much that all evidence of the veining and structure of the leaves is lost. It should be flaky rather than powdery.

5. PEAT MOSS

Often used as a substitute for leaf mold, peat moss is generally satisfactory. For some plants—azaleas, heathers and other acid-soil plants, for example—it is better than leaf mold. It is sold in bales of various sizes and should be finely broken before being added to the soil. Always use a horticultural grade of peat moss; that sold for bedding horses and other non-gardening purposes is not as satisfactory.

6. HUMUS

Commercial humus of good quality is a light, fluffy black organic matter formed by the natural decay of vegetation under

HOUSE PLANTS

Next add charcoal that has been chopped and broken into pieces the size of peas. This helps prevent souring in soil that contains organic matter.

The addition of extra leaf mold, humus, or peat moss plus charcoal makes the woodsy mixture best suited for ferns, African violets, and begonias.

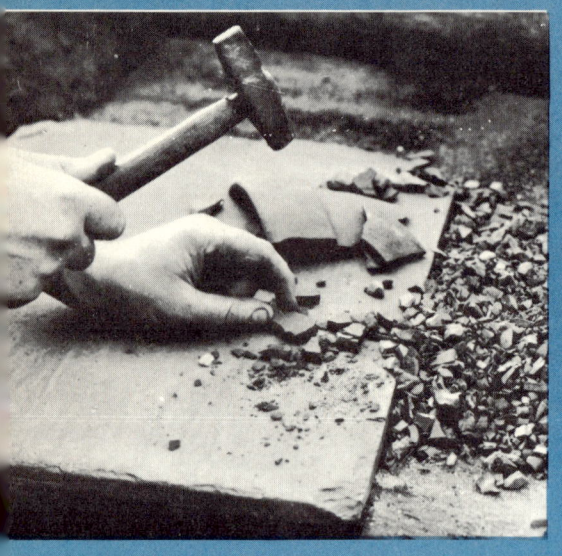

Desert plants require variations of the general potting mixture. Add small bits of broken crocks and bricks or gritty cinders prepared pea-size.

Then mix in a generous amount of really coarse sand or fine grit. This will help simulate the plant's natural desert-habitat soil conditions.

Now you have a soil suitable for your cactus or other succulent. Fertilizer may be added for the strong-growing kinds like century plant and aloes.

New York Botanical Garden photos

HOUSE PLANTS

water. Because of its fine texture it is less satisfactory than either peat moss or leaf mold for mixing with heavy (clayey) loam but it may be used with advantage with light loam. I personally prefer good leaf mold to humus but gladly use the latter when the former is unavailable.

7. DRIED COW MANURE

This is practically an essential ingredient of many soil mixtures. Undoubtedly the best is obtained by drying fresh manure in the sun or in a shed and then crumbling the cakes until the pieces range from the size of peas to the size of half walnuts. If you cannot do this, substitute the dried cow manure that is offered for sale by seedsmen and dealers in garden fertilizers.

8. BONE MEAL

One of the safest fertilizers to add to potting soil is bone meal. I know of no plants that do not respond favorably to it; so far as I know none are harmed by it.

9. WOOD ASHES

Provided they have not been rained upon or in other ways wetted, wood ashes are a most excellent fertilizer to add to potting soils for many plants. They supply much-needed potash but as this is very soluble it is quickly washed away by water. Ashes that have been kept dry and retain their potash content are sold as *unleached* wood ashes.

10. CHARCOAL

Soils that contain a large proportion of organic matter (leaf mold, peat moss or humus) are apt to become sour as a result of repeated watering. Broken charcoal added to them does much to prevent this. Chop the charcoal into pieces ranging in size from that of a pea to that of a peanut.

Use this test for physical quality of mixture:
A. As shown in the top photo, turn over your prepared soil mixture and then take a handful and squeeze it. Soil should feel moist but not wet.

B. Open your hand and tap the lump of soil lightly with your finger. If it remains in a lump, as in center photo, the mixture is too heavy. Remedy is the addition of more sand and organic matter.

If, when you tap the lump of soil with your finger, it falls apart as shown in the bottom photo at the right, the proportion of ingredients that determine its texture and physical quality are now correct.

HOUSE PLANTS

Good leaf mold can be found in woods. This compost results from the decay of leaves; oak and beech are good. The new top leaves are scraped away and the decayed and rotted leaves below are collected.

PREPARING SOIL MIXTURES

The bulk ingredients you use in soil mixtures—loam, leaf mold, sand, etc., should be moist but not water soaked at mixing time. If the loam is so wet that it sticks to shovel and fingers it is unsatisfactory—let it dry somewhat before mixing. If the components are too dry correct this by sprinkling with water occasionally during the mixing process. The objective is a mixture that is agreeably moist, not dry enough to be dusty, not wet enough to make your fingers muddy.

Don't sift the loam unless the soil is for seed sowing, transplanting tiny seedlings, or potting newly rooted cuttings. Then it may be passed through a half inch or three quarter inch mesh. For ordinary potting, break the loam with the fingers or chop it with a spade—leaving it as coarse as may conveniently be packed about the roots of the plants that are to be handled. In this way the valuable fibrous material is left in the soil instead of being removed. Mix the ingredients thoroughly.

Because loams, sands, and leaf molds differ somewhat, it is not possible to state exactly the proportions in which they should be mixed for any specific purpose. If your loam is heavy and on the clayey side, more sand will be needed than if you begin with a light sandy loam. More leaf mold, peat moss, or humus is needed if the loam is poor in organic matter than if it is black and rich. The mixtures suggested here are based on the use of a fertile loam of medium lightness and humus content. Modify the proportions of the ingredients used under other circumstances. Choose the mixture best suited to your purposes.

RECIPES FOR SOIL MIXTURES

FOR SEED SOWING

All ingredients should be fine enough to pass through a half inch mesh. *Rub* the loam and leaf mold through so that as much of their fibrous parts as possible are retained.

Seed Soil No. 1. *A mixture for the seeds of the great majority of plants.* Loam one part, leaf mold, peat moss, or humus one part, coarse sand one part.

Seed Soil No. 2. *A mixture suitable for cacti and other succulents.* Loam one part, leaf mold, peat moss, or humus one part, coarse sand four parts, crocks, broken brick or gritty cinders (passed through a quarter inch sieve and with all fine dust removed) four parts.

Seed Soil No. 3. *A mixture suitable for plants that require a woodsy, humusy soil such as begonias, gloxinias and African violets.* Loam one part, leaf mold, peat moss, or humus two parts, sand one part, crocks, cinders or broken brick (passed through a quarter inch sieve and with all fine dust removed) one quarter part, charcoal (passed through a quarter inch sieve) one quarter part.

FOR TRANSPLANTING SEEDLINGS

Soil for the first transplanting of seedlings should be similar to that recommended for seeds of the same plants except that it may be coarser and may have a little fertilizer added. If it passes through a three-quarter inch mesh it is fine enough. Add half a pint of bone meal and a pint of dried sheep manure (or two quarts of dried cow manure) to each bushel.

1752

HOUSE PLANTS

The rotted leaves you bring home must have decayed sufficiently so that they can be rubbed through a one-half or three-quarter inch wire mesh.

The splendid leaf mold that will result should be flaky in quality. It is the very finest organic matter for mixing with the soil for potting plants.

FOR POTTED CUTTINGS

Cuttings rooted in sand and other well aerated media need a loose, porous soil at their first potting. Use the same type of mixture that the plant is known to favor at later pottings but leave out all fertilizers and double or treble the proportion of sand used. Pass all ingredients through a half inch sieve.

FOR POTTING

Don't make the mixture finer than necessary to permit packing it about the roots. Within reason, the coarser the soil the better. When potting into large pots or tubs you will be able to use coarser material than for smaller receptacles.

Potting Soil No. 1. A general purpose mixture suitable for most strong rooted plants such as *geraniums, chrysanthemums, fuchsias, palms, snake plants,* and *English ivy.* Loam four parts, leaf mold, peat moss, or humus two parts, dried cow manure one part (or one-third as much dried sheep manure), coarse sand two parts (this may be replaced in part by chopped crock, brick or gritty cinders), bone meal a pint to each bushel, wood ashes two quarts to each bushel, complete garden fertilizer half a pint to each bushel.

Potting Soil No. 2. A woodsy mixture for plants that need a soil having a high organic matter content. These include *begonias, African violets, gloxinias* and *ferns.* Loam two parts, leaf mold, peat moss, or humus two-and-a-half parts, coarse sand half a part, broken crock, brick or gritty cinders one part, charcoal half a part, dried cow manure one part, bone meal a pint to each bushel.

Potting Soil No. 3. A mixture for *succulent plants such as cactuses.* Loam two parts, leaf mold, peat moss, or humus two parts, coarse sand two parts, broken crocks, bricks, or gritty cinders two parts, bone meal a pint to each bushel, lime a pint to each bushel, wood ashes two quarts to each bushel. For strong growing kinds such as *century plants* and *aloes* add one tenth part by bulk of dried cow manure.

Potting Soil No. 4. For acid soil plants such as *heathers, azaleas, camellias* and *gardenias.* Loam two parts, leaf mold, or humus one part, peat moss two parts, coarse sand two parts, dried cow manure one part.

Potting Soil No. 5. For forcing bulbs and plants such as *daffodils, hyacinths, tulips, spireas,* and *fuchias.* Loam four parts, leaf mold, peat moss, or humus two parts, coarse sand three parts, bone meal a pint to each bushel.

Potting Soil number one can be adapted for plants that need a woodsy mixture by mixing with it three additional parts of leaf mold, humus or peat moss and one-and-one-half parts of chopped charcoal or it can be adapted to the needs of castuses and succulents by mixing with it one part of sand and three parts broken crocks or broken bricks.

Do not hesitate to mix the special soil your plant will need. Ingredients for each are more or less the same, only proportions differ, and in this way you can best simulate the shaded, woodsy soil your ferns will like, or the drier, sandier anchorage necessary for cactuses and other succulents. Good soil will give plants a good head start for indoor living. •

HOUSE PLANTS

Irving Kaufman Studios

Plants with smooth leaves are benefited by having leaves sponged often with diluted insecticide. Don't wait until plant is infected before treatment.

Note characteristic ring-shaped markings on the leaves of this African violet. This leaf spot disease is probably due to a virus infection. Pick off all infected leaves.

Bugs and Blights

Bugs and blights bedevil the best of plants. Here's how to recognize problems and prevent or cure them.

HOUSE PLANTS

IT IS not difficult to keep house plants free of pests and diseases. The reasons for this are simple. The air indoors is too dry to encourage the growth of many fungus diseases that plague the greenhouse gardener, and the plants are usually few enough for you to examine every one at frequent intervals.

Do just that. Be curious. Look at the undersides of the leaves at least every week or two. Carefully examine the stems. Check the crowns (centers) of the plants. If at all suspicious that something may be wrong with the roots, carefully remove the plant from its container and inspect the root ball. Early detection of trouble is imperative in keeping house plants healthy.

But detection is not enough. You must be able to correctly identify the causes of troubles. It's no use treating a plant suffering from mildew diseases with a spray intended for killing aphids, or a plant that has nothing wrong with it but that it needs fertilizing or a different temperature with a fungicide or insecticide. Correct diagnosis is vital.

Once the cause of trouble is ascertained take prompt remedial measures. Clean plants depend upon three D's: Detection, Diagnosis, and Do Something—the something being the application of the best cures and preventatives. Many plants are ruined because diseases and pests are permitted to become too well established before control measures are taken.

WHAT TO LOOK FOR

What should you look for when you examine your plants? First note the over-all appearance of the foliage. Is there any change in its coloring that cannot be accounted for by normal seasonal variation such as the gradual yellowing and dying of caladiums before they go dormant, and the greening of hyacinth foliage after the pots are transferred from darkness to light? If you notice an unaccounted yellowing or other loss of leaf color, are you quite sure that it is not because the plant is suffering from too low a temperature, from drafts, from an atmosphere that is too dry, from lack of nourishment or from having been either too dry or excessively wet?

A few plants, notably gardenias and azaleas, exhibit a special yellowing of their foliage known as chlorosis if their soil is insufficiently acid. Unseasonal yellowing and other discoloring of the foliage is no sure indication that your plant is attacked by bug or blight. It merely signals *some* unfavorable condition.

If satisfied that the loss of leaf color is not due to cold, starvation, dryness, wetness, drafts or unfavorable soil conditions or if you are doubtful about this, look more closely for bugs and diseases. Inspect the above ground parts of the plant first.

THE BUGS YOU MAY FIND ON STEMS AND LEAVES

Examine with great care the undersides of the leaves for—

RED SPIDER MITES

These are tiny roundish creatures scarcely visible even when full grown.

Typical injury by red spider mites is shown on leaves. Look for a finely mottled or peppered appearance—yellow, gray, or silver.

When only a few plants are involved, it is often simpler to dip plants in insecticide. Paper held over pot prevents loss of soil.

HOUSE PLANTS

Dept. of Entomolgy, Cornell Univ.

Whiteflies, both mature insects and nymphs, crowd the underside of infested leaf.

Scale insects attach to the undersides of leaves. They move only when young and are scarcely visible at that stage.

Scale insects like these on English ivy leaf can be removed with sponge or soft brush dipped in a nicotine insecticide.

They congregate chiefly on the undersides of foliage where they spin frail mealy webs. They suck the plants juices. Red spider mites are pale yellow, orange, red or greenish and move with fair rapidity. A keen eye can detect them running along their webs but it is easier to see them with a hand lens. Red spider mites are particularly fond of English ivy, aspidistras, fuchsias, amaryllis, pick-a-back plant, asparagus ferns and ageratums, and occur on a great variety of other plants. They cause the foliage to have a finely mottled or peppered appearance, yellow, grayish, or silvery. In severe infestations the whole plant looks sickly, and older leaves turn brown. Much leaf dropping may occur. Growth is severely checked.

Red spider mites thrive where the air is hot and dry. They are likely to infest plants located in sunny windows, near radiators and against walls that reflect much heat. They are also fond of places where air circulation is poor even though the atmosphere is humid. They are easily controlled. Dipping the plants in, or spraying them with, a nicotine insecticide—a teaspoonful and a half of Black Leaf 40 (nicotine sulphate) and a heaping tablespoonful or two of soap flakes disolved in a gallon of warm water—is effective. Spray with sufficient force to break the fine webs the mites spin and hide under. Thoroughly wet the underside of every leaf. Repeat this treatment two or three times at weekly intervals.

An extremely effective method of preventing infestations of red spider mites and of reducing those already established is by forcefully syringing or spraying the plants, particularly the undersides of the leaves, with clear water once a week. This can be most conveniently done in the sink or bath tub. Use sufficient force to break the webs and wash away the mites but not enough to damage the foliage. Daily spraying with water and the maintenance of a moist atmosphere and a good circulation of air discourage this common pest.

If the leaves are silvery and bleached and perhaps eventually become brown and wilted and drop and you find no red spider mites look carefully for—

THRIPS

These are yellowish, brownish or black creatures that move rapidly and when disturbed tend to hide in leaf bases and other crevices. They are only just visible to a keen naked eye. A magnifying glass is a great aid in detecting them. Thrips are slender, pointed at both ends, and their bodies lie close to the surface upon which they travel. With their mouthparts they rasp the plant and suck its juices. It is the rasping or scarifying that gives a characteristic streaky silvery appearance to attacked foliage.

Thrips are especially likely to occur on begonias, gloxinias, dracaenas, aralias, amaryllis, spider-lilies, crotons, fuchsias, cyclamens, orchids, ferns, and palms. They are easy to eliminate by dipping or spraying with a nicotine insecticide as recommended for red spider mites, or better still by using a DDT insecticide diluted as recommended by its manufacturer.

HOUSE PLANTS

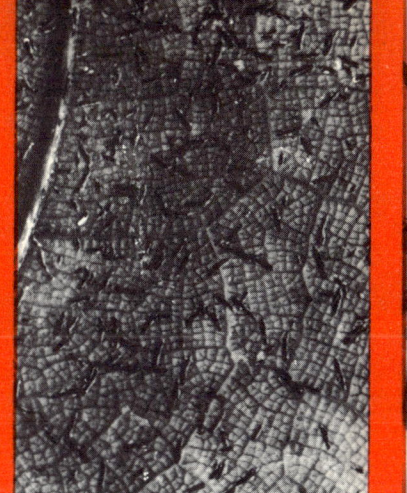

N. Y. Botanical Garden

This euonymus, above, is infested with both scale insects on the stems and aphids on the undersides of the leaves.

Here is another kind of scale insect—the thread scale. Note characteristic scars on this fiddle-leaved fig plant.

A toothbrush dipped into you[r] insecticide is a useful tool fo[r] removing these scale insect[s].

Perhaps you will find on the undersides of the leaves small but easily visible moth-like insects that are pure white in color and rather triangular in shape, and give to flying away in clouds if the plant is disturbed and to returning promptly when disturbance subsides. These are—

WHITEFLIES

Associated with the fully grown insects you will almost surely see oval, flat, semi-transparent white or pale green egg-like bodies which do not move. These are a younger (nymphal) stage of the whitefly. Like the mature insects they live by sucking sap. Whiteflies are especially likely to infest fuchsias, pelargoniums, geraniums, coleus, ageratum, begonias, hibiscus, lantana, flowering-maple, Christmas-cherry, primroses, calendulas, chrysanthemums, cinerarias, ferns and heliotrope.

Infested plants lack vigor. Their leaves turn yellow and may drop. The uppersides of the foliage is often covered with a soot-like deposit which is a fungus that grows on the honeydew secretion that the insects excrete and drop on to the leaves beneath.

Whiteflies are not easy to control. One of the reasons for this is that they are so lively. Even before a spray hits them they are likely to be on the wing. They are, however, sluggish on dull days and at night. Act then. Once a week for a period of a month or six weeks spray infested plants with, or dip them in, a nicotine insecticide as recommended above for red spider mites. Before beginning this treatment pick off and burn leaves that have yellowed or that are severely infested.

Even uninfected plants benefit from leaf washing if gently done. Give only smooth-leaved plants this treatment. After scale insects are swabbed off with the insecticide, rinse plant with clear water.

The undersides of fern fronds often have spore-containing organs that superficially resemble scale insects. Do not mistake them for insects and attempt to remove or scrub them off the plant.

HOUSE PLANTS

Cornell Univ. photo
Aphids are soft bodied insects that like young shoots.

Mealy bugs are sucking insects that can cause injury to many house plants.

This crassula is heavily infested with mealy bugs. Note cluster on new shoot.

Your investigation of the leaves may disclose small, but easily visible, round or elongated lumps attached to them. These lumps will probably be most abundant on the undersurfaces but may occur on the upper sides too and are often plentiful along the stems. They may be black, brown, yellow or white. You will find that you can dislodge them with your finger nail. There are several distinct species of these—

SCALE INSECTS

They infest many kinds of plants including palms, ferns, crotons, English-ivy, fatshedera, aralia, clerodendron, citrus fruits, rubber plants, gardenias, oleanders and cactuses.

The newly hatched scale is almost invisible. It crawls from its mother, finds a tender leaf or stem, inserts its proboscis and remains in that spot for the rest of its life, sucking sap and growing bigger. It is common to find scales of various sizes on the same plant. Look not only for the old, dark colored ones but also for the youngsters which are, smaller, flatter and often much paler in color. It is important to kill them as well as the mature ones. Do not mistake spore bearing organs of ferns (which are on the undersides of the leaves) or the natural scales that occur on some cactuses for insect scales. Insect scales do not ordinarilly form the nearly regular pattern that these do.

Scale insects seriously reduce the vigor of infested plants. Foliage turns yellow and growth slows. Like whiteflies and aphids they excrete a sticky honeydew which coats the foliage on which it falls and encourages the growth of a black fungus that looks like soot.

Eradication of scale insects is not difficult when the infested plants can be sponged or brushed to physically remove the insects. This is easy with palms, dracaenas, oranges and many other kinds. It is more difficult with some cactuses. With ferns it is often impossible.

To clean a plant of scales mix a nicotine insecticide as recommended by the manufacturer, dip a sponge in it and squeeze it nearly dry, place each leaf in turn on the palm of the hand and rub it with the sponge hard enough to remove the scales but not to scratch or damage the plant. For stems and difficult-to-get-at spots dip a toothbrush in the insecticide and use it instead of the sponge. When the plant has been thoroughly cleaned rinse it with clear water. Success depends upon removing every scale, even the tiniest. This means going over every part of the plant including those parts where no scales can be seen, but where very young ones may be. Don't forget the corners and crevices. Always clean a plant of scale when the first individuals appear. Don't wait for a bad infestation.

Ferns are difficult to sponge or brush and often re-act badly to insecticides. The best method of ridding them of scale is to pick off or cut off all badly affected parts (in extreme cases cut away all the foliage) and then to dip the rest in a lemon oil or a nicotine insecticide prepared at the weakest dilution recommended by the manufacturer. Three or four hours after

HOUSE PLANTS

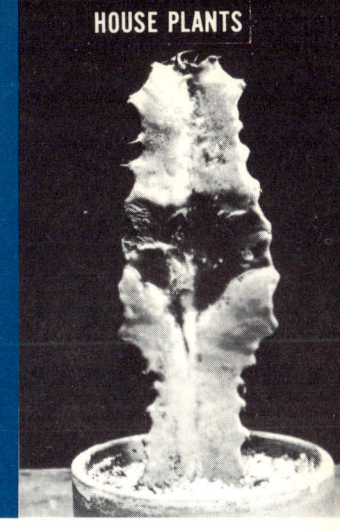

N. Y. Botanical Garden photos

Distortion, crinkling, and brittleness of center leaves indicates cyclamen mites.

Shoot with stem rot should be cut off below infection; cut is sulphur-dusted.

Stem rot disease of this euphorbia is now beyond point of cure.

dipping rinse with clear water. Repeat this treatment two or three times at weekly intervals.

If when you examine your plants you notice soft bodied pear-shaped insects clustered and crawling on the younger stems and beneath the leaves, insects that are green, black, pinkish, or purplish and that when mature raise their bodies above the leaf or stem on spidery legs, you have an infestation of—

APHIDS OR PLANT LICE

These creatures are common on a great many plants. They occur on calendulas, English-ivy, lantanas, fuchsias, hydrangeas, heliotropes, German-ivy, cinerarias and other kinds. They live by sucking the plant juices. They multiply very rapidly. As a result of their activities the plant is weakened and its foliage deformed.

By dipping a plant in or spraying it with a nicotine insecticide (the formula recommended above for red spider mites is fine) or a pyrethrum insecticide, aphids are quickly killed. Remember that every aphid must be thoroughly wetted to cause its death and it is sometimes difficult to reach those hidden in the folds of twisted leaves. Half measures when spraying are no good. Dipping is better in such cases.

Possibly your examination of stems and leaves will disclose easily seeable slow-moving pinkish soft-bodied insects that are oval, are fringed with short white filaments, and are covered with a white powdery waxy substance. You are likely to find, too, particularly in the leaf axils, cottony masses that are their egg cases. These insects are—

MEALY BUGS

They live by sucking sap and are likely to occur on a great variety of plants. Among their favorites are coleus, African violets, kalanchoes, crassulas, oleanders, dieffenbachias, fuchsias, gardenias, amaryllis and citrus fruits.

Control of mealy bugs is not difficult. The important thing is never to let them get numerous and well established. If you do the affected plants will cease to thrive and will develop sickly and undersized foliage and flowers. A sooty fungus that lives on the honeydew that these bugs excrete is likely to grow over the leaf surface.

One of the best preventatives of mealy-bug infestations is the weekly forceful syringing or spraying with clear water that I advocated above for the control of red spider mites. Not all plants (African violets for example) will stand this. Those that won't must be cleaned by removing the mealy bugs with a toothpick or soft brush. This is easily done when only a few are present. Another method is to attach a small cotton swab to a stick, dip it in alcohol and touch each mealy bug with it. Do not let the alcohol come in contact with plant.

The physical removal of mealy bugs with a stream of water, toothpick or brush is usually the most satisfactory treatment. In serious cases nicotine and white-oil-emulsion insecticides are helpful if carefully used. Volk is an excellent white oil emulsion. Use it at exactly the strength recom-

1759

HOUSE PLANTS

The younger leaves of this tuberous begonia are badly deformed and brittle from mite infestation.

N. Y. Botanical Garden

Scorching of leaf margins, at left, is caused by fungus anthracnose disease. Geranium leaf marks are the result of a bacterial leaf spot disease.

mended by its manufacturer for various kinds of plants and either dip them in it or spray them with it. Keep treated specimens out of sunshine and rinse them thoroughly with clear water a few hours after treatment.

If you find—

ANTS crawling over your plants look for other troubles. The ants themselves do no harm except that they carry the young of mealy bugs, aphids and scale insects from place to place.

Ants are there in search of food and the food they seek is the sweet, sticky secretion known as honeydew that is given off by scale insects, whiteflies, aphids and mealy bugs. Therefore if ants are present look carefully for one or more of these pests. Remove these and the ants will cease visiting your plants.

If, despite a most careful inspection, you find no visible creatures on the leaves or stems but if the leaves, particularly the younger ones, are distorted, crinkled, turned upward or downward at their edges, brittle and do not grow as fast as they should but remain stunted and puckered you may be sure that mites are the cause of the trouble. The kinds responsible are—

CYCLAMEN MITE AND BROAD MITE

These are invisible to the naked eye. Under the microscope they appear as nearly transparent white or greenish eight-legged oval creatures less than a hundredth of an inch long. The broad mite moves rapidly, the cyclamen mite moves slowly.

The broad mite feeds on exposed undersurfaces of the leaves. It is readily eliminated by dusting with finely powdered (special dusting) sulphur. Two or three applications at weekly intervals are usually sufficient. The cyclamen mite is more difficult. It feeds largely in the crevices of opening buds and leaves and is hard to reach. Mite killing dusts that contain azobenzene (such as Azo Fume 10 Dust manufactured by Plant Products Corporation, Blue Point, Long Island, N. Y.) are effective if thoroughly dusted among the young leaves and foliage. Submerging the plant in water that is kept at 110 degrees F. and keeping it there for fifteen minutes will kill mites without harm to the plant. The temperature must be accurately maintained.

Be careful not to bring mite-infested plants indoors. Destroy badly infested specimens. Give prompt treatment to those lightly infested. Never touch a clean plant after handling one that has mites.

Possibly the only insects you can find on or near your plants are—

BLACK FLIES, small creatures that hover in the air around them or—

SPRINGTAILS, tiny white jumping insects that appear on the soil surface, particularly after the plant has been watered. Neither is harmful. Both live on organic matter in the soil. If you feel you must eradicate them water the soil with water to which Black Leaf 40 (nicotine sulphate) has been added at the rate of two teaspoonfuls to each gallon.

DISEASES ON STEMS AND LEAVES

Look for diseases as well as pests. Perhaps sections of the stems have turned black, softened, and died. These STEM ROTS are particularly likely to affect geraniums, euphorbias, coleus, cactuses and begonias. The best treatment is to cut away promptly all diseased tissue, to dust

HOUSE PLANTS

the cut surfaces with powdered sulphur and to keep the plants rather "on the dry side." Avoid wetting stems and foliage.

In stemless and essentially stemless plants such as African violets, pick-a-back plants and calla lilies, rot may affect the centers of the plants causing them to decay and become wet and slimy. These are

CROWN ROTS

Clean out all decayed parts, dust with sulphur and keep on the dry side as advised for stem rots.

When leaves are marked with unnatural yellow or brown spots it usually indicates the presence of a—

LEAF-SPOT DISEASE

These are caused by fungi, bacteria and viruses. The spots vary in shape and size in different kinds. Pick off and burn every affected leaf promptly. Spraying with bordeaux mixture will help if a fungus is the cause of the trouble but probably not otherwise. Keep the plants widely spaced and avoid wetting their foliage. Leaf spots affect begonias, geraniums, philodendrons, rubber plants and many others.

A gray-white powdery or mealy covering on stems and leaves indicates—

POWDERY MILDEW

This fungus is found on kalanchoes, begonias, primroses and some other plants. It usually occurs when the atmosphere is too humid and stagnant. Good air circulation is a preventative. The application of dusting sulphur cures it.

Gray or yellowish gray moldy, water-soaked areas on the leaves and stems of such plants as primroses, begonias and Christmas cherries denote—

GRAY MOLD BLIGHT

This occurs when the atmosphere is too moist and circulation of air is poor. Correct these by better ventilation and careful watering. Pick off badly infected leaves and blooms and dust lightly infected parts with sulphur.

If young seedlings simply rot at ground level and topple over the cause is—

DAMPING-OFF DISEASE

This is encouraged by crowding (caused by sowing too thickly) by weakness (lengthening or "drawing") due to too high temperatures and insufficient light, and by careless watering and spraying. It rarely occurs among seedlings grown in vermiculite or sphagnum moss. Seedsmen sell anti-damping-off preparations that offer some protection if used at seed sowing time. When damping off affects a pot of seed-

Pick off and burn leaves of leaf-spot-diseased English ivy. Spray plant with bordeaux mixture.

N. Y. Botanical Garden
Damping-off disease, caused by keeping soil and foliage too wet, has effected begonia at right.

lings, keep them dryish, dust the soil surface with sulphur. Transplant as soon as they are large enough to handle to new soil.

BUGS AND OTHER TROUBLES UNDERGROUND

Not all pests and diseases occur on stems, foliage and flowers. Some inhabit roots and bulbs. Watch for these. If growth is unthrifty though the plant's surroundings seem satisfactory, if stems shrivel or leaves wilt without such obvious cause as draft or dryness, and if you find no pest or disease on the above-ground portions, suspect trouble below.

Don't turn plants out of their containers more frequently than necessary but don't hesitate to do so if it seems desirable to inspect their roots. To remove a plant invert it and tap the rim of its pot smartly on the edge of a firm bench or table.

Examine the outside of the soil and root ball. Perhaps there is nothing wrong other than the specimen is starved for food and is in need of repotting or fertilizing. If

1761

HOUSE PLANTS

N. Y. Botanical Garden photos

Here is the root of calla lily in excellent condition. Note root structure is completely intact.

Root rot disease has killed this lily. Roots are destroyed, leaves yellow, and flowers fail to open.

the roots are alive and healthy and are a dense firm mass that completely or almost completely fills the container, this is probably the case.

If, on the other hand, roots are comparatively few or they have rotted and died look further. It is possible, of course, that growth is not good because of unsuitable soil. A plant potted into this will not root vigorously and does not grow thriftily. Such a situation become evident within a few weeks of potting. The soil of plants that have grown well and have established themselves in their pots may be harmed by overwatering until it becomes soured and unsuitable for root growth. As a result, roots decay even though no disease or pest is present. This condition is reflected in poor top growth and often by wilting of the foliage. Therefore when you examine a root ball, check its drainage first.

Has the hole in the bottom of the pot been stopped so that excess water could not escape? Does it appear that the soil has remained in a wet, muddy condition for long periods? If your answer to either of these questions is "yes" then there is the probable cause of the unhealthiness of the plant. There is a good chance that no pest or disease is involved. In such cases remove as much of the old soil as possible without breaking any active roots and repot into a well drained container of fresh soil. Use as small a pot as the roots will easily fit into.

Let us consider other possibilities. You may detect—

EARTHWORMS in the soil. Perhaps you see them or maybe all you observe is the tunnels they make through the root ball or the coarsish castings (excreta) that are deposited on the soil surface (no need to remove the plant from its pot to detect these). Earthworms are admirable creatures in the good earth outdoors but they are completely out of place in the soil of potted plants. They disturb roots and grind the soil to a harmfully fine condition that prevents adequate aeration and drainage. Get rid of them. The simplest way of doing this is to soak the soil with water in which freshly slaked lime has been steeped or with water to which mustard of the hot, yellow, "English" type has been added at the rate of a teaspoonful to each quart.

Occasionally, in clusters on the roots, are found grayish slow-moving bugs that resemble the mealy bugs found on stems and leaves. These are—

ROOT MEALY BUGS

They secrete masses of waxy fibers and harm the plant by sucking its juices. The surest treatment is to gently wash all the soil off the roots and to dip them in a properly diluted nicotine insecticide before repotting them in clean pots and fresh soil.

Don't be alarmed if you find in the soil and especially on rotted roots and bulbs tiny slender thread-like—

WHITE WORMS

These are scavengers that live on dead and decaying plant tissues. They are not the *cause* of harm or death.

Amaryllis, narcissi, daffodils and some other bulbs may rot and collapse as the result of the infestation with grubs of the—

NARCISSUS BULB FLY

The grubs are fat white worms half an inch or more long. Bulbs that contain them feel light and soft. Burn all infected bulbs as soon as detected.

Earthworms here have tunnelled through the soil, disturbed the roots of the plant, clogged some of the drainage passages, and retarded its growth.

The earthworms may be brought to the surface by pouring lime water on the plant's soil. Pick the worms off and return them to the outdoor garden.

SUMMARY

The above-mentioned are the principal pests and diseases that attack house plants. A few others that are limited to special kinds of plants are dealt with under the discussions of those particular plants.

Always be alert for signs of attack but don't make the mistake of supposing that *because* your plant is not doing well it *must* be the victim of bug or blight. An unfavorable location or wrong care in such matters as watering, fertilizing, providing atmospheric humidity, etc., can soon cause a plant to look sickly.

Yellowing, dying and dropping of leaves beginning with the lowermost and working upward is a common trouble. Most usually this is due to excessive dryness of the atmosphere, lack of light, the soil having been too dry on one or more occasions, repeated overwatering, gas injury or simply age.

Plants that you obtain from the florist at full maturity such as poinsettias, cinerarias, and cyclamen are likely to lose a few leaves under the best conditions. If they are moved from a humid greenhouse to the dry atmosphere of a home the loss is apt to be more serious. Only by keeping such plants as cool as is practical for their kind and keeping the air as moist as possible can losses be kept at a minimum.

For those plants that will stand it, and only a few will not, a weekly hosing with a fine spray of water does wonders in keeping down insects, removing dust and promoting general health. Give this treatment in the bathtub or sink or out of doors in warm weather. •

These surface earthworms are the result of lime water soaking. Rough soil is from casts of worms.

Prevention is always the best cure; a weekly hosing in sink removes grime, helps keep down insects.

1763

HOUSE PLANTS

Transplanting and Repotting

Plants need larger pots as they grow bigger. Each begonia above is ready now for a transplanting.

The more successful your indoor gardening, the more often you will want and need to transplant and repot your house plant specimens.

FROM time to time you will have to transplant your house plants. This is done to give them additional root room and to provide them with fresh soil. The frequency with which they will need this attention depends upon the kind of plant and upon some other circumstances. Certain plants such as clivias, lilies-of-the-nile, Christmas cactuses, aspidistras, and palms need transplanting at long intervals only. This is especially true if they are established in largish pots. In their younger stages more frequent shifting is desirable. Even then a "move" every one to three years is usually all that is needed. Specimens contained in large receptacles may go five years or more without shifting.

Not all plants are satisfied with such infrequent transplanting. Quick-growing, soft-wooded kinds such as begonias and geraniums ordinarily need operating upon at least once a year, oftener while they are young. In all cases young specimens need more frequent transplanting than do older individuals of the same kind. It is the practice to begin with small plants and "grow them on" until they are in receptacles of good size and then to transplant at much less frequent intervals.

"Of good size" is a relative phrase that can be interpreted in terms of actual pot size only if the kind of plant is specified. An amaryllis may remain in a six-inch container for several years before it is moved to one seven inches in diameter whereas a geranium will need accommodating in a pot larger than the six-inch size before it is two years old. But a container eight inches in diameter is a "good sized" receptacle for a geranium and repotting will normally not be done oftener than once every year or two after this size is attained and even then the plant will not be given a *larger* pot on each occasion.

1764

HOUSE PLANTS

Many amateurs make the mistake of over-potting, of putting their plants into containers too large for their immediate needs. This leads to depletion of nutrients by leaching before the new roots occupy the soil and often to souring and stagnation of the earth because of over-watering. A mark of good culture is to develop fine healthy specimens in comparatively (but not ridiculously) small containers.

When a plant is transferred from a seed bed, cutting bed, flat, or the ground outdoors to a pot the operation is known as "potting." The same term is used to describe the planting of bulbs in pots and the transplanting of specimens from one pot to another. This latter is also called repotting. If wooden tubs are used instead of pots, "tubbing" and "retubbing" are the better terms, but potting and repotting are often used to cover these operations, too, and will be so applied here.

At potting time plants may be put into larger containers, into those of the same size as they have occupied, or into smaller receptacles. This last procedure is known as "reducing." It is employed if the specimen has a poorly developed root system in relation to the size of the container it is in. Reducing is also part of the annual cultural routine of a few specific kinds of plants even though they have good root systems. Martha Washington geraniums are notable examples of this.

Repotting without increasing the size of the container gives opportunity to provide the roots with some fresh earth. To do this necessitates disturbance of the roots; therefore, it should be undertaken at the *beginning* of the growing season only, not *while* the plant is in full growth. An exception may be made when dealing with a sick plant that has a poor root system. Special "hospitalization" treatment is then needed afterward.

"Moving on" or transplanting into larger receptacles provides new soil *and* increased root room. It may be done at the beginning of the growing season and, provided the roots are not disturbed, *during* the growth cycle. Always, however, it should be done sufficiently in advance of the plant going to rest for the roots to occupy the new soil before this happens.

HOW TO POT

Let the operations connected with potting be orderly. Have at hand enough of an appropriate soil mixture and see that it is in suitable condition. It must neither be too wet nor too dry, neither dusty nor muddy, but just comfortably in between. Assemble the pots or tubs you are likely to need. See that they are clean inside and out and dry. If you are using *new* clay pots, submerge them for about a minute in water and then let them dry. As they come from the kiln they are parched and the roots of plants potted into them are likely to stick to their sides and make later removal of the plants difficult unless this immersion treatment is given.

Pots are of various kinds. Watering practice is adjusted to meet the differing rates at which water is lost from the soil in them; good plants can be grown in glazed, painted and other nonporous containers just as in the ordinary porous clay pots where the finest of specimens can be produced.

It is possible to grow some plants (and I am not referring to bog plants) for long periods in pots that have no drainage holes in their bottoms. By expert adjustment of the amounts of water provided skilled gardeners can do this. But the game is not worth the candle. Ordinarily it is court-

For drainage, place over the bottom hole of the pot a large "crock"—a piece of broken flower pot, brick, clinker, or pebble for good drainage.

Over the large crock place additional crocks and then leaves or moss to prevent soil from washing down and clogging drainage through bottom hole.

1765

HOUSE PLANTS

Sift loam only when preparing soil for seed sowing, transplanting tiny seedlings, or potting newly rooted cuttings. Then use three-quarter inch mesh.

ing disaster to attempt it. It is so much simpler and surer to arrange for sharp drainage which automatically adjusts for modest excesses in the matter of watering. See, therefore, that your pots are provided with drainage holes.

Over these place a layer of crocks (pieces of broken flower pots), coarse cinders or small pebbles. Put one crock piece large enough to cover each hole—concave side downward immediately over it—and then an inch or two or three (depending upon the size of the pot) of smaller drainage pieces. To prevent the new soil from washing down and clogging this, cover it with a layer of half rotted tree leaves, moss, or similar material before you add soil.

Plants that are to be potted should be watered well a few hours beforehand. If transplanted when dry they are bound to suffer more than if their tissues are charged with moisture. Don't, however, soak them immediately before potting. If you do their soil is so wet that you are

Repotted geranium in section photo show new soil around old root mass. Note ample crocks in the bottom, for drainage; also that all flowers and buds have been picked off plant at time of the new potting.

HOUSE PLANTS

bound to puddle it in the potting process. Let it drain awhile.

Remove the plant from its container either by inverting it and tapping its rim sharply on a firm table or bench, at the same time covering the mouth of the pot with the hand to catch the ball when it slides out, or, if the specimen is too large to be handled in this way, by taking hold of the plant and lifting it slightly above the ground and tapping the rim of its pot or tub with a wooden mallet or heavy piece of wood. Examine the ball. Carefully consider to what extent it is advisable to disturb the roots.

WHEN GROWTH IS BEGINNING AND FOLIAGE IS SPARSE

If the season of active growth is just beginning and the plant has little or no foliage (as with a poinsettia, calla lily or cyclamen that is just coming out of its dormant season) or if you are pruning the plant quite severely and so are removing a goodly portion of its foliage as you might well do with a fuchsia, hibiscus, geranium, or begonia at the beginning of their growing seasons, then you can safely loosen the soil between the roots and shake out as much as can reasonably be removed without seriously damaging the roots. To do this, knead the ball gently with the fingers. With a sharp-pointed stick pick from its outer parts as much of the old soil as you safely can. Take away all old drainage material.

Now look at the ball. In its center a solid mass of soil remains. Frayed out from this are the roots you have disengaged from the soil. Don't let them dry.

Consider whether you can get the plant back into the same size pot. If it is a pretty big specimen of its kind you may want to do this—otherwise you will probably want to "pot it on." Whether or not you *can* pot it into a container of the size it previously occupied depends upon whether there is room to work new soil among the roots.

If you decide on a larger pot don't select one too big. Allow half an inch to an inch of space between the outside of the old ball of roots and the sides of the pot for new soil, perhaps a little more if the plant is being moved from a really big container.

Now you are ready for the actual potting. The plant is prepared, a suitably sized pot with drainage in it and good soil are at hand. Throw a little soil into the pot. Tamp it. Put the plant in place. Center it. It should be at such a depth that when the job is finished its upper roots will be covered with a quarter of an inch to half an

Plant is removed from old pot by tapping edge of pot on bench or table. Plant shown below has fine mass of healthy roots. Since, in this case, the gardener did not plan to prune back the foliage or divide the plant, he repotted the plant in a larger pot but did not disturb any of the roots.

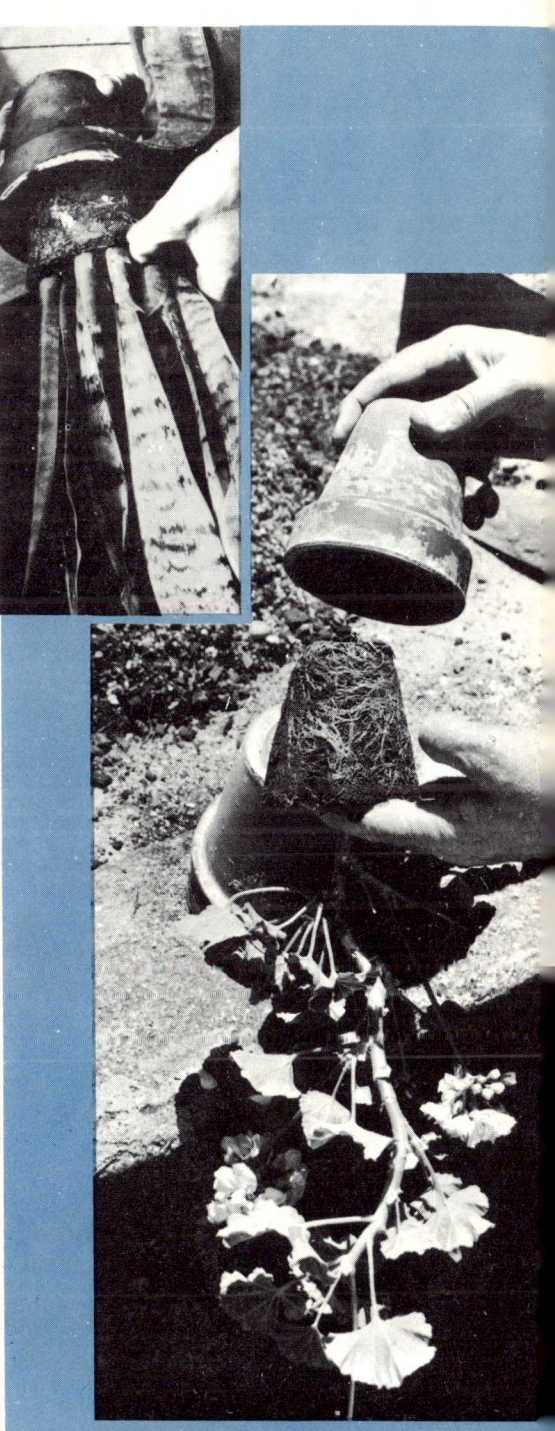

Irving Kaufman Studios

1767

HOUSE PLANTS

This plant is quite pot bound. Its roots have little further room for growth. Most plants need repotting when they have reached this development.

This plant is very pot bound. Its roots are now practically a solid mass and have exhausted the soil. Usually it is best to repot plant sooner.

Flourishing geranium at left is ready for a larger pot. The plant at right is in unsuitable pot and soil; needs transplanting to a smaller container.

inch of fresh soil. Allow ample room for water between the finished soil surface and the rim of the container. This means about three quarters of an inch with a five-inch pot, more for larger, less for smaller sizes.

If when you set the plant in position it is too low, lift it out and put more soil beneath it. If it is too high take away some of the soil that you put over the drainage.

With the plant in position fill soil around its roots and jar the pot a few times on the bench to settle it. Pack the soil with a potting stick or a wood lath until it is evenly firm throughout. The degree of firmness depends upon the kind of plant. For those that like loose potting such as begonias and ferns you should, by exerting considerable effort, be able to push your finger to a depth of perhaps half an inch into the surface of the newly packed soil. With firmly potted plants you cannot do this. Still you must not ram the soil until it is compressed to a state approaching that of a hard tennis court, a garden path, or of a school play yard. Use reasonable restraint. My impression is that women tend to pot too loosely, men too firmly.

When the soil is packed uniformly, and ordinarily to the same density as that of the old ball, finish the surface by levelling it with the fingers and pressing it to test its firmness. Don't leave finger marks or potting stick marks on the surface. Let the upper quarter of an inch be as loose as newly cultivated ground.

WHEN GROWTH IS BEGINNING AND FOLIAGE IS PLENTIFUL

All plants have their seasons of rest but not all lose their foliage and go dormant during such periods. Nor is it always possible or desirable to prune away a considerable portion of leafage at potting time. The beginning of the growing season (early spring for most plants) is the best time to pot leafy subjects such as dracaenas, ferns, dumb-canes, peperomias and pick-a-back plants. The actual method of potting is precisely that detailed above for "When Growth is beginning and Foliage is Sparse" except that you must not do as much violence to the root ball. If you do, a good proportion of the leaves will turn yellow and drop or die.

When such plants are well rooted simply remove the old drainage material from the bottom of the ball. Then with a pointed stick pick away a little of the old surface soil from the top of the ball and, without breaking them, loosen the tips of the roots on the outside of the ball slightly and pick out whatever old soil you are able to. This slight roughening of the outside of the ball makes contact between the new soil and the old more intimate and facilitates rooting.

If you find that your leafy plant is not well rooted but that its soil is in poor condition and you believe it would benefit from repotting, then remove as much of the old soil as possible with a pointed stick. Try not to break a single root and pot it into the smallest pot that will contain the roots with just a little to spare all around.

WHEN IN FULL GROWTH

Quick growing plants, particularly in their young stages, need potting more than once a year. Some of these transfers must be made while they are leafy and growing actively. The whole secret of success lies in not disturbing the roots. If possible, carefully remove the drainage and, with a pointed stick, tickle away a little of the surface soil—just enough to roughen it—not more. Then pot exactly as recommended above for "When Growth begins and Foliage is Sparse."

The potting of plants during their growing season should be done before they become excessively pot bound, that is before their roots form a solid mass around the outside of the soil ball.

PLANTS LIFTED FROM FLATS OR GARDEN

When you pot plants not taken from other pots but lifted from the garden or from flats or other receptacles in which several have been growing together you, of necessity, disturb their roots. Keep the disturbance at a minimum. Preserve the maximum amount of roots and keep as much soil as possible attached to them. Don't let them dry. From the time they are dug keep the plants out of drafts and sunlight.

The actual potting is exactly as described for "When Growth is beginning and Foliage is Sparse" except that you must handle the ball more carefully so that it will not fall apart. For this reason try to put the right amount of soil in the pot at first to bring the plant to its correct level. Lifting it out to correct the height of the soil beneath it is likely to break the ball. Take care, too, to work soil among the loose roots. Don't clump them together.

ROOTED CUTTINGS AND SEEDLINGS

Pot newly rooted cuttings more loosely than you would older plants of the same kinds. That is, do not pack their soil as firmly. Pots two to two and a half inches in diameter are ordinarily big enough. Put a single crock or a few cinders in the bottom of each and over this a bit of half

Here the small retarded plant has been removed from pot and crocks are picked out.

Now its soil ball is kneaded and the roots frayed out so that ball is reduced in size.

HOUSE PLANTS

Note the frayed-out roots and smaller soil ball of the small geranium above. Now it is ready for transplanting in fresh soil and in a smaller pot this is more suited for its size and development.

For transplanting to a larger pot, the healthy geranium is removed from its pot and, as was shown before, the pieces of crocks are carefully removed from between the roots without disturbing them.

rotted leaves. Throw a little soil on top. Place the rooted cutting in position, then lightly toss in more soil until the pot is filled to its brim. Then firm the earth about the roots with the tips of the fingers and level its surface.

From seed pots, seedlings are usually transplanted to flats, pots, or pans that hold several to many.

Sometimes plants are potted individually directly from seed pots. To do this, prepare small pots as advised above for rooted cuttings. Fill each to the brim with soil—then with a dibber or with the finger (as in pricking off) make a hole of ample size to hold the roots. Lower them into it. Press the soil lightly on the bench to level the surface soil. Seedlings should be planted at such a depth that the bases of their seed-leaves (the first that appear when the young plant emerges) are barely above soil level.

BULBS

The depth at which bulbs are planted in pots is important. It bears no relation to outdoor garden practice. For instance tulips and daffodils are covered with five inches or more of earth outdoors but are potted with their noses just showing above the surface. The important detail to consider is from where do the roots originate. Bulbs such as tulips, daffodils, hyacinths and amaryllis that are of considerable size and that produce all their roots from their bases are set high, with their tips level with the soil or in some cases, as with amaryllis and crinum lilies, considerably above the surface. This permits the downward growing roots to make maximum use of the available earth.

Bulbs that root from their tops as do calla lilies and tuberous begonias are set with their noses an inch or so beneath the surface so that roots are encouraged to develop and so that they find earth to root into. Easter lilies that produce roots from the base of the stem that grows from the bulb are set low in their pots and as the stem lengthens soil is added to encourage rooting.

Small bulbs such as freesias, tritonias and oxalis are set beneath the surface, with their tops just covered.

HOUSE PLANTS

After crocking the new larger pot, put in the plant without disturbing its root ball and then pack new soil around it. Photo at far right shows two geraniums now in proper pots.

The geraniums are given a spray watering after having been repotted. Just as you choose the right soil for each plant you pot, check water needs so it gets right amount.

Bulbs may be planted singly or several in a receptacle. When the latter plan is followed it is customary to set them much more closely together than in outdoor planting.

As roots develop from bulbs they press on the soil beneath and may lift the bulbs out of their pots. When this happens press them back. Such happening can be partially prevented by taking care when potting that the soil beneath the bulbs is left fairly loose and that the surface soil is packed quite firmly.

IN OSMUNDINE

Plants that naturally grow attached to trees instead of in the ground as do most tropical orchids and bromeliads will not live in soil. Pot them in osmundine (osmunds fiber) which is the roots of the osmunda fern. This can be obtained from dealers in horticultural supplies and usually from commercial greenhouses where orchids are grown. A special potting technique is called for when using this tough, wiry material.

Soak the osmundine in water overnight and chop most of it into egg-size pieces. Remove the plant to be potted from its container by slicing around the inside of its pot with a knife and then inverting it and tapping the rim of its container on a table or bench. Cut away any old growths that need removing. Pull off old osmundine that can be removed without damaging the roots. If the roots of the plant to be potted have little old osmundine attached to them, wrap a new piece under and around them. Now slip the plant into a pot that has been prepared by crocking it to a much greater depth than is usual for soil grown plants. Fill it one-third with crocks.

With the plant in position, begin packing around it pieces of osmundine. Put them into position with their fibers running vertically. If necessary, fray them out a little to achieve this. Between each newly inserted piece of osmundine and the pot slide a long-wedge shaped potting stick, and by using its lower end as a fulcrum and by pressing its top inward toward the plant squeeze the osmundine against the roots. Keep going around and around the pot adding piece after piece until even by the exercise of considerable strength it is im-

HOUSE PLANTS

Tubers are transplanted after well started. Here caladium tuber is started in the spring.

Roots of caladium come from top of tuber. It must be planted deeply so roots will be below surface.

Started in peat moss and sand, caladium is now transplanted for further growth in soil.

Here a transplanted young calla lily is filling out. As the plant matures the soil is topdressed, more water is given.

possible to push more in. Then finish off the top by clipping it neatly with a pair of scissors. The top of the fiber may be level with, or crowned slightly above the rim of the pot. It is important that osmundine be packed very firmly in the manner detailed, not by ramming it down from above as is done with soil. It is possible to pick up by its leaves a plant well potted in osmundine without danger of the pot falling off.

CARE AFTER POTTING

Immediately a plant is potted, water it thoroughly. Do this with a fine spray or by setting it in water to about half the depth of its pot. Don't disturb the soil by pouring a stream of water on it as from a hose or faucet. For a week or two after potting, keep it out of strong sunlight and make special efforts to maintain a humid atmosphere about it. Unless it is a kind known to resent water on its foliage, spray it lightly two or three times a day. Avoid drafts.

If the plant is small enough and particularly if it has few roots or if its roots have been disturbed much, it is a good plan to hospitalize it in a terrarium for two or three weeks or longer after potting.

Avoid overwatering newly potted plants. It is so easy, and so fatal, to do this before new roots have ramified through the new soil. After the initial soaking, let as long a period go as you safely can before you water again.

SUMMARY

Potting a living plant is something like performing an operation on a human being. It is a disruptive procedure in which part of plant body is lost because even though the greatest care is taken some fine roots are broken and destroyed. The operation

1772

HOUSE PLANTS

Too many roots are pushing this plant up; some are cut off, plant returned to same pot. For few roots, right, put new soil in same pot.

Slow-growing dracaena is getting a slightly larger pot, but plants like poinsettias and hibiscus sometimes are pruned for smaller pot.

Orchid potting requires a special procedure. Plant is removed from pot, old back bulbs cut away, old osmundine trimmed, four strong bulbs repotted with more osmundine.

must be regarded minor or major in proportion to the amount of root damage that is done. Just as a surgeon prefers to operate when the patient is in the best possible condition to withstand the shock and just as he provides the finest post-operative care, so the skilled gardener times his potting to coincide with that period of the plant's yearly cycle when it will do least harm, and so he takes measures to encourage the plant to re-establish itself as speedily as possible.

Bear in mind that one of the chief needs of any plant is water and that the roots collect this from the soil. Interference with or destruction of even some of the roots reduces the plant's ability to get needed moisture.

For this reason, potting that involves serious root disturbance should be done when the plant's *need* for water is at or near its minimum. Yet it is important that new roots be generated quickly after potting. The period that best meets these two requirements is just as new growth begins after a period of partial or absolute rest. This means, in the vast majority of cases, late winter or early spring.

Leaves give off large quantities of water in the form of invisible vapor and this loss must be made good, otherwise they turn yellow and die. When a plant is in full foliage the roots have all they can do to replace the water lost from the leaves. Any reduction of the plant's ability to absorb water then brings serious results. That is why I advise you that when potting plants in full leaf, not to disturb their roots at all. Because shade, a humid atmosphere, and freedom from drafts minimize loss of water from the foliage, take care to provide these conditions for your newly potted plants until they recover from the shock of transplanting. •

1773

HOUSE PLANTS

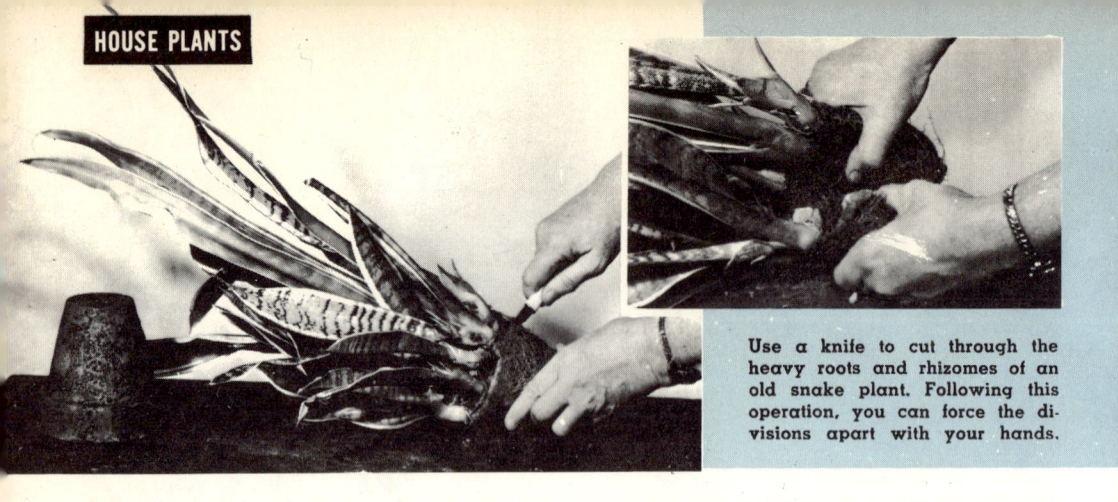

Use a knife to cut through the heavy roots and rhizomes of an old snake plant. Following this operation, you can force the divisions apart with your hands.

Divide to Multiply

The best way to increase or rejuvenate many types of plants is to divide them at the roots. This should be done as new growth starts.

DIVIDING a plant is the simplest method of obtaining increase and, if you do it carefully, one of the surest. It is also an excellent way of rejuvenating old, overgrown specimens that you do not want to put into larger containers but that need new soil and more root room.

Unfortunately not all plants lend themselves to this method of multiplication and restraint. Palms, dracaenas, Australian silk-oak and others that have a solitary central stem belong here. The kinds that can be divided easily are those such as aspidistras, snake plants, Boston ferns, lily-turf, and spider plants that form broad clumps with shoots arising from all over their surface soil.

The best time to divide is just as new growth begins; when, after a period of comparative rest, roots are becoming busy and new shoots are about to pop. Don't wait until these latter are half grown or even well advanced. Act as soon as you see them *beginning* to grow. Most plants start their new growth cycles in late winter or spring.

A few hours prior to dividing soak the plant in water. At operating time, spread the fingers of one hand over the top of its pot and between or around the shoots; turn it upside down; take hold of the bottom of the pot with the other hand and tap the pot's rim sharply on the edge of a bench or table. This will remove the plant from its container.

Now decide upon the most effective means of separating the clump before you into pieces—each consisting of a portion of leafage with a generous amount of roots attached.

Vary your technique according to the character of the roots. If they are massive, heavy, and densely packed as those of old snake plants, aspidistras, or ferns are likely to be, you will find a sharp heavy knife of great assistance in cutting through them. In extreme cases you may simply have to slice the root ball into thirds, quarters or smaller pieces with this tool, but it is always better to do no more cutting than necessary and then to pull the pieces apart by hand. In this way the most roots are preserved. When dealing with rhizomatous begonias, snake plants, and aspidistras of moderate root growth and other kinds that have a few thick stems or roots and a greater mass of fibrous roots, it is necessary to use the knife on the thicker members only.

Such lightly rooted plants as African violets and strawberry-begonias can be easily pulled apart after loosening the soil with the fingers into separate crowns.

The size of divisions depends upon what you want them for. If your purpose is to

HOUSE PLANTS

Place large piece of crock, hollow side down, in pot. Next comes gravel, leaves for good drainage.

Put each division into pot which does not crowd the roots and pack soil firmly around the plant.

get as many young plants as you can then let each be as small as possible. But if all you want is to reduce the size of an old fern, aspidistra or such like plant to more reasonable proportions then each division may be half as big as the mother specimen. Between these extremes, divisions of various sizes may be made. The most important thing to remember is that each should have as many healthy roots attached to it as possible. The greater the amount of roots in proportion to the amount of top growth, the surer is your success.

As soon as the divisions are made and before they have a chance to dry, pot them into pots as small as will easily contain their roots without crowding. If they have excessive foliage and seem to be top heavy, trim some of the oldest and largest leaves back moderately. Small divisions should be potted in the manner advised for potting cuttings, large divisions according to the method recommended for potting plants that have been lifted from flats or from the garden.

Newly potted divisions need some special care to encourage them to root and reestablish themselves. If small, they appreciate being kept in a terrarium or similar device for a while where the air about them is humid. Freedom from drafts, shade from strong sunlight, and a slightly higher temperature than normal (so long as the atmosphere is not too arid) are all helpful. It helps, too, to spray the foliage (except that of plants known to resent this) with water two or three times daily. After the initial soaking of the soil following potting, take great care not to overwater. Newly planted divisions need moderate amounts of water only until they readjust themselves to living a new life on their own. •

Divide old multiple-crowned African violets by pulling them apart with hands. Repot each crown.

A healthy, large-sized division of a fern is put into a new container. Care is taken to save roots.

1775

HOUSE PLANTS

N. Y. Botanical Garden photos

Prepare soil carefully and you'll be rewarded by better seedlings. Here the gardener presses soil with fingers to make an even degree of firmness for planting.

Indoor Plants From Seeds

Indoor planting pleasure may be derived by starting from scratches in the soil sown with the seeds of your favorite indoor flowers.

AS YOU study plants you'll read of many plants that can be grown from seeds—coleus, asparagus-ferns, eucalyptus, Australian silk-oak, patience plant, kalanchoes, gloxinias, cactuses and other succulents, and many begonias, to name but a few. It's fun to raise plants in this way, and not difficult if a few basic principles are followed.

The requirements of planted seeds and seedlings are simple. They need a medium into which to root, a supply of moisture, a suitable temperature, reasonable atmospheric humidity, nutrients, and adequate light. The most suitable time of the year to sow seeds of permanent house plants is in late winter or spring when the days are lengthening and the urge to grow is greatest. A few garden annuals may be seeded outdoors in summer for lifting in the fall and flowering in the winter but these are not, of course, permanent indoor plants.

Sow your seeds in clean pots or pans (shallow pots). Drain these by placing an inch or so of coarse cinders or crocks (chips of broken flower pots) over the holes in their bottoms. Put one large crock, hollow side down, over each hole, and a layer of smaller pieces over it. Spread coarse leaves or moss thinly over the crocks, then fill the pot or pan nearly to its top with seed soil and press it moderately firm with your finger tips. Let the finished surface be slightly lower than the rim of the container and quite level. Soil that has passed through a half-inch sieve will be fine enough, but when sowing very small seeds such as begonias and African violets top this off with a quarter-inch layer of the same soil sifted through a quarter-inch mesh or even through a piece of window screening.

Before scattering the seed, water the soil thoroughly with a fine spray or by immersing the containers nearly to their rims and letting the moisture seep to the surface from below. Use boiling water if possible; it serves to some extent as a sterilizing agent. Let the pots drain for ten or fifteen minutes, then scatter the seeds at such density that the distance between neighboring seeds is about four times their average diameter. Sift fine soil over them to a depth of once or twice their own diameters. Extremely small seeds such as begonias, gloxinias, and African violets need no soil covering.

Cover the containers with sheets of glass and place them where they are to germinate. The best place is in a moist terrarium or in a box that has an inch or two of damp moss or cinders in its bottom and is covered with a sheet of glass. These devices make it possible to maintain a humid atmosphere around the seed receptacles so that they do not dry too rapidly. Another method of checking drying is to place the seed pot inside a larger pot and pack the space between with peat

1776

HOUSE PLANTS

Water soil thoroughly; then sow seeds and press under lightly. Sift on fine soil; cover with glass.

Remove glass and give light when seedlings can be seen. They are watered, above, by immersion.

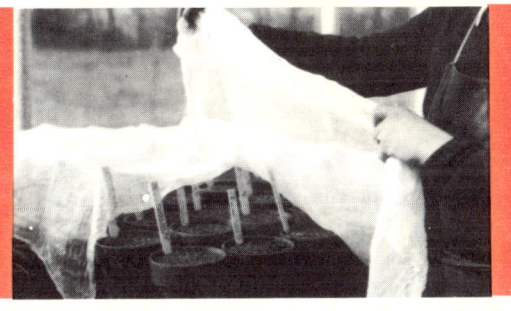

Seedlings must not receive strong sun when they have first sprouted; shade them with cheesecloth.

Keep track of the seedlings' progress. Once first leaves have unfolded, they can stand more light.

moss or sand which is kept moist. A temperature of sixty to seventy degrees is suitable for the germination of most seeds and it is best to keep them dark until they begin to break ground. Examine the containers daily and when the first seedlings can just be seen remove the shade and glass and give them good light, but continue to shade them lightly from bright sunshine at least for a few days. Never permit the soil to dry. Don't maintain it in a constant bog-like condition either.

Depending upon their kind, the young plants will need a location in sun or shade, in a warm temperature or in a lower one. Whatever you do, don't let the seedlings "draw" (become lanky and weak) as they will if they get insufficient light or too high a temperature.

SOIL SUBSTITUTES

Seedlings can be raised on media other than soil with the advantage that they are much less likely to suffer from damping off disease. Sphagnum moss and vermiculite are preferred soil substitutes. Because these substances, unlike soil, do not supply nutrients, it is necessary to provide for these in other ways.

Sphagnum moss occurs in bogs in many parts of the country and is usually obtainable from greenhouses where orchids are grown. It may be used alive or dead. Vermiculite is sold by dealers in horticultural supplies. Prepare sphagnum by re-

Seedlings can be transplanted when second leaves have formed. The plants may be lifted with dibber.

Prying plants out may break root structure. A better method is to turn plants out and drop ball on table.

HOUSE PLANTS

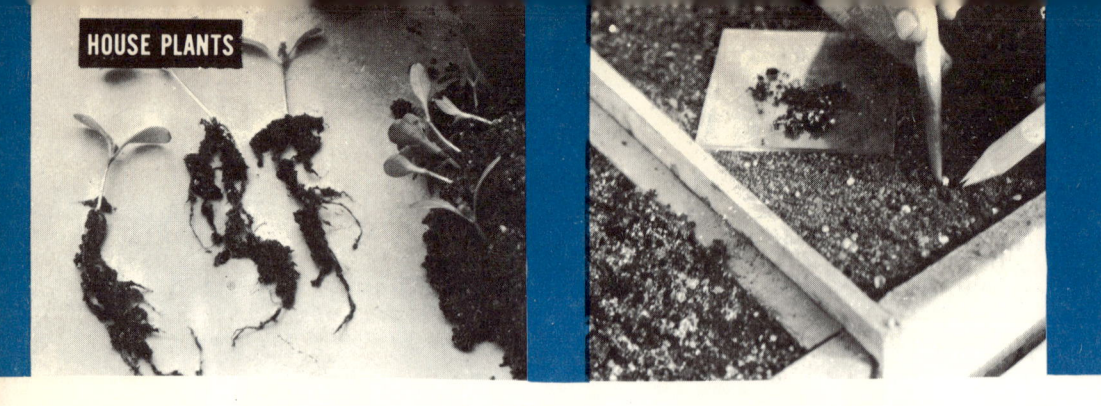

Separate plantlets without damaging roots, left. Young plants looking like this have an adequate healthy root system. Do not cut or shorten them.

Very tiny seedlings, like the begonias shown above, are picked up with a notched label stick rather than fingers; transplanted without handling.

When pricking off, use a blunt wooden dibber to make a hole large enough not to crowd roots. Hold the seedling by leaf and lower gently. Firm soil.

moving from it sticks and other foreign matter and by rubbing it through a screen having a quarter-inch mesh. Vermiculite needs no preparation.

Whichever is used, simply fill well drained pots or other containers nearly to their brims with it and then soak with water in which an ordinary 5-10-5 garden fertilizer has been stirred at the rate of five or six teaspoonfuls to the gallon. Don't pour the undissolved residue of the fertilizer on the pots. Throw it away. Vermiculite needs no pressing down but sphagnum should be firmed moderately before it is soaked with the fertilizer solution.

Scatter the seeds evenly. If they are tiny they will need no covering of sphagnum or vermiculite, but if they are sizable cover them to about twice their own average diameters with one of these materials.

After sowing, treat exactly as you would seeds planted in soil with these differences: always water from above in the form of a fine spray. The immersion method of watering, particularly for seeds sown in sphagnum, is not satisfactory. Water once every week or two with the fertilizer solution recommended above.

THE MASON JAR METHOD

With little or no trouble you can raise seedlings in a Mason jar, or other glass container. It is a method particularly adapted to the requirements of begonias, gloxinias, African violets, primroses and other kinds that have small seeds and need a moist atmosphere.

Instead of soil, use screened leaf mold, leaf mold and sand or peat moss and sand. Have this quite moist but not so wet that water runs freely from it if you squeeze it. Lay the Mason jar on its side and spread in it a layer of the soil substitute. Press this down, smooth it and level it with the blade of a table knife so that the finished surface is level with or is slightly higher than the lower edge of the jar's mouth.

Put the seeds to be sown on the end of a knife blade. Insert this through the neck of the jar and by jiggling it or tapping it lightly, scatter the seeds evenly. No soil covering is necessary. Fasten the jar's cover in place without using the rubber ring that makes it airtight and place the jar out of direct sunshine in a well lighted position. Shade with paper until the first signs of germination are evident. If weeds come up snip them off with a pair of scissors.

When the young plants appear, ventilate by removing the cover for all or part of each day. Much moisture condensing on the inside of the glass indicates a need for such airing. It is unlikely that any watering will be necessary until the plantlets are ready for transplanting but should the sowing medium become too dry it can be moistened with a spray of water. When the seedlings are large enough to be pricked off, remove them with a fork or

HOUSE PLANTS

Young seedlings should be planted in this manner with seed leaves (first leaves) level with soil surface and a moderate space left for watering.

Note that the seedling, upper center, is planted too low in a pot insufficiently filled with soil. It may get too much shade or be flooded with water.

The seedling, upper right, has been planted too high in its pot. Also note long sensitive stem exposed; leaves should be even with soil surface.

spoon and transplant them as you would seedlings raised in more conventional fashion.

TRANSPLANTING OR PRICKING OFF

As soon as the seedlings have formed their first true leaves—that is those which develop immediately after the original leaves that uncurl from the seed "prick them off" (transplant them) either individually into small pots or better still several in a pot, pan (shallow pot) or flat, spacing them two to three inches apart in order to give them adequate room for growth.

Make sure the containers into which you transfer them are well drained. Handle the plants so that all possible roots are saved. Don't crowd them into holes too small to easily accommodate the roots. Avoid pinching or breaking their delicate stems. Of course, don't let the roots dry. Make each hole with a dibber (a pencil will do) or with your finger. Lower the plant into it so that the bases of its first true leaves are almost down to ground level, then firm the soil moderately with the finger tips. Water well immediately after transplanting and keep the young plants shaded lightly and out of drafts. A humid atmosphere is of great aid in preventing wilting. Take particular care to let the soil dry out moderately, but not become dry enough to cause wilting, between waterings. Overwatering is fatal to recently transplanted seedlings. •

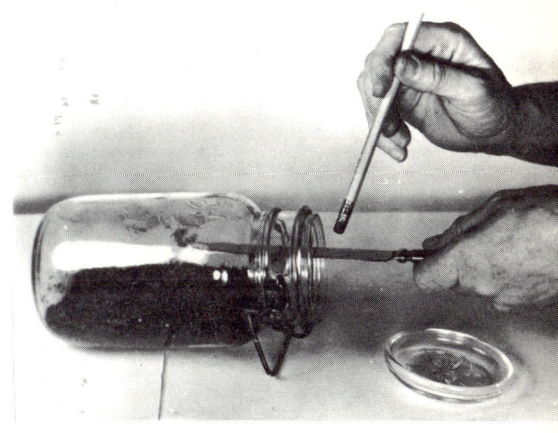

For a miniature terrarium for small seeds that need moisture, sow seeds by tapping off blade in jar.

Plants from small seeds like begonias and African violets are lifted out when big enough with fork.

After taking them from Mason jar, transplant them into pans or flats with holes two inches apart.

HOUSE PLANTS

Shown here are leaf and stem cuttings, left and right, from plants which will propogate from slips.

Irving Kaufman Studio photos

New Plants from Cuttings

Large plants from little cuttings grow—and easily indoors when carefully planted after selection from suitable healthy parents.

A CUTTING is a slip. It is a piece of a plant without roots which properly prepared, planted, and cared for will develop into a new individual. A surprising number of different kinds of plants can be raised from slips. The technique is simple once you've mastered a few rudiments.

The most important fact to grasp is that unrooted cuttings have extremely limited ability to absorb moisture and therefore if you don't take measures to protect them they will dry and die. Until they have adequate roots, cuttings dessicate easily even though the sand, peat moss, vermiculite or other medium in which they are planted is kept wet.

Watering is not enough. To prevent moisture being lost faster than it can be replaced you must take other measures, too.

The methods of preventing excessive moisture loss are: provision of a humid atmosphere, shade from direct sunshine and protection from drafts. It's as simple as that.

The easiest way to ensure these conditions is to keep newly planted cuttings inside a container that admits light. A satisfactory device is a terrarium. An aquarium emptied of water will do, or, in a pinch, a wooden box with a sheet of glass over it, although this latter is scarcely light enough for some plants. An inverted glass or glass bowl or a bell jar made by cutting the bottom out of a gallon cider jar are other possibilities. Such containers are in effect little greenhouses. They afford protection from drafts, and the air inside is made humid by moisture given off by the slips and the material in which they are planted. In terrariums and similar devices, additional atmospheric humidity can be provided by standing the cutting pots on a layer of gravel, cinders or peat moss that is kept moist.

KINDS OF CUTTINGS

Cuttings may consist of single leaves or parts of leaves, pieces of stem without leaves or, more usually, a piece of stem with leaves attached. Most often the stem is a terminal portion, the end of a shoot, but this is by no means necessarily so. Many plants can be successfully grown from mid-section stem cuttings—that is from pieces of stem severed at both ends. Let's consider different cutting types.

The chief veins of a rex begonia leaf can be cut several places to form roots from each incision.

HOUSE PLANTS

Place a small pot, with drainage hole plugged, inside a larger pot that is well drained. Pack space between with 50-50 mix of sand and peat moss. Insert cuttings; water center.

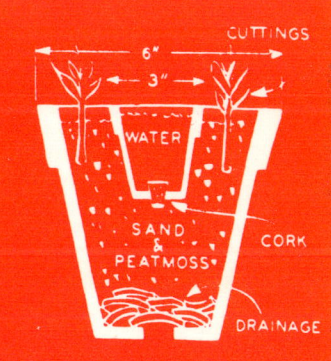

A three-inch pot is a good choice to place in a larger six-inch pot. With hole in small pot plugged, water will seep through porous clay wall and moisten the new cuttings' soil.

Cover with a bell jar or cider bottle with bottom cut off. Use blocks to raise jar slightly to admit a small amount of fresh air. Alternatively, pot may be placed in a regular terrarium.

HOUSE PLANTS

A Christmas begonia leaf cutting is prepared by cutting its stalk with sharp knife to an inch long.

Now poke a small hole and insert the newly-made leaf cutting in a flat of sand or other medium.

N. Y. Botanical Garden photos

LEAF CUTTINGS

Not all plants can be rooted from single leaves. African violets can be. So can gloxinias, peperomias, snake-plants kalanchoes, echeverias, many begonias, and a number of other items. Select mature leaves—not those that have not yet reached full size nor individuals so old and tired that they are already beginning to die. See that they are disease-free and without pests. If they have stalks (echerverias and the panda plant are examples of kinds that do not) cut these so that they are not more than an inch long. Plant the cuttings in well-drained pots of firmly packed sand, or sand and peat moss or in pots of loose vermiculite. Set them at an angle of about thirty degrees from the vertical with their bases about half an inch beneath the surface.

Each leaf so treated gives rise to one new plant. In some cases more than one plant can be gotten from a leaf. If you cut a snake-plant leaf into pieces three to four inches long and insert them top sides up as single leaf cuttings, each will give rise to a new plant. If you cut the leaf of a rex begonia into wedges, each two or three inches long and each with a strong vein down its center and plant these as leaf cuttings, each will give rise to a new in-

Shown upper right are typical cuttings of cactuses and succulents not needing moist atmosphere.

Dark leaf at right was the original leaf cutting of a peperomia. New shoots and roots have developed.

This cutting consisted of a wedge-shaped leaf portion from a rex begonia. New leaf is sprouting.

N. Y. Botanical Garden photos

1782

HOUSE PLANTS

Panda plant leaves inserted nearly upright in a bed of firm sand soon root and produce new plants.

After about two months this Christmas begonia leaf cutting has developed roots and is ready for potting.

dividual. Another method is to take a rex begonia leaf, slice through its main veins just beneath each of several points where they fork to form branch veins, and lay it underside down on two or three inches of sand, sand and peat moss or vermiculite. Put a few pebbles on it to keep it flat. If treated then like other leaf cuttings a new plant will develop from every incision.

STEM CUTTINGS

Make stem cuttings from healthy shoots only. Don't use very soft or very weak ones. In most cases you will use terminal or tip cuttings which are actually shoot ends. Three or four inches is a good length for most cuttings but some kinds, such as English ivy, may be made longer, and other kinds root readily from shorter pieces. Usually it is desirable to include three or four nodes (stem joints) in each cutting, more if the leaves are close together.

Prepare the slips by removing all leaves from the lower inch or two that will be below the surface of the rooting medium. With cuttings such as hydrangeas that have very big leaves, cut away the upper third as well of each of the full-sized ones that remain.

Cut across the bases of the cuttings with a sharp knife or razor blade. A square cut

With a sharp knife, lower leaves are being removed from geranium, upper right, to prepare stem cutting.

Stem is cut squarely across just below node—the joint on stem from which a leaf has been growing.

With a dibber (a peg of wood) the cutting is then firmly planted in a well-packed bed of potting sand.

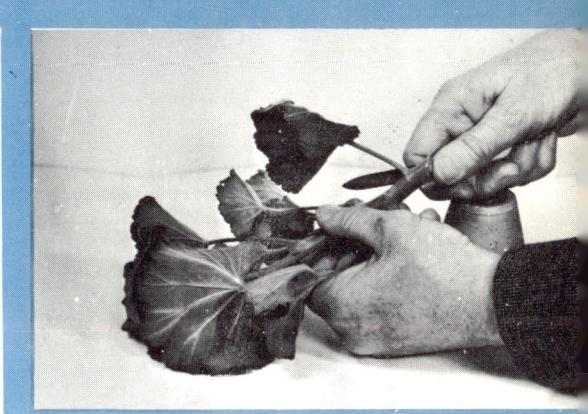

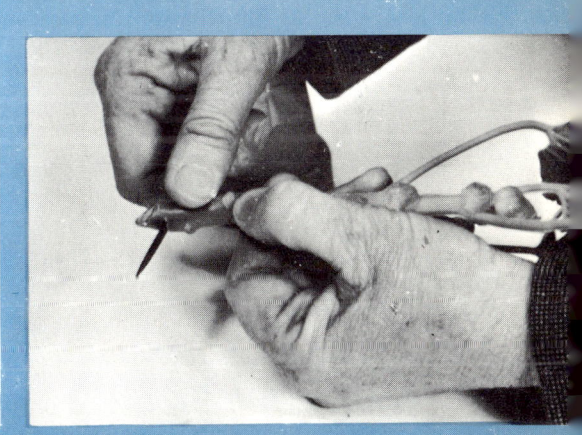

HOUSE PLANTS

When vermiculite is used as a rooting medium, do not pack it firmly. Merely push cuttings into it; no dibber is needed.

Here hydrangea cuttings from the mother plant are being made. For propagation select only strong and healthy shoots.

Because hydrangeas have large leaves, the lower ones are removed and those left are cut back before slips are planted.

is better than a slanting one. Let the cut be at a distance beneath a node (joint on the stem from which a leaf develops) equal to half the thickness of the stem.

Sectional stem cuttings are a satisfactory means of propagating many plants including English ivy, philodendrons, geraniums, dumb-canes and dracaenas. They may be leafy or without leaves. If they have foliage, prepare and insert them exactly as you would terminal cuttings but cut their upper ends slantwise in such a fashion that the lower part of the cut begins just above a node. If the stem you use is without leaves, as the old stem of a dracaena or dumb-cane will be, then simply cut it into sections—each two to three inches long.

Both terminal and sectional cuttings may be planted in pots of sand, sand and peat moss, or vermiculite. If you use the latter do not pack it. Merely push the cuttings into it until they stand erect and then water thoroughly with a fine spray. If you use sand or a mixture of sand and peat moss see that the material is moist but not wet and pack it as firmly as you can by pressing it with your fingers and pounding it with a beater or rammer. Level the surface now with a pencil or with a thicker dibber. If the cuttings are too thick to go into holes made by a pencil, make holes of such depths that the bases of the cuttings will rest upon the bottoms of them. Pack the root-medium firmly around the base of each cutting and soak it with a fine spray of water.

Instead of inserting them vertically it is often just as satisfactory to lay leafless sectional stem cuttings horizontally with their upper edges showing above the rooting medium. This is commonly done with dracaenas and dumb-canes. The shoots that grow from laid down cuttings assume a normal vertical position and new roots are produced from the entire length of the piece of old stem.

CUTTINGS IN WATER

Cuttings of many plants root readily if they are placed with their lower ends in water. Pothos, philodendrons, English ivy and a host of others respond to this treatment. Yet I have never felt that as a means of propagation it is quite as satisfactory as is planting the slips in a more solid

Cuttings need special care to survive first shock of separation. Shelter them from sun and drafts.

Cuttings of wandering Jew have been started in sand and have sufficient roots for planting in pot.

HOUSE PLANTS

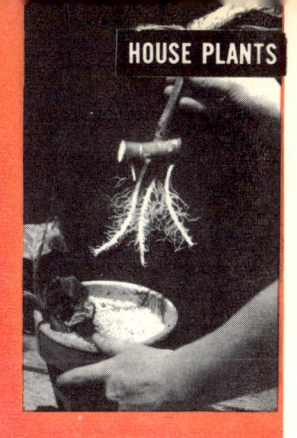

This cutting has been started in water. Plants like coleus and wandering Jew may be propagated easily in this way.

This section stem cutting of a philodendron was planted vertically in peat moss and has rooted and developed shoot.

After a few weeks, lift out your cutting to examine the rootlets. This dumb-cane has developed enough to be ready for potting.

rooting medium. Difficulty is likely to occur when the rooted cuttings are transferred to pots of soil. Roots developed in water are especially brittle. You must take great care at potting time not to break them and you should use a very sandy soil at the first potting as they adapt themselves to this more quickly than to a heavier earth.

CARE OF PLANTED CUTTINGS

Cuttings of cactuses and other succulent plants that grow naturally in dry desert atmospheres do not need a moist atmosphere. Other kinds do, and after planting should immediately be given the protection of a terrarium or one of the substitute devices discussed at the beginning of this chapter. Keep them out of direct sunlight but where they get good light. A temperature slightly warmer than that enjoyed by mature plants of the same kinds suits them best.

At first little or no ventilation will be required—only enough to prevent the air being so heavily charged with moisture that it condenses conspicuously on the inside of the glass. After a week or two the cuttings should begin to perk up and later to send out roots. Then you may gradually accustom them to more ventilation and finally to normal atmospheric conditions. To promote humidity and to prevent wilting sprinkle the cuttings lightly with a fine spray of water once or twice a day when the weather is bright but never do this so late that the foliage is still wet when night comes.

When you suspect that they are rooted, cautiously dig up one of the slips. If it has a good number of roots that are from one to two inches long it is time it was taken up and potted. If not, replant it carefully and wait a while longer.

The rooting medium in which your cuttings are planted should be kept always evenly moist but not constantly saturated. This latter condition soon results in decay and death. If any leaves show signs of decay, pick off the affected parts at once. Remove promptly any cuttings that die. A review of the "Bugs and Blights" chapter will help you recognize any diseases.

The most favorable time for inserting most cuttings is from February to October inclusive. The dead months of winter are generally less satisfactory. •

N. Y. Botanical Garden photos

Short sections from the stem of a dumb-cane are laid horizontally in sand or other suitable soil.

Your result is a new plant with attractive shoots and healthy roots, ready to be individually potted.

INCINERATOR

BACKYARD INCINERATOR

This attractive unit contains storage facilities and garbage disposal

By David X. Manners

HANDSOME FACE BRICK makes a structure that dresses up your back yard, as the photo shows.

CHIMNEY CAP prevents rain from wetting refuse in unit. Make cap as described in text.

YOU can solve the twin problems of where to burn trash, and where to store lawnmower, garden furniture or tools, with a single unit. By using an attractive face brick in the structure's construction you can further enhance its pleasing design.

A six-inch concrete slab affords firm support for the project and provides the floor for both the storage section and the ashpit. The slab is reinforced with six-inch mesh placed at the halfway point.

The partition wall between storage and incinerator sections is of masonry block. The incinerator may be lined with either hard-burned or firebrick. For the incinerator grate, use either a 12x24-inch cast iron affair, supported on a ½x2-inch steel strip set between fourth and fifth brick courses, or—less expensively—mortar ⅝-inch rods, on three-inch centers, between those courses.

Chimney Support

Support brickwork over the ashpit opening with a steel T. A 2x2-inch angle supports the chimney masonry at the point where smoke enters the flue. Note the piece of angled brick at the chimney throat and the smoke shelf behind it. These serve as a baffle against downdrafts and insure

STORAGE UNIT DOOR is made of heavy aluminum with edges bent over ½ inch for reinforcement.

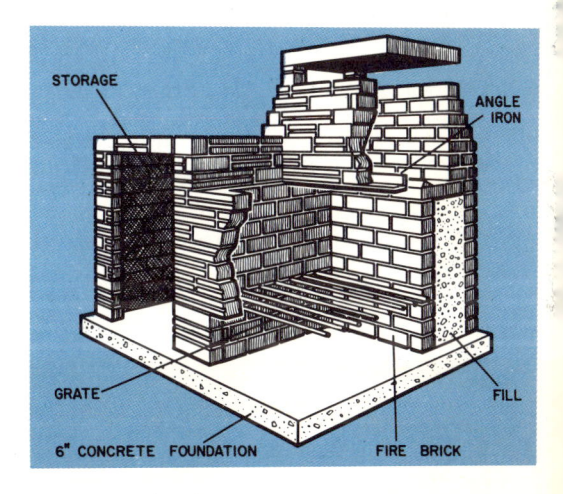

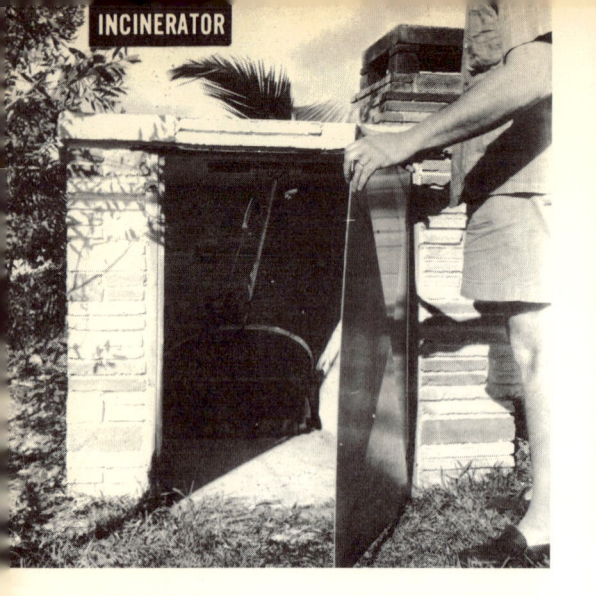

INCINERATOR

DOOR OPENING is framed with 2x4's nailed to mortar joints. Hasp closure permits padlocking.

SPACE IS ideally suited for storing power mower, gas can, etc. Grade-level slab makes easy entry.

proper operation of the incinerator unit.

The lid covering the incinerator opening, a 1/8x16x16-inch steel plate, can be fabricated at any local forge or metal working shop for about $5. The four-inch lengths of steel rod welded to corners of the plate serve as hinge pins. The pins are set into eye-bolts cemented between bricks. Another length of rod welded to the front of the plate at midway point serves as lid handle.

The interior of the chimney base is filled with rubble or compacted dirt. Finish the inside of the chimney smooth with a coating of mortar. A spark arrestor screen safeguards against fire hazards, and a chimney cap prevents wetting down of unburned trash by rain.

A 3/4x24-inch pipe set as a threshold in the storage section protects the edge of the slab against damage and also serves as a stop for the door. Door is of aluminum

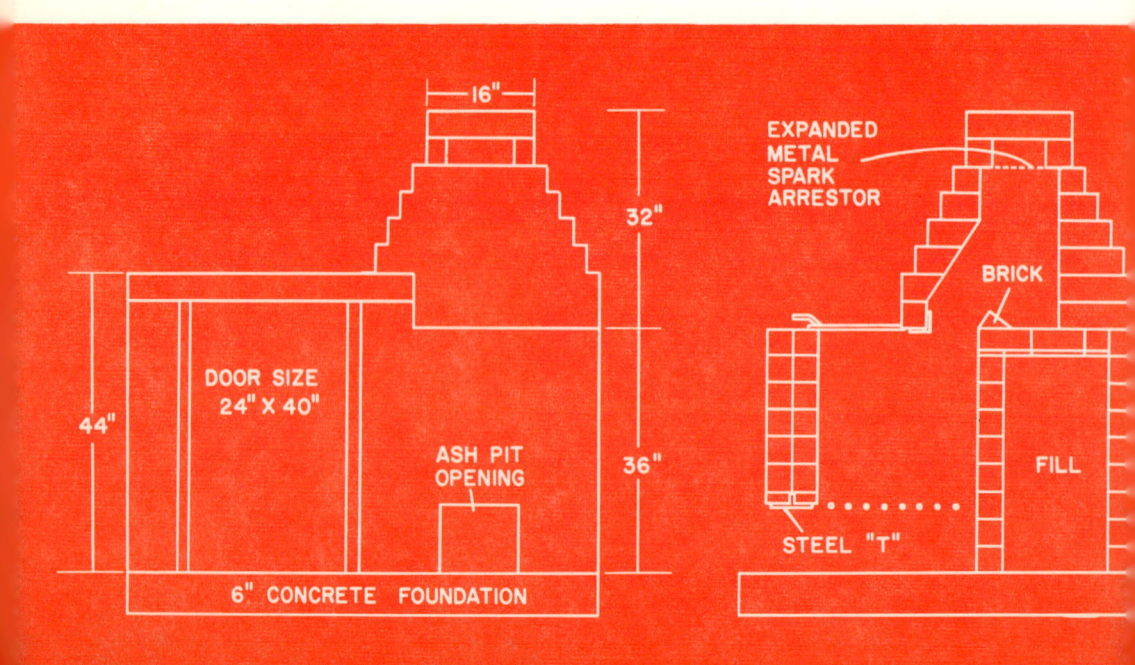

INCINERATOR

INCINERATOR LID is ½x16x16-inch steel. Rod pins set in eyebolts act as hinges. Cost: $5 at local forge.

INSTALL LID with sufficient clearance so it can be tilted back slightly when open, as shown above.

and can be made at any sheet metal shop. However, you can make an equally satisfactory door of tongue-and-groove boards, joined on the inside face by battens. Door opening is framed on each side by 2x4's nailed to mortar joints. The front edges of the 2x4's are rabbeted so that when the door is closed it fits flush.

The opening above the door is bridged by a 2x2x36-inch steel angle. Roof over the storage section is a 4-inch concrete slab poured after brick facing is in place and has set hard. The facing serves as outside edges of the slab form. The bottom of the form is made of tongue-and-groove boards set across the span and left in place after the slab is poured. These boards are supported underneath with props at 16-inch intervals until the slab has set. The slab is reinforced with ½-inch rods, laid checkerboard style, with intersections wired together. Space rods a foot apart. •

MATERIALS NEEDED:

- 00 standard-size bricks (8¼x3⅝x2¼ inch approximately)
- 15 masonry blocks
- 3 sacks portland cement
- 3 sacks lime
- ½ yard sand
- 15 cu. ft. concrete for foundation
- 8 cu. ft. concrete for storage roof and chimney cap

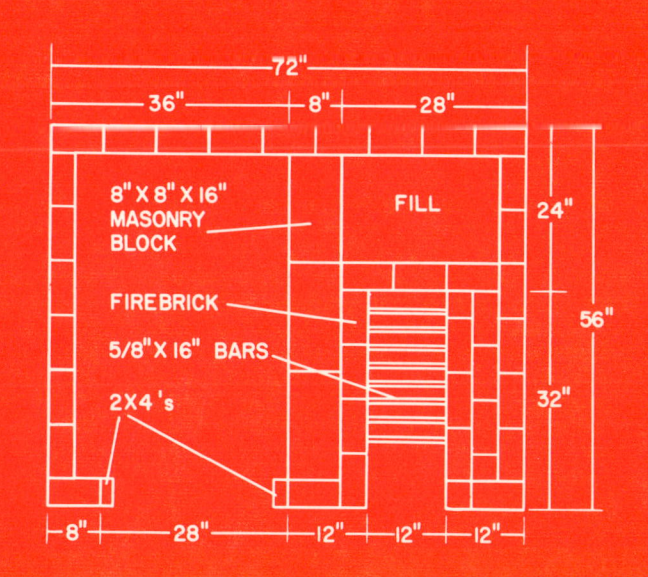

JOINTS

The strength, the durability and the appearance of any project will depend quite heavily on both the type of joint which is decided upon as well as how well the job is executed by the builder.

Wood Joints You Should Know

Discover the correct joint for your project and the easiest way to construct it

THERE is one cardinal rule to joint-making. Choose the easiest-to-make joint that is adequate for the job. It doesn't make sense to go through the trouble of constructing a dovetail if a simple rabbet will do. This is truer today than ever before because new and available adhesives now make a bond which holds together under tremendous stress.

Of course, if you are a particular craftsman and get your kicks from precise fitting of intricate cuts you'll still be making dovetails and mortise-and-tenon joints just for the joy of it. And this is fine. But for the practical, week-end carpenter who has limited time and wants a job done —choose the simple joints, especially if the cuts are possible on available power tools.

There's another angle to this business of joint-making, too. Times have changed. It wasn't too far back that joints were made by hand. A well executed dovetail was the mark of craftsmanship, and projects were often designed so the joints were visible. Pride prompted this and it was also a way that the quality of the piece could be judged.

Today you don't have to rely on hand

JOINTS

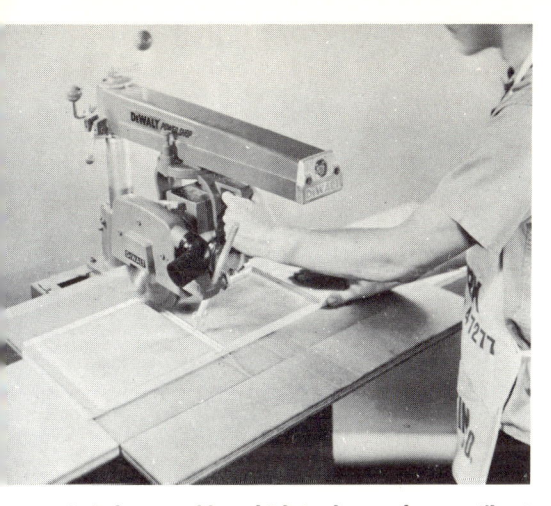

A dado assembly, which is shown above, will cut dadoes and grooves as fast as the blade can be pulled across board, and with greatest precision.

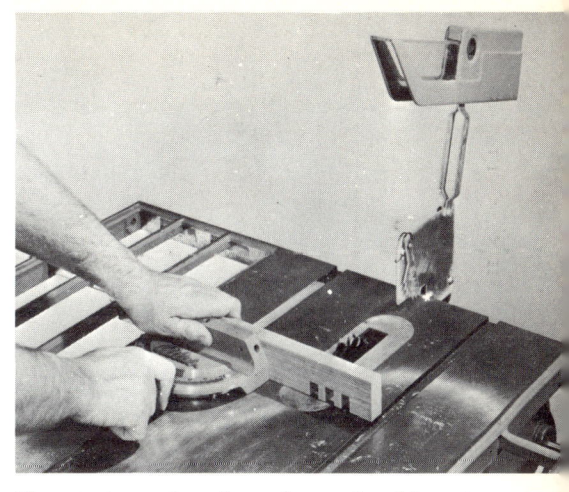

The surest way to make a clean cut and to mate a joint properly is to have correctly aligned power tools. Check your machinery periodically.

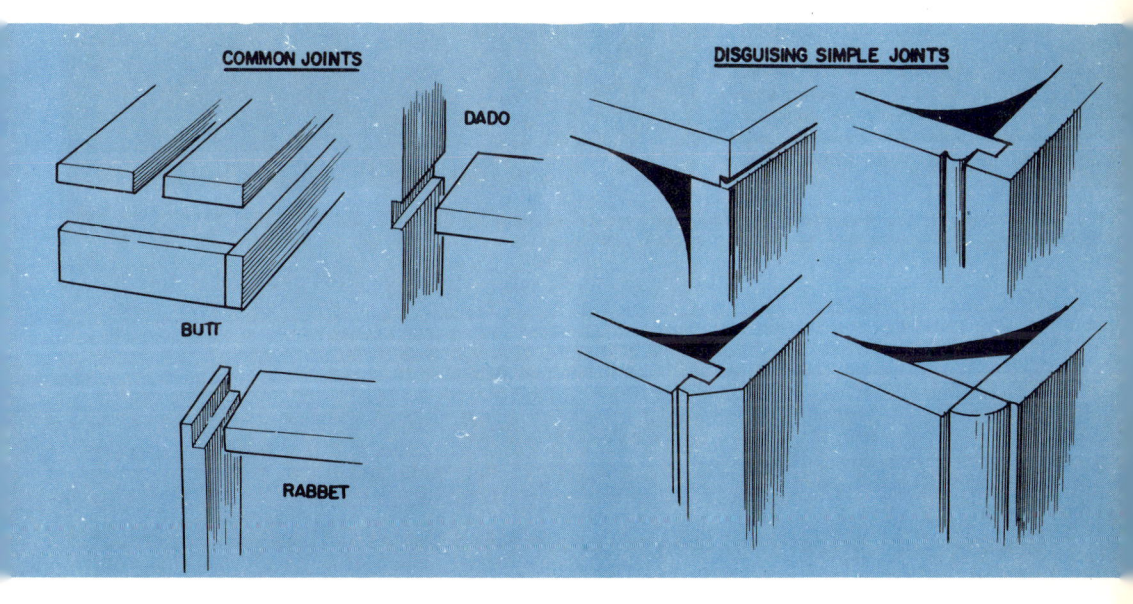

COMMON JOINTS: BUTT, DADO, RABBET

DISGUISING SIMPLE JOINTS

skill. You can do the jobs with power. Dovetail attachments are available for drill press and router so you can produce such an assembly fast and accurately.

In the final analysis you choose a joint for two reasons, appearance and strength.

A miter joint puts together two pieces of wood so the corner does not reveal any unsightly end grain. If you were making a piece of furniture for the house, you would consider this angle. But if you were making the project for the garage, you could use a butt joint instead.

If you needed a horizontal piece between two uprights and it was going to hold up nothing but itself, a butt joint could be used. But if the horizontal piece was a shelf that would have to support a load of books, then a dado in the uprights would give the shelf a ledge to sit on.

When you pull on a drawer front, you're applying a stress that tends to pull the drawer front away from the drawer sides. So any joint you use here should tend to fight this. That's why dovetails are used so often at this point. The interlocking fingers of the joint tend to fight this strain even if the glue fails.

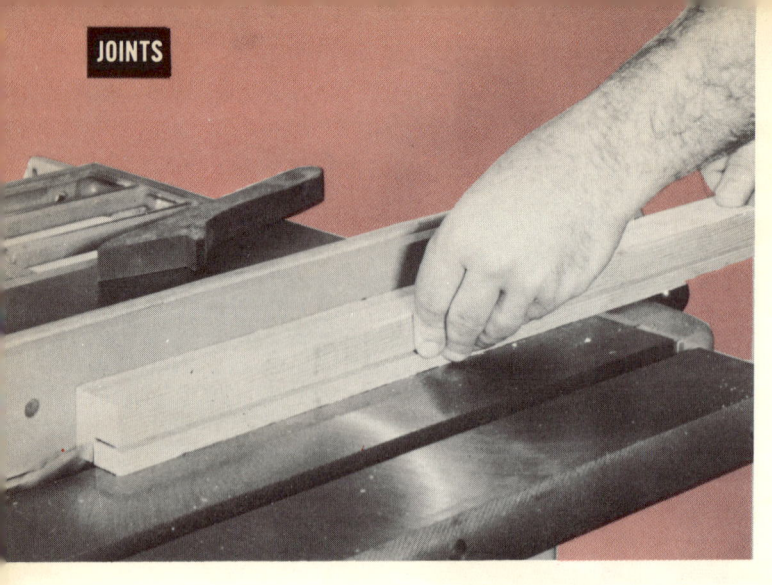

JOINTS

An easy way to cut a simple rabbet is to use a standard saw blade, as shown at left. Just make two passes to trim away excess wood and to form L-shape which is needed.

It is advisable to make an outline of all cuts with a backsaw if hand tools are to be used; any waste stock left from cut must be cleaned with sharp chisel.

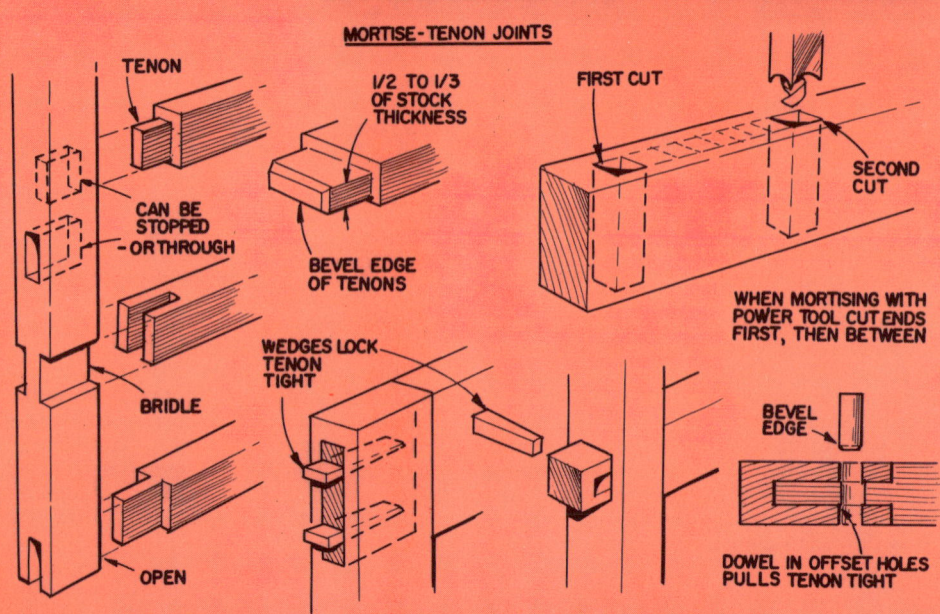

MORTISE-TENON JOINTS

TENON

1/2 TO 1/3 OF STOCK THICKNESS

FIRST CUT

CAN BE STOPPED -OR THROUGH

BEVEL EDGE OF TENONS

SECOND CUT

WHEN MORTISING WITH POWER TOOL CUT ENDS FIRST, THEN BETWEEN

BRIDLE

WEDGES LOCK TENON TIGHT

BEVEL EDGE

OPEN

DOWEL IN OFFSET HOLES PULLS TENON TIGHT

JOINTS

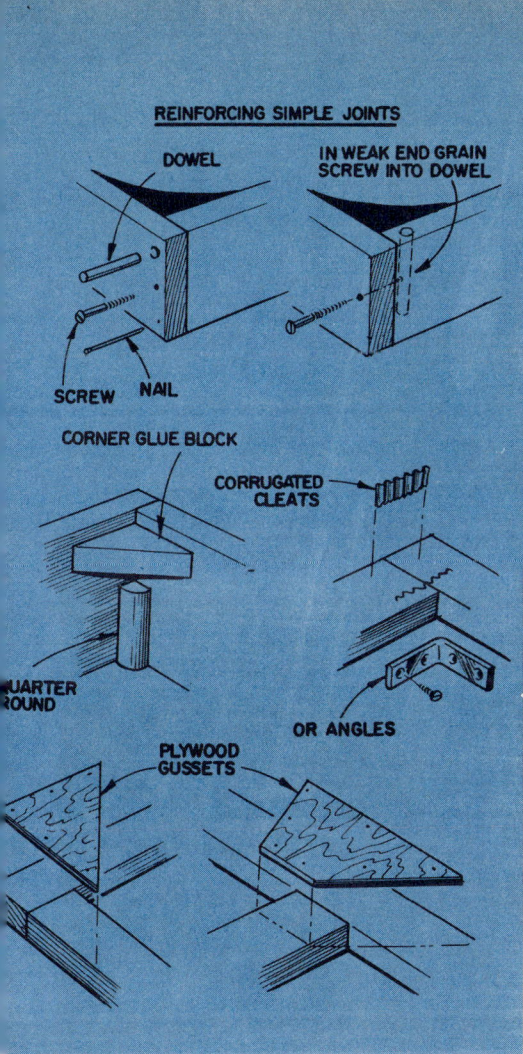

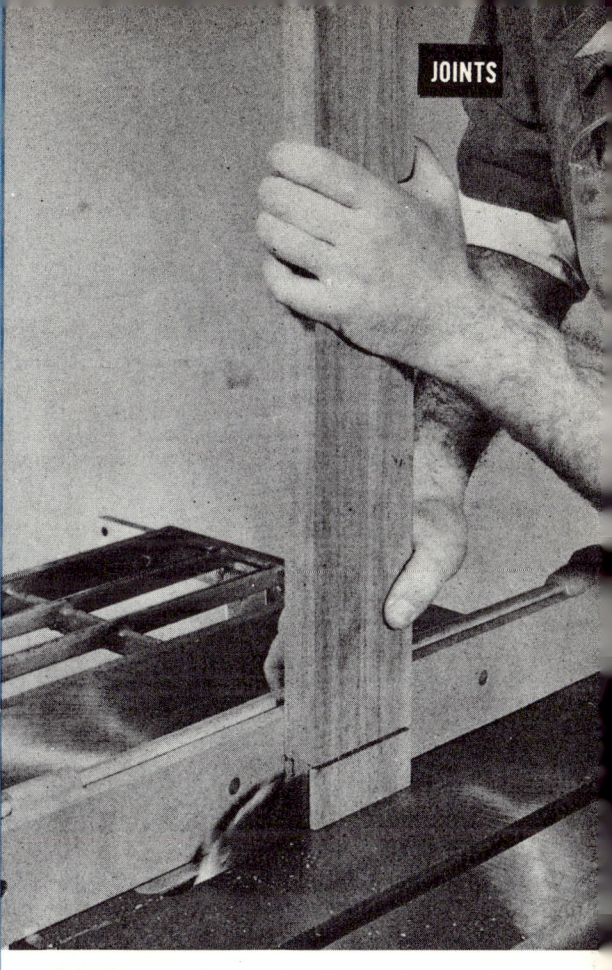

REINFORCING SIMPLE JOINTS
- DOWEL
- IN WEAK END GRAIN SCREW INTO DOWEL
- SCREW
- NAIL
- CORNER GLUE BLOCK
- CORRUGATED CLEATS
- QUARTER ROUND
- OR ANGLES
- PLYWOOD GUSSETS

A fast way to form a shoulder cut for a tendon is to use two saw blades separated by washer-spacers. Otherwise cut is made with two passes.

When you use a simple rabbet in the drawer front and set the drawer sides in this, it's wise to drive nails through the sides into the front, rather than through the front of the drawer into the sides. For one reason the nails would be in a better position to fight the strain; for another, nail heads in the drawer front would spoil the appearance.

On a bench or table project that has stretchers between the legs, weight on the table tends to spread the legs and thus part the joint between stretchers and legs. If you used a butt joint here, you would not get the strength you should have. But a mortise-tenon (especially if a peg were driven through the tenon) or a lapped dovetail could hold the two parts together under stress even if glue were not used.

So these are two things to consider—looks and strength. Determine how the joint must carry the load. Will it be under stress? Will it tend to pull apart? Will it tend to twist? Ask yourself, is it in a spot where appearance is important? Then choose the simplest joint to do the job.

Beyond this it's a question of accuracy. It doesn't matter what joint you decide to use. Even the two parts in a butt joint must meet flush and square to achieve maximum strength. Sloppy fitting is the death knell of any kind of joint. You might conceal a poor fit with wood dough and heavy paint, but you're not adding strength in the doing.

When you're working with power tools, be sure they are in correct alignment. When your miter gauge is at normal cross-cut position, you want to be sure the cut you get is exactly 90 degrees. If you can't rely on this, it's not possible to make a good joint. The drill press table must be at right angles to the spindle center and so on. It's these periodic checks for correct alignment of power tool components that

1793

JOINTS

Cutting and gluing are only part of making good strong joints. It is essential that a good set of clamps be used to hold the boards together while drying. Start by buying at least three or four bar clamps.

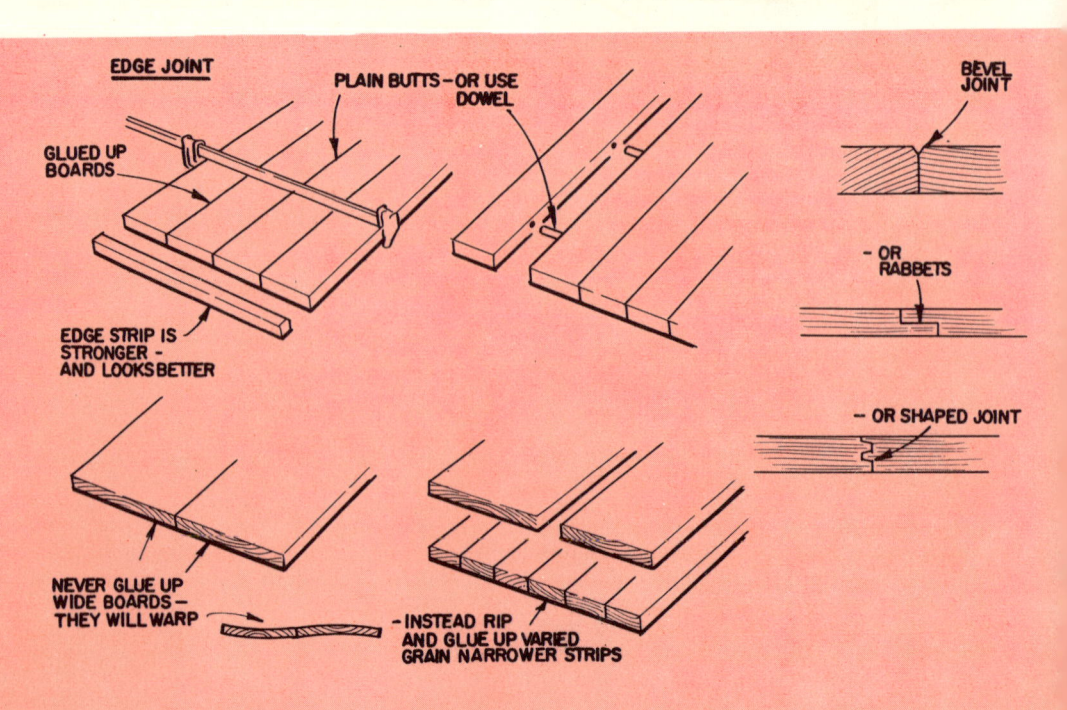

EDGE JOINT

- GLUED UP BOARDS
- PLAIN BUTTS – OR USE DOWEL
- BEVEL JOINT
- EDGE STRIP IS STRONGER – AND LOOKS BETTER
- – OR RABBETS
- – OR SHAPED JOINT
- NEVER GLUE UP WIDE BOARDS – THEY WILL WARP
- – INSTEAD RIP AND GLUE UP VARIED GRAIN NARROWER STRIPS

1794

JOINTS

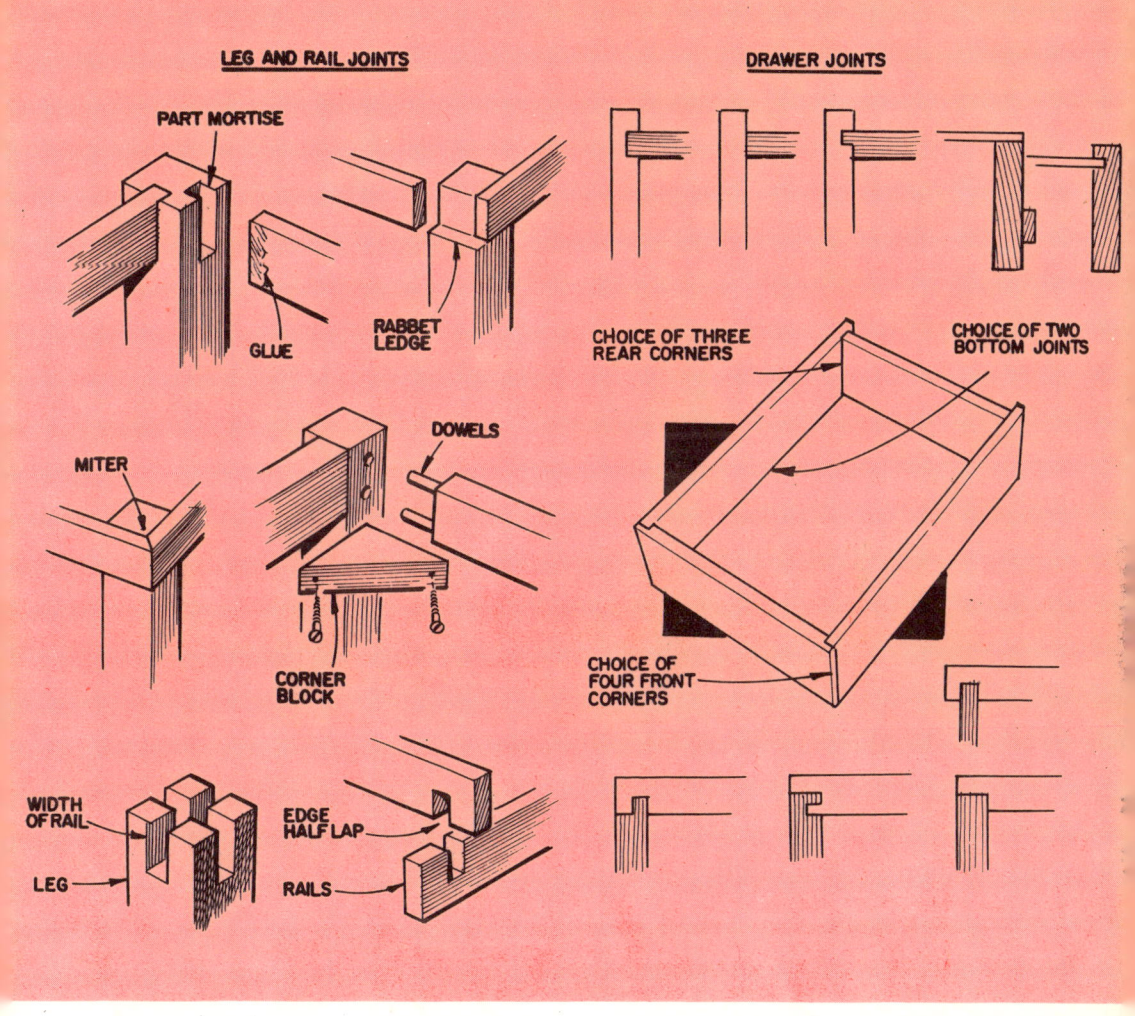

LEG AND RAIL JOINTS

DRAWER JOINTS

will result in accurate cuts that lead to good joints whether they are simple or intricate.

Hand tools require more skill because, usually, it's how *you* hold and use the tool, that determines how accurate the cut will be. But you can help yourself a great deal if you work slowly and measure carefully. Use a square for all lines that must be at right angles to an edge. Be sure the ruler you use is straight. Measure twice so you only have to cut once. Many handmade joints rely heavily on a back saw and a set of chisels. So these are good tools to own, and they should be good tools. Keep the saw clean and sharp; keep the chisels in the same condition.

Actually, for most of your projects, you'll find that butt, dado, and rabbet joints will do nicely. Where stress is such that these joints don't appear strong enough, each of them can be reinforced—blind, if appearance matters, or with visible mechanical additions if looks are secondary.

Both the dado and the rabbet joints are quickly accomplished on a table saw if you have a dado assembly available. This is a set that consists of two outside blades and an assortment of "chippers" that fit between them. The two outside blades usually cut a ⅛-in. kerf, so two together will cut a groove or dado ¼ in. wide. Beyond this, you add chippers which clean away the stock between the two outlining cuts. A conventional dado will allow you to cut from ¼ in. up to ¾ in. wide.

When you form a U-shaped groove with the assembly that runs across the grain of the wood, it's called a dado. The same cut *with* the grain of the wood is called a groove (sometimes referred to as "ploughing"). When you use the dado to make an L-shaped cut along the edge or across the end of a piece of stock it is called a rabbet.

1795

JOINTS

When putting blind, round tenon in position, as is shown in photo above, use a wedge which will spread the tenon into hole as part is inserted.

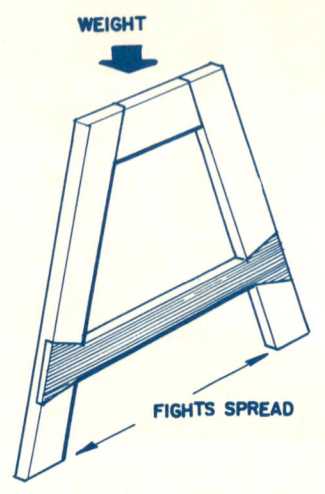

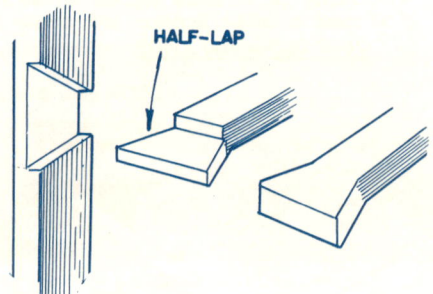

MODIFIED TRESTLE LAP OR DOVE TAIL LAP

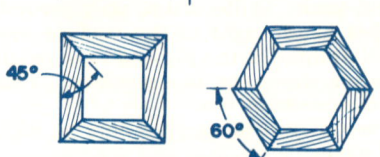

WEIGHT

FIGHTS SPREAD

HALF-LAP

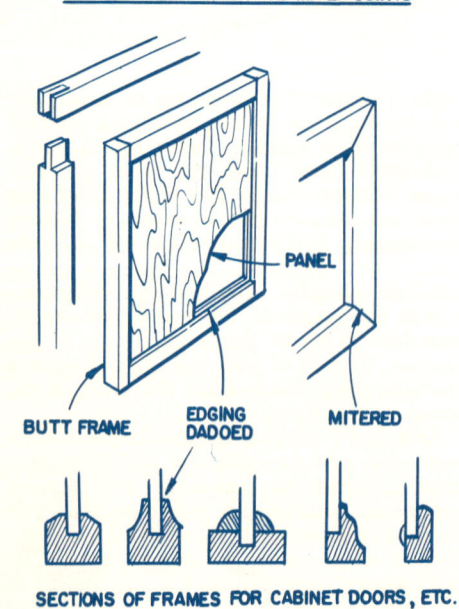

FRAME CONSTRUCTION AND MITER JOINTS

PANEL

BUTT FRAME — EDGING DADOED — MITERED

SECTIONS OF FRAMES FOR CABINET DOORS, ETC.

BAD ANGLE MAY MEET, BUT FRAME CAN BE OUT OF SQUARE

LESS THAN 45°
MORE THAN 45°

45°
60°

THIS IS A MITER — AND SO IS THIS

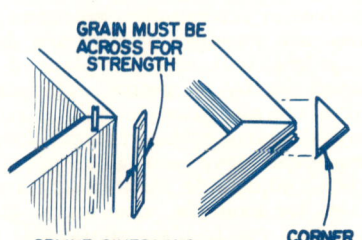

GRAIN MUST BE ACROSS FOR STRENGTH

SPLINE GIVES LONG MITERS GREAT HOLDING

CORNER SPLINE

1796

JOINTS

Above is a portable router which is being used with router bit to make rabbet. A useful tool, it is used to make intricate and simple joints

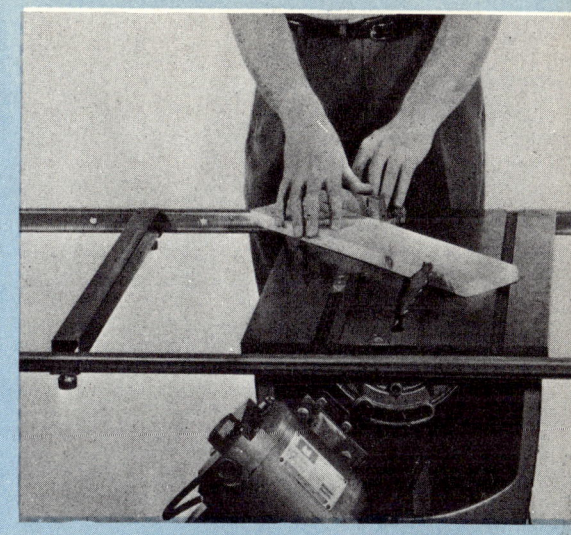

Compound angle joint must be precise. To form this joint, as shown above, it is necessary to use both a blade tilt and a miter gauge setting

CRATE DESIGN AND JOINTS

DEPTH – 1/2 STOCK
WIDTH – STOCK THICKNESS

GRID DESIGN AND JOINTS

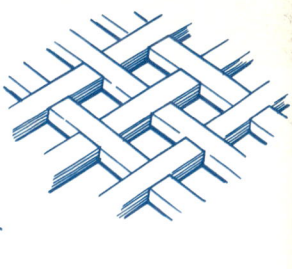

DEPTH – 1/2 STOCK
WIDTH – STOCK WIDTH

The advantage of the rabbet over the butt joint, at a corner, for example, is that it offers more gluing surface and conceals more end grain. Quite often, on plywood, the rabbet is cut right to the surface veneer so that none of the plywood sandwich shows after the joint is assembled. This really amounts to no more than a butt joint with a flap of veneer carried over to hide the end grain.

Dadoes and grooves are usually used to fit shelves or intermediate uprights. Book shelves are stronger if they are dadoed. An upright will stay in place if it is hemmed in by a groove. Dadoes and grooves are also used to hold moving or removable parts. Sliding cabinet doors, for example, can move easily in grooves. When you want adjustable partitions, in a record cabinet, for example, a series of grooves will permit you to place removable partitions where you need them, at any time.

Many times it is possible to save time and to do a job when you lack specific equipment: a mortise-tenon for example. Ordinarily these are cut with mortise-tenon bits and chisels. But if you don't own these you can form a mortise by drilling overlapping holes and cleaning out the waste stock between. The tenon is cut as usual on the table saw. The only difference is that the edges of the tenon have to be rounded off to fit the round ends of the mortise. The drill you use should have a diameter that matches the thickness of the tenon you will cut.

And don't neglect the mechanical fasteners that add strength and will often save time. Corrugated fasteners and similar items can reinforce a miter so that you don't have to spline it. Glue blocks, screws, dowels, cleats, and gussets all should be used where they will do the job and fit in with appearance. •

JOISTS

Setting a 4x8 sheet of Plyscord in place. It is a common and good construction practice to use the plywood from the forms for the sub-flooring. Note the double joists, called "trimmers," which are always located under wall partitions. Stagger joints when placing plywood. Spacers hold joists perpendicular.

setting the
FLOOR JOISTS and SUB-FLOORING

Laying the "deck" will only take a few days. Here are some details to watch.

SETTING your floor joists in place is especially satisfying and requires a day or two at the most—but if you don't pre-plan the joist setting you will create many future time-consuming and wasted-money complications.

All fir floor joists for the maximum span of 15 feet call for 2x10s located 16 inches on center. If your plan works out where some joists are less than 16 inches you are getting a floor that is more sturdy; never place joists more than the prescribed distance apart as recommended by your local building code which covers both span, spacing and type of material.

If you are using a warm air heating-air conditioning system your placement of partitions must be such that a joist underneath is located to the side of the interior partition to make way for the future heating duct. This will usually apply to main entrances, kitchen and bathroom, where high heating registers are common. Your future plumbing plan must also be considered in the placement of floor joists, and since plumbing and heating layouts will vary greatly depending upon the local requirements in your areas, you should have your plumbing and heating plans worked out in great detail before you nail the floor joists in place. Each 2x10x16-foot joist will costs you about $3.40 which you can easily waste unless you plan placement very carefully.

Before resting the joists on the sill and steel beam, toenail a 2x10 around the complete perimeter of the outside of the sill if

JOISTS

After the plywood panel is in place, nail at six-inch intervals to the floor joists. Use 8-penny nails, driven home. If edge of plywood splinters in places, do not be alarmed because the area is covered with 15-pound felt and then the finish flooring is nailed in place with 8-penny rosin-coated nails.

Perspective view showing typical floor construction. Note that the wood exposed to the brick area is generously coated with waterproofing before brickwork is started. Only nail top of bridging in place.

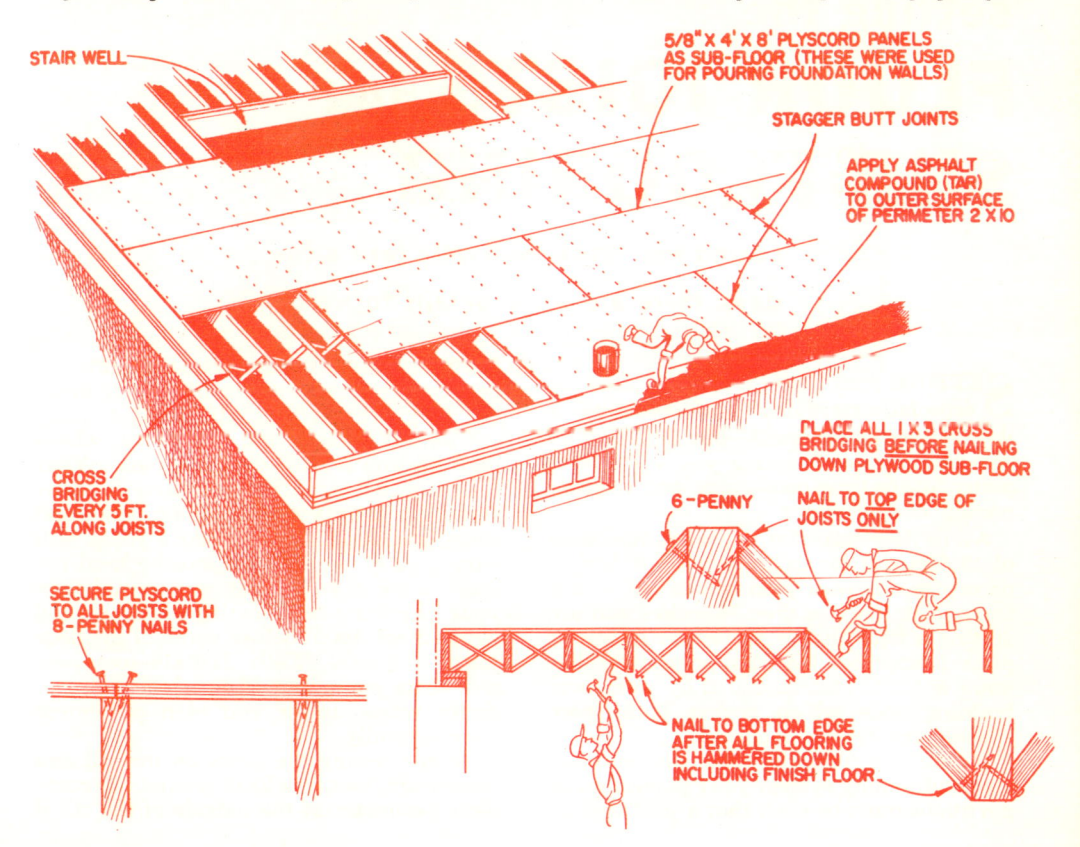

STAIR WELL

5/8" X 4' X 8' PLYSCORD PANELS AS SUB-FLOOR (THESE WERE USED FOR POURING FOUNDATION WALLS)

STAGGER BUTT JOINTS

APPLY ASPHALT COMPOUND (TAR) TO OUTER SURFACE OF PERIMETER 2 X 10

CROSS BRIDGING EVERY 5 FT. ALONG JOISTS

PLACE ALL 1 X 3 CROSS BRIDGING BEFORE NAILING DOWN PLYWOOD SUB-FLOOR

6-PENNY

NAIL TO TOP EDGE OF JOISTS ONLY

SECURE PLYSCORD TO ALL JOISTS WITH 8-PENNY NAILS

NAIL TO BOTTOM EDGE AFTER ALL FLOORING IS HAMMERED DOWN INCLUDING FINISH FLOOR

JOISTS

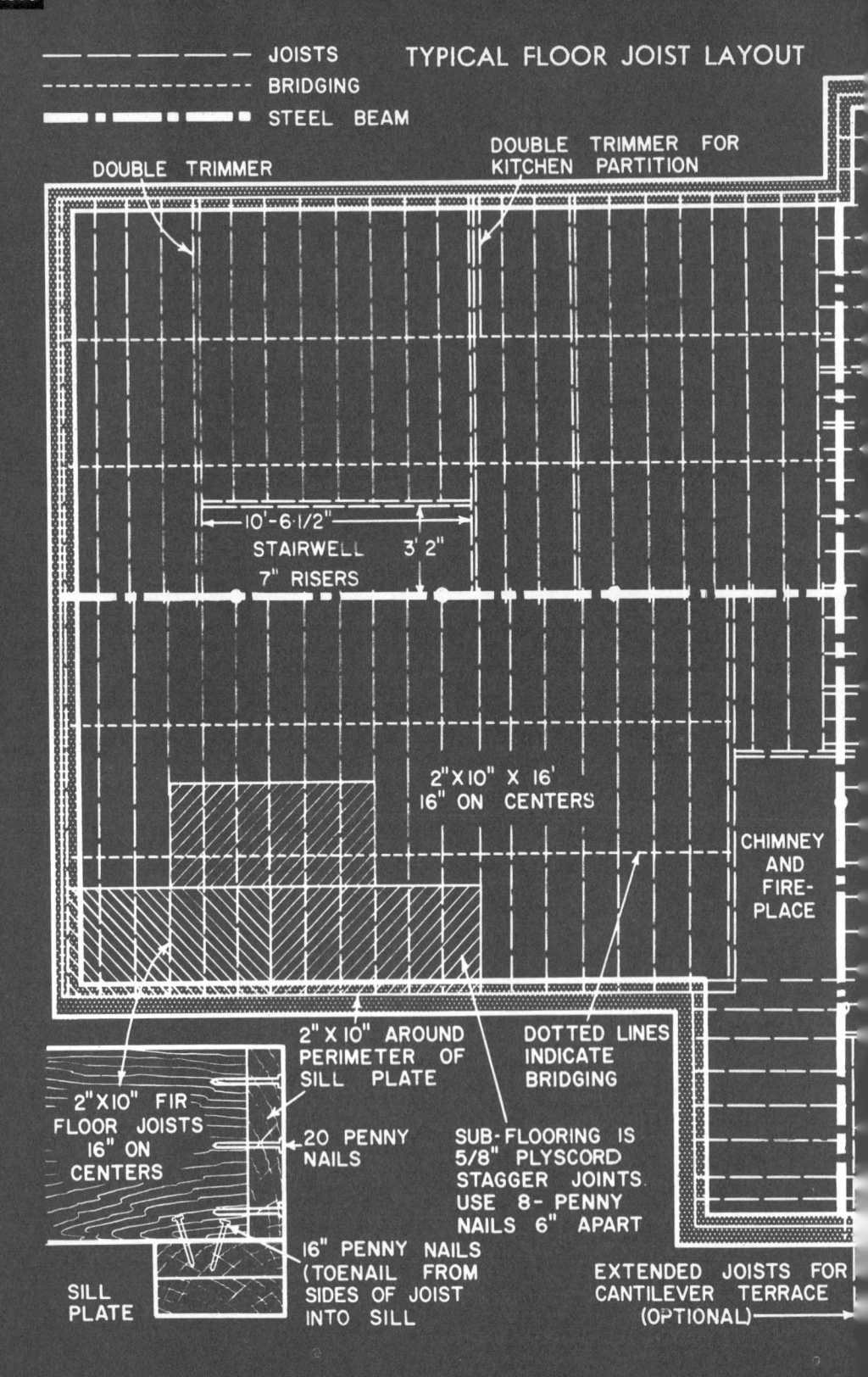

TYPICAL FLOOR JOIST LAYOUT

— — — — — JOISTS
- - - - - - - BRIDGING
▬ ▪ ▬ ▪ ▬ STEEL BEAM

DOUBLE TRIMMER

DOUBLE TRIMMER FOR KITCHEN PARTITION

10'-6 1/2"
STAIRWELL 3' 2"
7" RISERS

2" X 10" X 16'
16" ON CENTERS

CHIMNEY AND FIREPLACE

2" X 10" AROUND PERIMETER OF SILL PLATE

DOTTED LINES INDICATE BRIDGING

2" X 10" FIR FLOOR JOISTS 16" ON CENTERS

20 PENNY NAILS

SUB-FLOORING IS 5/8" PLYSCORD STAGGER JOINTS. USE 8-PENNY NAILS 6" APART

16" PENNY NAILS (TOENAIL FROM SIDES OF JOIST INTO SILL

SILL PLATE

EXTENDED JOISTS FOR CANTILEVER TERRACE (OPTIONAL)

1800

JOISTS

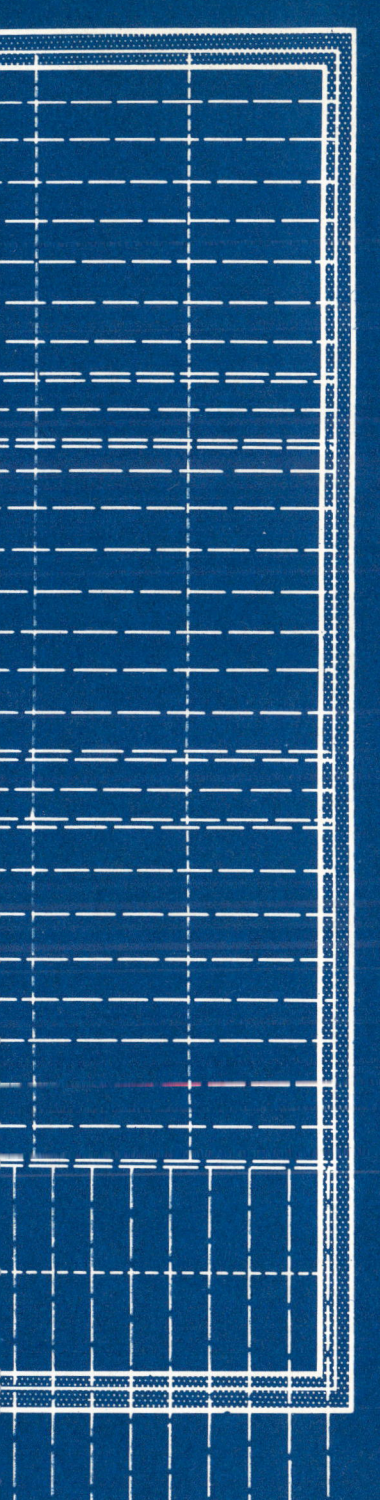

Nail a 2x10 to the sill plate and carefully mark off the position of each joist. Then span plate, steel with 2x10s.

your foundation is 12 inches thick. If you are using a 10-inch thick foundation, which is entirely adequate if your code and type of terrain permit a wall of this thickness, extend the joists over the complete sill and block between each. You must have at least four inches of joist resting on the wall.

Mark off the position of any partitions on either the face of the sill plate (for ten-inch foundations) or the perimeter 2x10 (for 12-inch foundations) and place the double joist, or trimmer, to the most convenient side of the partition.

Mark off 16-inch intervals and set the joists in position. If you have a perimeter 2x10 use two 20-penny nails driven through the 2x10 into the end grain of each joist and also toenail the joist to the sill with 10-penny nails.

Another important point to consider when positioning your joists is to make certain the "crown" is up. Lumber is rarely straight, and if you are fortunate enough to receive material that appears to be straight, the fact that it is not kiln dried and contains up to 20 percent moisture means it is merely a matter of time before it will warp. Look down the edge of each piece and place the concave side up. Don't worry about twisted lumber; you can easily twist it straight when the joists are nailed permanently in place. If all of your joists have the "crown up" you will end up with an even floor that will have less chance of squeaking.

The well for the basement stairs or your chimney will also be flanked with a double joist—and a double 2x10 referred to as a "header." The joists will butt into the header

JOISTS

Your masons will require scaffolding where necessary on the outside wall and the sub-flooring in place at least around the perimeter of foundation.

and are held secure with special bridle irons which actually make it possible to hang each joist. In many areas bridle irons are not required but if your code calls for this type of ironware you still should drive two or three 60-penny spikes through the double header into the end grain of the joists or else add a 1x2 "nailer" to the header and notch the joists. Framing lumber, not being kiln dried, will shrink and after a year or so if you use only bridle irons you will note the iron is not doing its job.

After the joists are secure, snap a line at the points indicated for the bridging. Your local lumberyard or hardware store usually sells one or more types of metal bridging and also beveled edge wooden bridging. We prefer the wooden bridging because it produces a sturdier floor in the long run, although metal bridging usually requires much less time to install—a good reason why some builders use this type exclusively.

Nail your bridging in place with two 8-penny nails and drive the top side in first. Do not nail the basement side at this time; wait until the sub-flooring is completely in

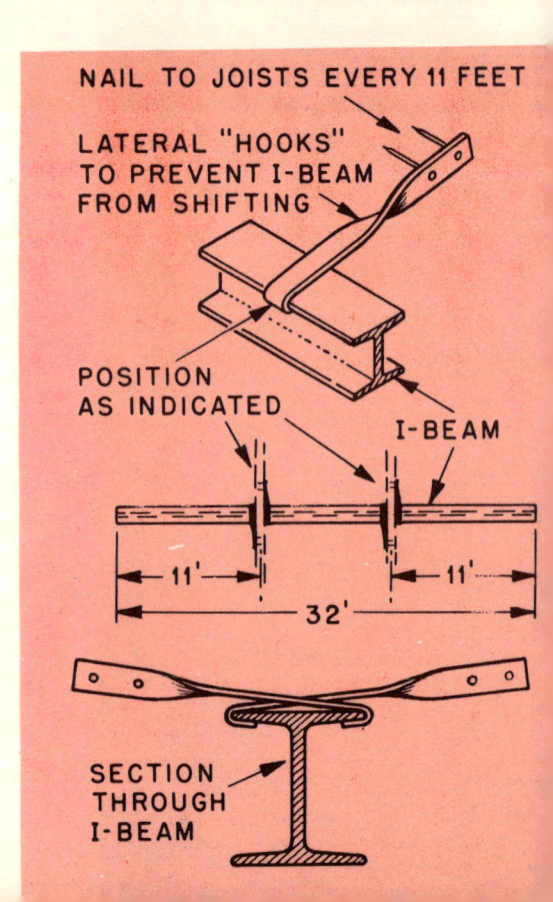

JOISTS

place before nailing from underneath.

With your deck in place, you will find it most convenient to stack up all of your remaining 2x4s and plywood to be used for the partitions, directly on the sub-flooring. Keep it out of the way of the bricklayers and plumbers who will soon add their bit. Lumber left out on irregular ground will become watersoaked and quickly follow contour of ground. This is especially true with sheets of plywood.

Your concrete forms, 5/8-inch thick Plyscord, is used for the sub-flooring. Logically, the 4x8-foot pieces are staggered, as shown in the illustrations. Nail the plywood sheets to the joists with 8-penny common nails at intervals of 6 inches over all nailing joists. Some builders nail 2x4 "cats" between the joists to permit nailing around the complete perimeter of the plywood but this is not really necessary. Use a 20-ounce hammer for the sub-flooring chore and expect two good men to lay down about 35 sheets in a full eight-hour day. Plyscord is an interior grade plywood which really does not mean it cannot withstand a month or so of average weather. To use waterproof plywood for sub-flooring—or even your forms—would be too expensive, and actually not necessary. If a few ends do have a tendency to delaminate, because of rain, this need not be of any great concern because on top of your sub-floor a layer of 15-pound felt is eventually laid after which the finish floor is added. The latter will either be oak (if you do not plan to cover it with carpeting or tile), otherwise an additional layer of A-D plywood is added. Once the sub-flooring is in place you can proceed to nail the basement side of the bridging and start to lay out the room partitions. Assuming you have a basement, the next most tempting step is to install your basement stairs to simplify the chore of gaining access to the basement. However, use a ladder until the roof is on because the ready-made pine stairs we suggest you purchase are made from kiln-dried lumber and should not be left exposed to rain. Your local lumberyard probably stocks an assortment of stairs for different basement heights. Also, the making of stairs is a profession in itself; it really doesn't pay to make your own.•

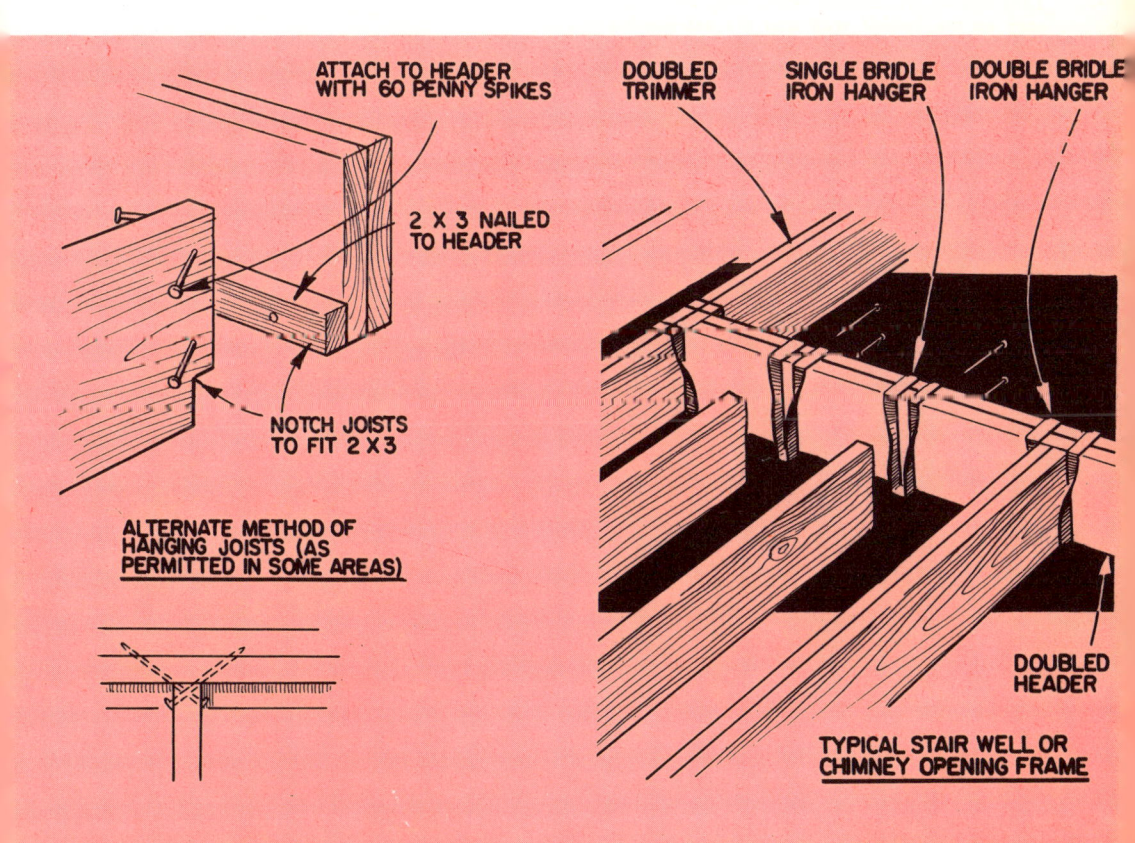

ATTACH TO HEADER WITH 60 PENNY SPIKES

2 X 3 NAILED TO HEADER

NOTCH JOISTS TO FIT 2 X 3

ALTERNATE METHOD OF HANGING JOISTS (AS PERMITTED IN SOME AREAS)

DOUBLED TRIMMER

SINGLE BRIDLE IRON HANGER

DOUBLE BRIDLE IRON HANGER

DOUBLED HEADER

TYPICAL STAIR WELL OR CHIMNEY OPENING FRAME

1803

JUNGLE GYM

Jungle Gym

by Hi Sibley

Here's another pipe structure the kids will be crazy about!

THIS type of climber gym is easy to assemble and can be made with as many squares as desired—playground size or a small home unit. Pine or redwood posts are bored, the holes being made larger than the pipe, and corners chamfered so they will not splinter. Select straight-grain material and apply an oil finish to preserve the wood. Pipe caps are screwed on the outer ends of each bar.

For the large gym, pipe lengths are 20, 56 and 92 inches respectively; for the smaller unit, 20, 38 and 56 inches. You can have them cut to size and threaded by your local plumber.

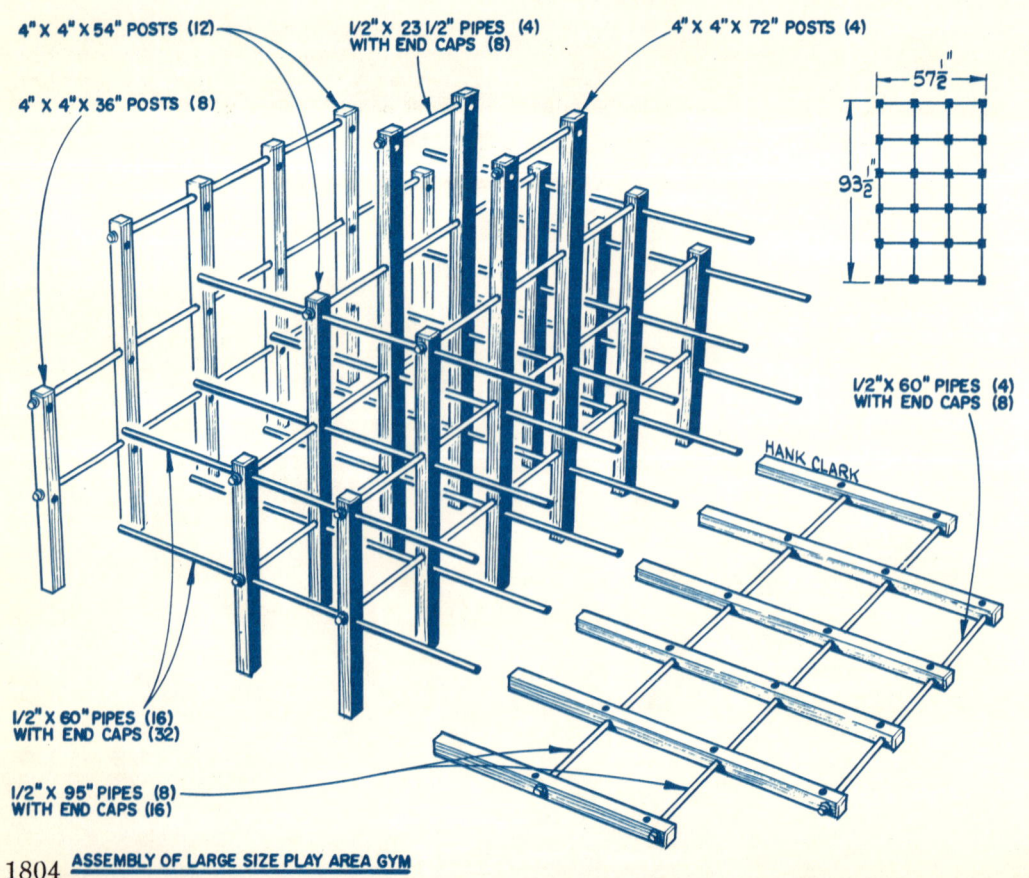

4" X 4" X 54" POSTS (12)
1/2" X 23 1/2" PIPES (4) WITH END CAPS (8)
4" X 4" X 72" POSTS (4)
4" X 4" X 36" POSTS (8)
57 1/2"
93 1/2"
1/2" X 60" PIPES (4) WITH END CAPS (8)
HANK CLARK
1/2" X 60" PIPES (16) WITH END CAPS (32)
1/2" X 95" PIPES (8) WITH END CAPS (16)

ASSEMBLY OF LARGE SIZE PLAY AREA GYM

LAYOUT FOR LARGE PLAY AREA GYM

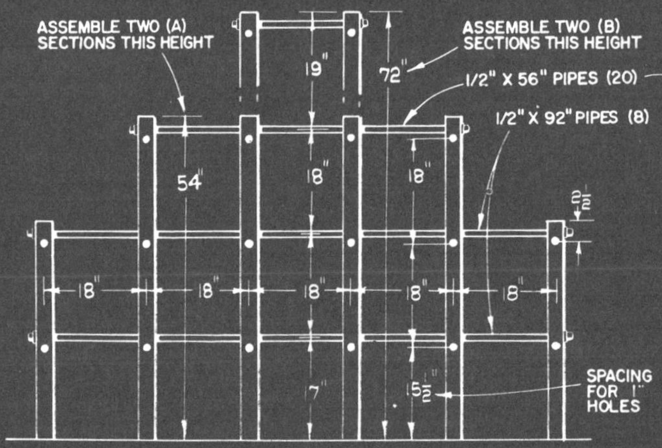

ASSEMBLY OF POSTS AND PIPES FOR ONE SECTION

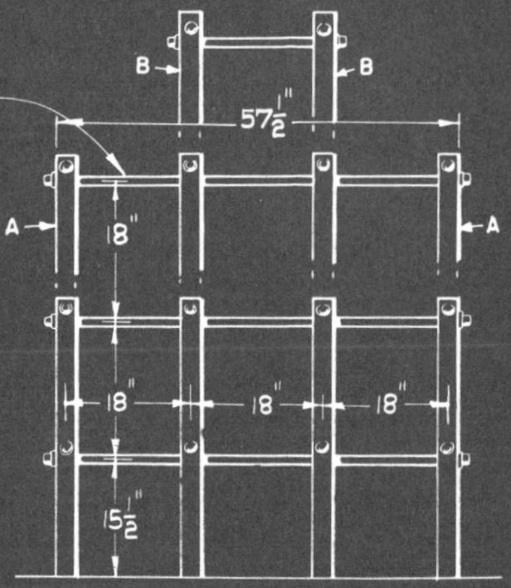

END VIEW OF JOINED SECTIONS

SIMPLE HOME BACK YARD GYM

SEE PERSPECTIVE FOR PIPE SIZES

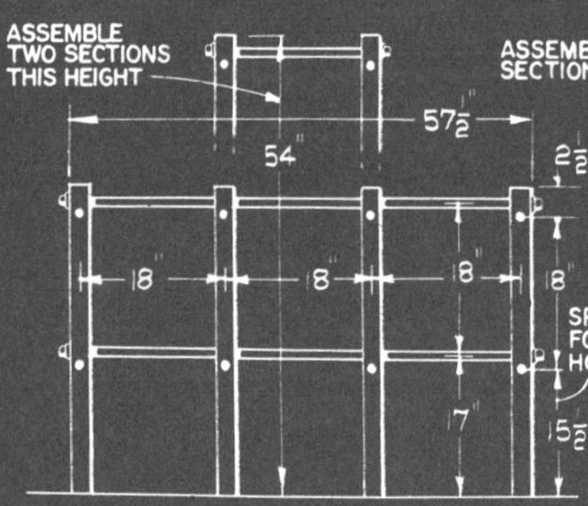

POSTS AND PIPES FOR ONE SECTION

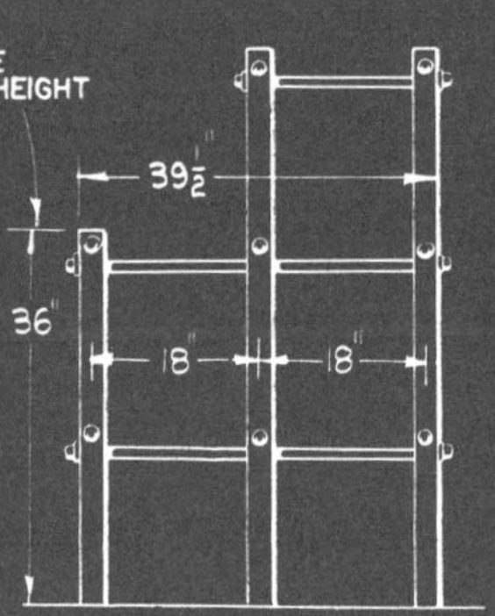

END VIEW OF JOINED SECTIONS

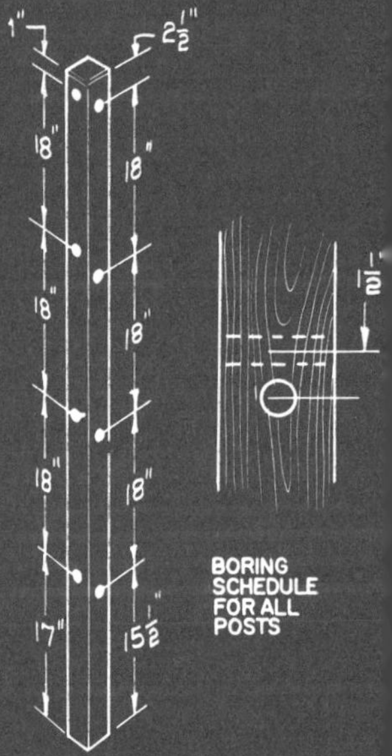

BORING SCHEDULE FOR ALL POSTS

ASSEMBLY OF SMALL BACK YARD GYM

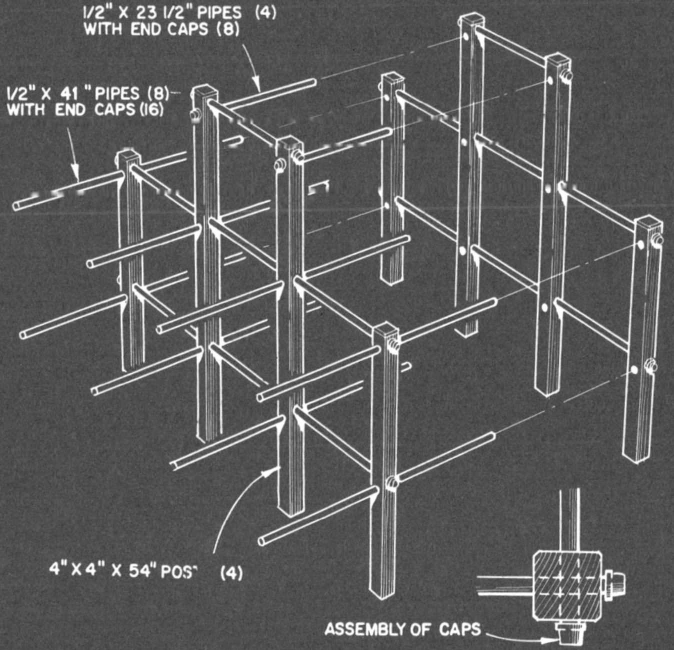

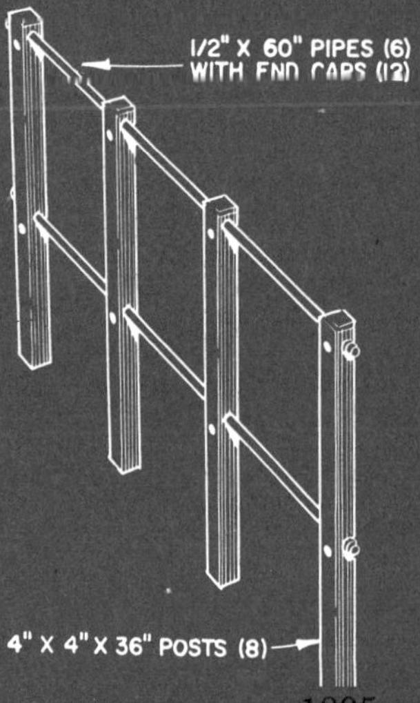

KARTING

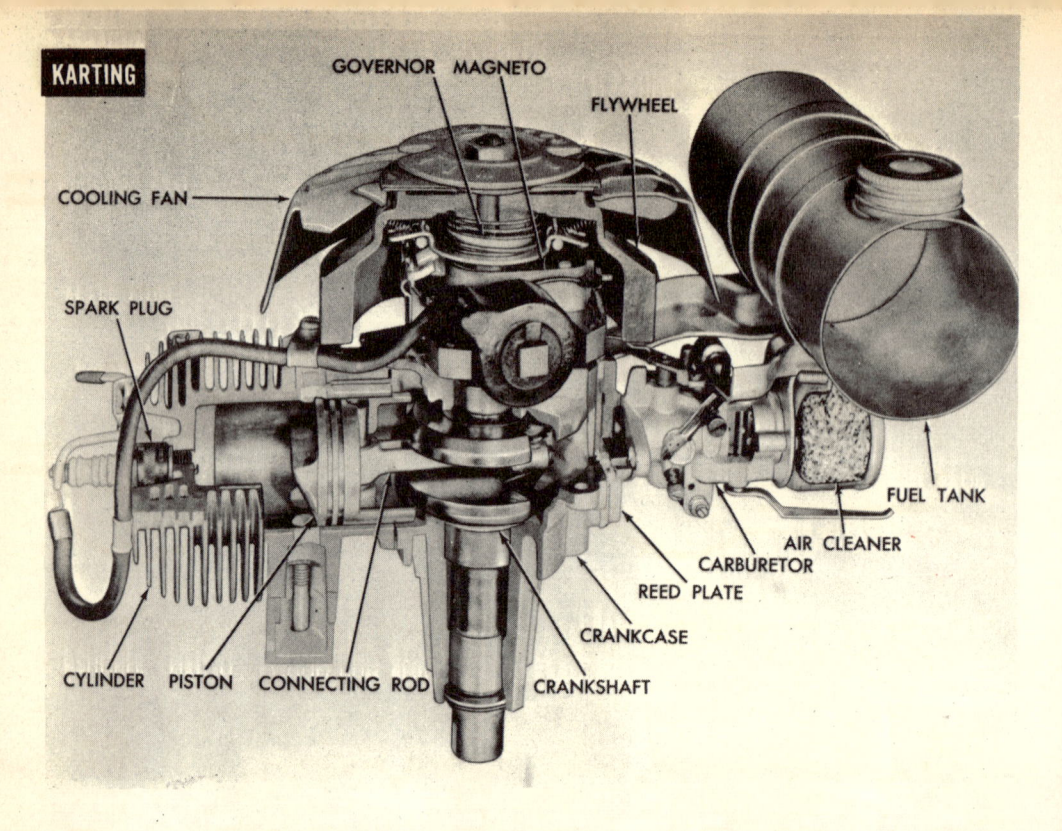

This is a cutaway of a basic 2-cycle engine, the Power products uniflow with typical deflector-head piston.

Two-Cycle Engine Fundamentals

Basic information about the two-stroke that all karters should know to get best results

THE 2-stroke-cycle engine dates back at least as early as 1878 and it was with this type of power plant that one of the fathers of the automobile, Carl Benz, did most of his early experimentation. However, in 1885 when he and Gottlieb Daimler built the first horseless carriages they sacrificed 2-stroke simplicity for 4-stroke efficiency.

Orphaned by 4-stroke fashion the 2-stroke principle was almost forgotten for decades by manufacturers of internal combustion engines. DKW in Germany almost single-handedly kept the 2-stroke alive down through the years in both automobiles and motorcycles. A few manufacturers of outboard engines here and in Europe accounted for most of the remainder of 2-stroke output until the beginning of World War II when a sudden, urgent need arose for light, highly-portable power packages. The most intensive development of the 2-stroke engine has taken place since then, resulting in the remarkably efficient, powerful, simple and durable engines that power our karts today.

To appreciate the 2-stroke's simplicity, it's best to compare it with the familiar 4-stroke engine. As the name indicates, with the 4-stroke only one stroke out of four is a power stroke. The cycle begins with the piston at the top of the cylinder,

1806

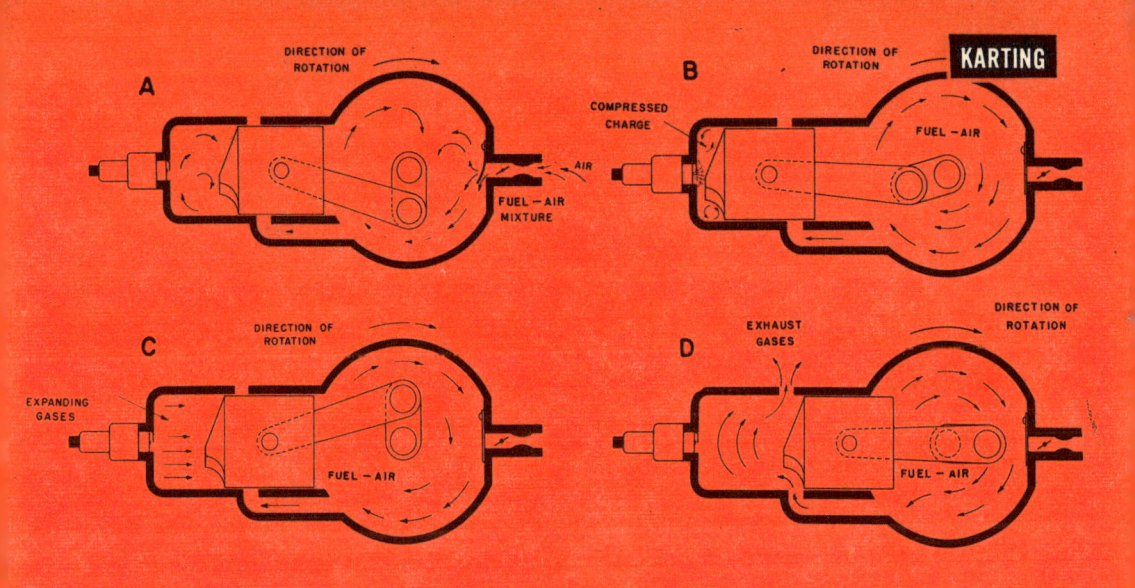

The 2-stroke cycle, above, with reed inlet valve and piston valves in cylinder, using the uniflow system.

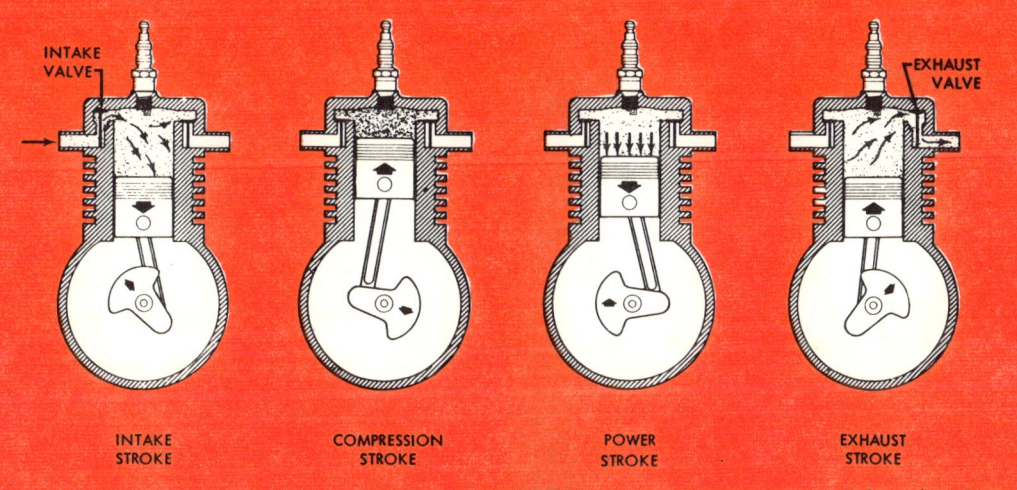

Illustrated above is the 4-stroke cycle. The obsolete T-head valve layout was used here for clarity.

with the poppet intake valve open. As the piston descends on the *intake* stroke it sucks fuel-air mixture through the intake valve. Near the bottom of the stroke the valve closes and the piston travels up the cylinder again, compressing the fuel-air charge for greater combustion efficiency. Near the top of the *compression* stroke a spark jumps across the spark plug gap and ignites the mixture. The expanding products of combustion force the piston down on the *power* stroke. Near the bottom of this stroke the exhaust valve opens and as the piston rises on stroke four, the *exhaust* stroke, the burned gases are pushed out through the exhaust valve. For this sequence of events to take place, many moving parts are needed which are unnecessary on a 2-stroke engine. These include poppet valves, valve springs, retainers, guides, tappets, cam shaft and timing gears, to name a few.

The 2-cycle engine, McCulloch explains, has to do in two strokes what is done by the 4-cycle in four. It also must charge its crankcase with fuel-air mixture so that this may be pumped into the combustion chamber. Thus, crankcase charging, mixture compression and ignition must occur on the upstroke and exhaust of the burned gases and intake of fresh mixture must occur on the downstroke. This is achieved

1807

KARTING

A FUEL-AIR MIXTURE

B FUEL-AIR MIXTURE / COMPRESSED CHARGE

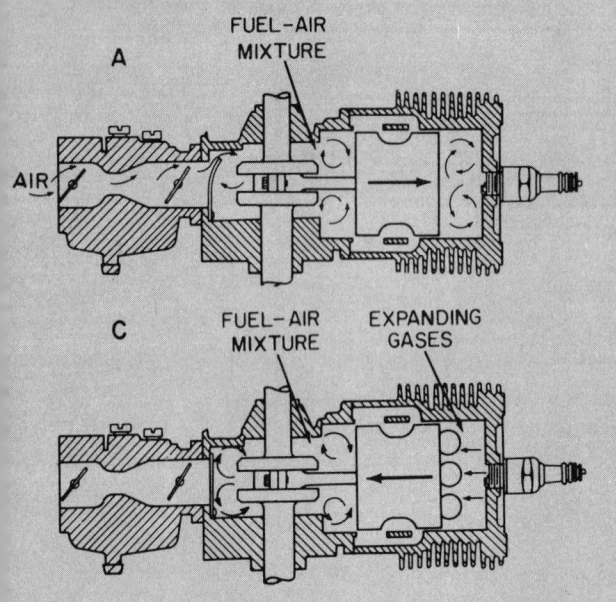

C FUEL-AIR MIXTURE / EXPANDING GASES

D FUEL-AIR MIXTURE / EXHAUST GASES

Loop-scavenge 2-stroke cycle provides superior breathing at the high end of the rpm range (above).

Another simplified illustration of the uniflow 2-cycle system. In practice, the crankcase is shrunken to just provide shaft clearance (right).

INLET FROM CARBURETOR — TRANSFER PORT — EXHAUST PORT

CRANKCASE
- INTAKE STROKE

CYLINDER
- COMPRESSION STROKE

CRANKCASE
- COMPRESSION STROKE

CYLINDER
- EXHAUST STROKE
- INTAKE STROKE

with the MC10 through the use of three openings or ports: two opening into the combustion chamber and one opening into the crankcase, from the carb.

The piston's upstroke creates a partial vacuum in the 'case which sucks in fresh mixture. During this stroke the piston also seals off the intake and exhaust ports and compresses the mixture in the combustion chamber. Near the top of this stroke the spark ignites the mixture and the piston is forced downward. It seals off the intake port and pressurizes the 'case. As the piston continues downward, the exhaust port is uncovered and the burned gases, still expanding, escape from the combustion chamber. Near the bottom of the downstroke the piston uncovers the transfer port, permitting the compressed mixture in the 'case to rush into the combustion chamber. Some fresh mixture escapes through the open exhaust port but this is minimized in good 2-strokes by design of piston heads and porting. Thus the elaborate and costly valve train of the 4-stroke engine is eliminated and one stroke in two becomes a power stroke instead of one in four.

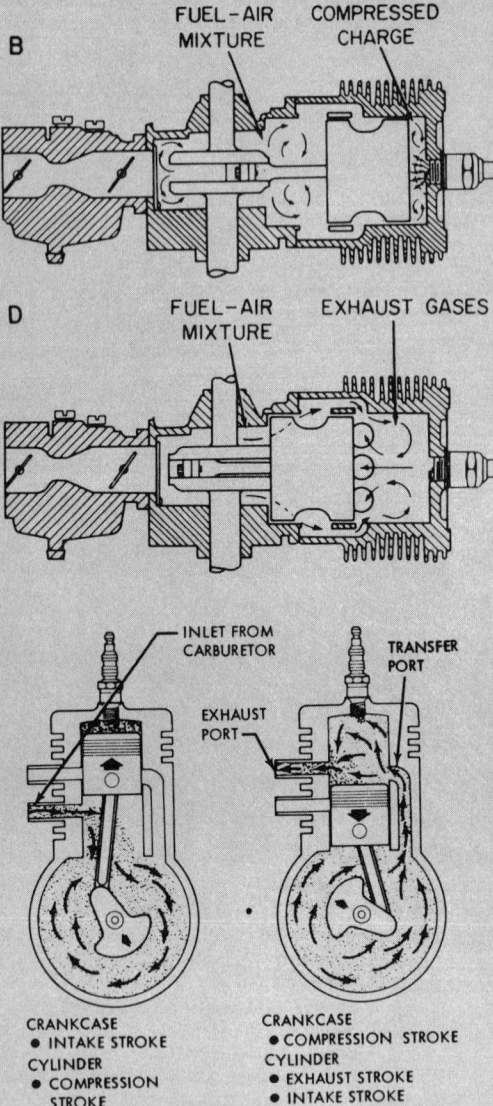

The main valves in popular 2-strokes, then, are slide valves composed of piston and cylinder wall. Frequently other simple valves also are used. The most popular of these is the reed valve, a thin piece of spring steel which is fitted to a machined seat which is placed between the carb and the intake port in the 'case. The reed is anchored at one end and its own tension holds the reed flat against its seat. Crankcase suction caused by the piston on the upstroke pulls the reed free and open, permitting mixture to be sucked into the 'case. As the piston nears the top of its stroke it slows down. The then-reduced suction lets the reed close, preventing

KARTING

Loop-scavenged PP AH-82 engine, as in A-D opposite page, with dual carbs. Note small crankcase.

Note twin inlet passages in cylinder, valve openings in piston of loop-scavenged Power Products.

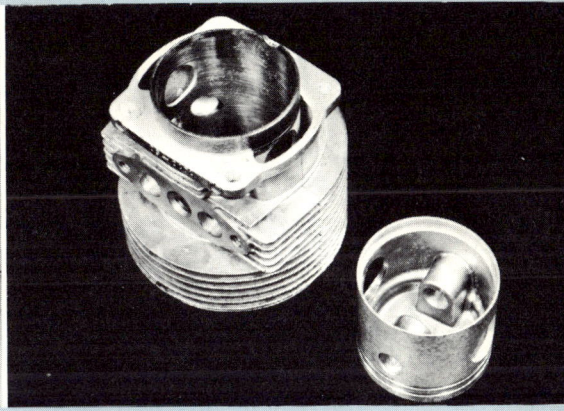

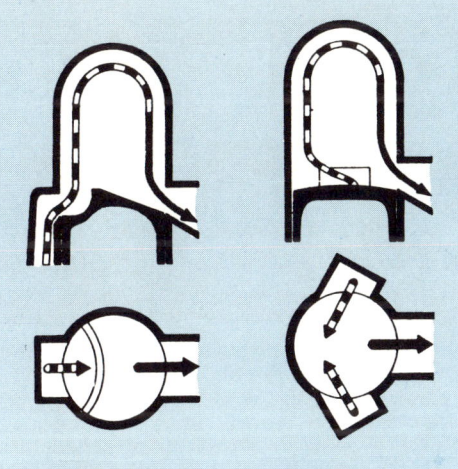

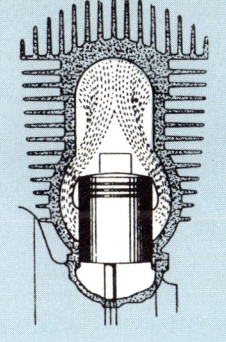

Ports are angled with loop scavenging so two streams of mix merge in chamber, loop toward exhaust port, illustrated left.

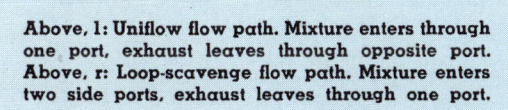

The cylinder block, dirt screen, reed plate, carb flange shown at left in a typical reed-valve layout.

Above, l: Uniflow flow path. Mixture enters through one port, exhaust leaves through opposite port. Above, r: Loop-scavenge flow path. Mixture enters two side ports, exhaust leaves through one port.

Reed valves, below, function just as harmonica reeds do. Crankcase size is greatly exaggerated in the illustration, for clarity.

mixture from being blown back out through the carb on the downstroke.

The rotary valve, although more positive, is seen less frequently. It usually consists of a circular plate which is mounted on the crankshaft. It covers the intake port except during a pie-slice which is cut from the plate. Reed plates and slide valves are those which are combined most frequently in high-efficiency kart engines because of their lower cost. Rotary valves are more positive, stay open longer. The fabulous Konig engines use rotary valves.

The porting of 2-stroke engines is a far more exact science than most karters imagine. Obviously, engine efficiency and

REED VALVE OPEN   REED VALVE CLOSED

1809

KARTING

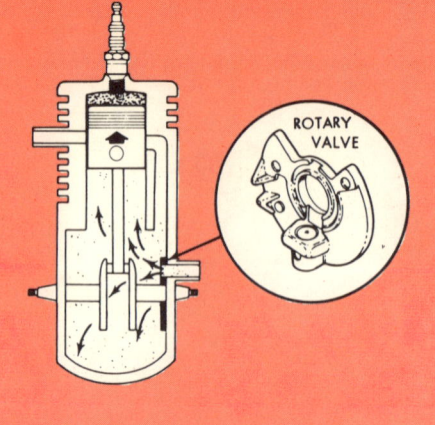

Typical port arrangement: left, inlet; center is transfer port; at the right' is the exhaust port.

Crankshaft-mounted rotary valves are more positive than reeds, stay open longer, but cost more.

Four approaches to loop-scavenging. Three inlet ports, far right, provide fine piston-head cooling.

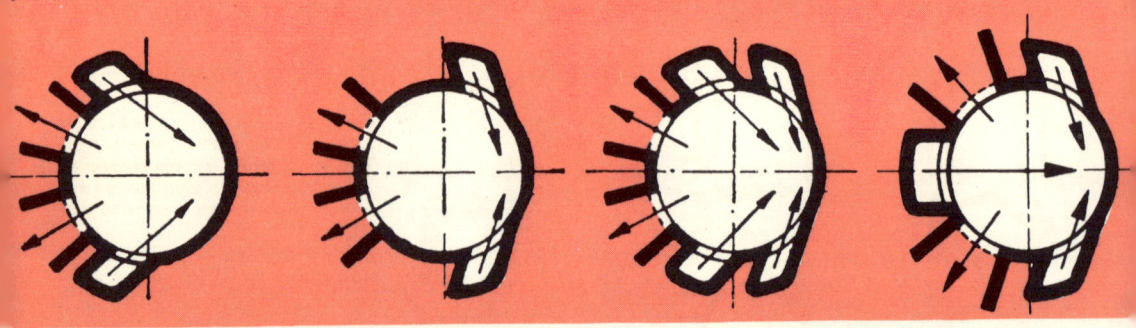

output are going to be profoundly influenced by the extent to which the cylinder is charged with fresh mixture and scavenged of burned mixture.

Basically, there are two approaches to the all-important problem of scavenging, or getting rid of the products of combustion that otherwise will contaminate fresh combustible mixture. The traditional scavenging method is termed *cross-scavenging* or *uniflow* and with it you induce mixture on one side of the cylinder and exhaust it on the other. The other approach is termed *loop-scavenge* and with it you induce mixture from ports on opposite sides of the cylinder in such a way that the two streams swirl in a loop which sweeps the combustion chamber, then join to exhaust through exhaust port(s) on a third side of the cylinder.

The fact that the screaming little McCulloch engines use loop scavenging suggests that this approach is the most efficient. McCulloch engineers, however, are the first to deny that this is an absolute fact. They point out that, when the emphasis is on low-rpm output, uniflow works splendidly. Loop-scavenge seems to do the best job in the higher rpm ranges. Both approaches are completely simple and in both cases the piston is the sliding valve for the transfer ports. Loop-scavenge cylinders are more costly to manufacture, however, due to extra coring, tooling, etc. One rule does stand out: you can get more mixture in faster with the loop layout.

Because the 'case of the 2-cycle engine acts as a transfer pump for the fuel-air mixture it is possible to lubricate the engine by the mere addition of oil (non-detergent!) to the gasoline. When the mixture passes through the carb it is vaporized and droplets of oil lubricate all the surfaces which they contact. That oil which is not deposited in the 'case is burned and leaves the engine as part of the exhaust.

What constitutes c/r in 2-strokes? This is the ratio between the volume in the combustion chamber when the piston is at top dead center and the swept volume above the piston as it just closes off the exhaust ports. As in the 4-stroke engine practice, the *effective* compression ratio is determined by the fit of pistons and rings and the amount of compression leakage that takes place past them. •

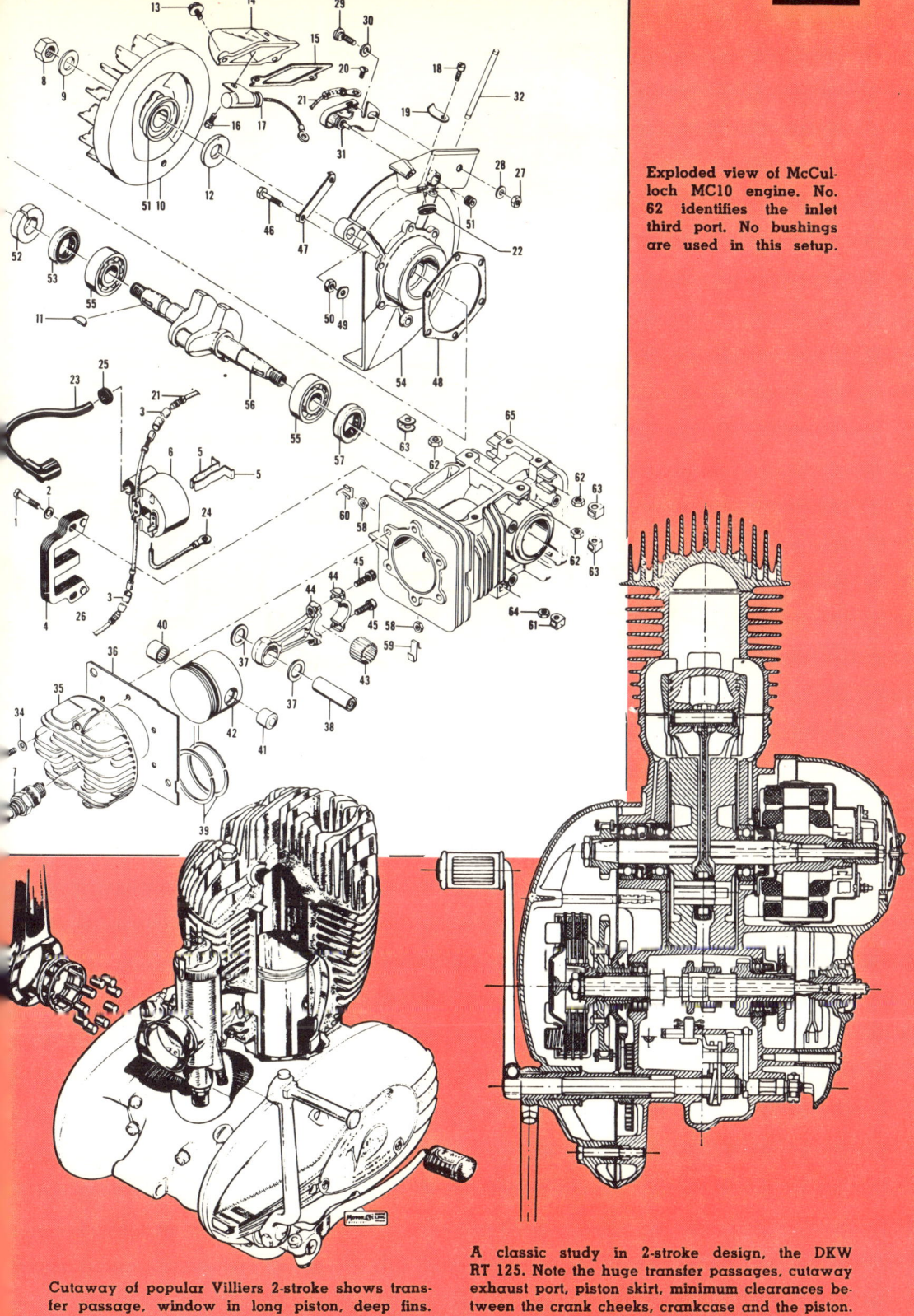

KARTING

Exploded view of McCulloch MC10 engine. No. 62 identifies the inlet third port. No bushings are used in this setup.

Cutaway of popular Villiers 2-stroke shows transfer passage, window in long piston, deep fins.

A classic study in 2-stroke design, the DKW RT 125. Note the huge transfer passages, cutaway exhaust port, piston skirt, minimum clearances between the crank cheeks, crankcase and the piston.

1811

KARTING

Remove flywheel by using knock-off nut, top center. Pull up on wheel, striking nut sharply with hammer.

Kart Engines —

their maintenance, tuning and souping

THIS IS PROBABLY the most important portion of this book, which is why it is the largest portion. Although it is presented in plain, direct language the subject matter is as technical as it is often controversial. The information which follows was drawn from many sources, but most of it was researched with the aid of the almost unique professional engineering staff (all ardent kart racers, of course) of Go-Power Corp. There were two reasons for this: (1) the availability of professional engineers who specialize in karting and (2) who have visited the plants and interviewed the engineers of nearly every two-stroke engine manufacturer in the U. S.

The McCulloch Breed

As engine rpm rises, getting good, clean scavenging of exhaust gases becomes an increasingly critical problem. The engine designer can achieve this by causing plenty of unburned fuel to be blown out the exhaust port, but this is the coward's way out. The ideal is to use only that amount of fuel that can be converted into kinetic energy and at the same time clear the cylinder of the products of combustion.

Probably the most important single factor contributing to the dominance of MC engines in kart competition is McCulloch's skillful use of the loop-scavenge principle, abetted by an inlet "third port" which charges the crankcase when the piston nears the top of its stroke, taking advantage of the last bit of motion left in the slug of mixture inside the engine after the main ports have been closed.

KARTING

MC-5 external appearance differs from MC-6 chiefly in sheet metal shroud details. Plug on other side.

MC-10, favorite of Super A and Super B classes, has differently shaped shroud for air ducting.

Kart engines are light and compact enough to go through mails. Packed MC-10 weighs 12½ pounds.

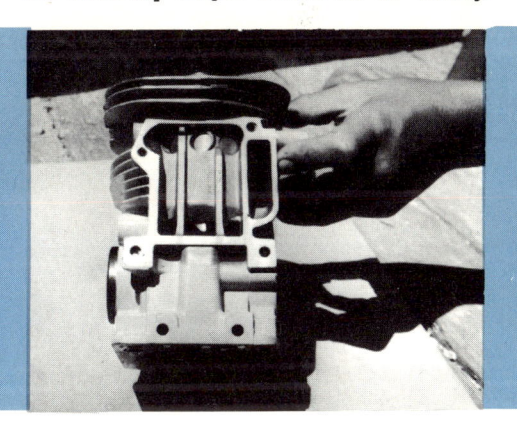

Vertical ribs may be beveled for smoother air-fuel flow. Unusual third port passage at right.

Many factors contribute to clean scavenging: port timing, port directivity, combustion chamber shape, plug location, piston design and ring location are among them. The *principal* problems, in achieving high hp per cubic inch, are concerned with charging and scavenging.

Since the edge of the piston is depended upon to accomplish valving, the shape of the edge and the fit of the piston and rings are vitally important. If the piston is loose, power will leak down its side. The *secondary* problems are related to how well you seal this top end during both compression and power strokes. The cylinder and piston castings must be designed so that, under all temperature conditions, they stay round. You can't seal a cylinder that has an irregular, hollow-spotted surface.

Facing the reed valves of the MC engines are vertical ribs or vanes. Because of the large size of the reed area there is a large area of the cylinder skirt which is unsupported; the ribs are there to keep the cylinder stiff and round. Many speed tuners will grind these ribs away entirely, in order to increase breathing area beyond the reeds. Doing so, they weaken the cylinder and risk poor piston sealing. In actual practice, however, MC engines that have been modified in this way seem to hold up just fine. Whether they put out any more hp is a moot point; there seems to be no dyno data on this.

The breathing area provided in the stock MC engine is very adequate. You can improve the flow of fuel-air mixture by beveling, streamlining both sides of these ribs.

1813

KARTING

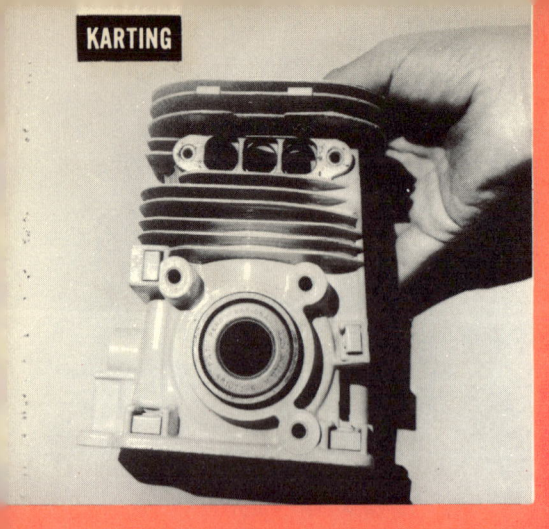

Round exhaust ports may be filed square, bridges thinned. Don't exceed top and bottom port edges.

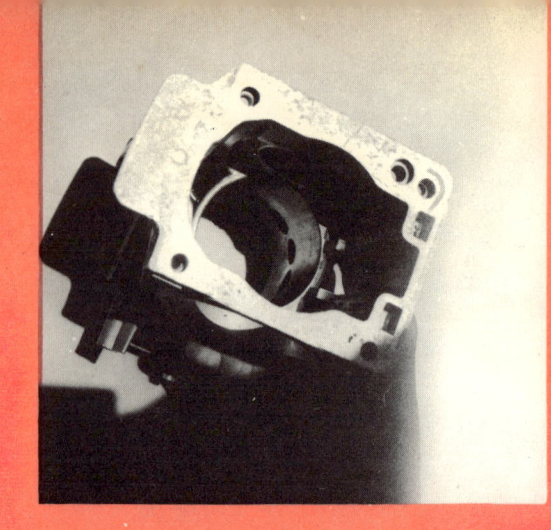

Looking into crankcase. Inner corners of cylinder skirt stiffening ribs can use streamlining.

McCulloch calls its crankcase stuffers "rabbit ears." Function is to improve pumping efficiency.

Stock finish is excellent, but "half golfball" combustion chamber is better when it's polished.

But don't bevel them so that they come to a knife edge. This concentrates all the stress on that thin edge which will tend to crack, and, if it does, the crack will spread. Streamline these ribs for better flow but don't overdo it. The cylinder block is filigree to begin with; use restraint in removing its metal.

The way a cylinder head is torqued down is important for all engines but is particularly critical with small ones. Uneven torquing causes distortion of the cylinder, with resulting wear at the high spots. They cause unnecessary friction losses and lead to blow-by. To be safe, apply 55 to 60 in-lbs. of torque to the Allenhead screws in opposite sequence.

Since the two-stroke crankcase and its contents function as a pump for the fuel-air mixture, the more pressure that can be applied against the mixture, the more vigorously it will be pumped into the cylinder. Close tolerances and crankcase stuffers are used to keep the 'case volume compact and the 'case compression ratio or pumping pressure high. The stock MC, being a high-efficiency engine, represents an excellent proportion of crankcase volume to cylinder

KARTING

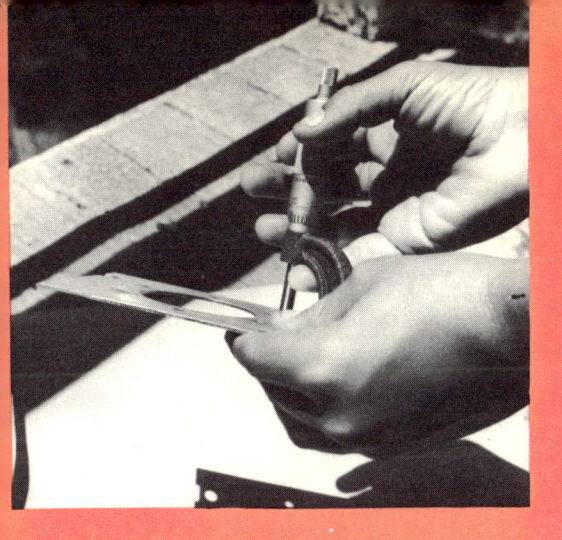

Head gasket is square aluminum sheet. Stock has an .066 thickness, giving about 8:1 comp ratio.

Effective carburetor throat area is greatly increased by removal of choke shaft and butterfly.

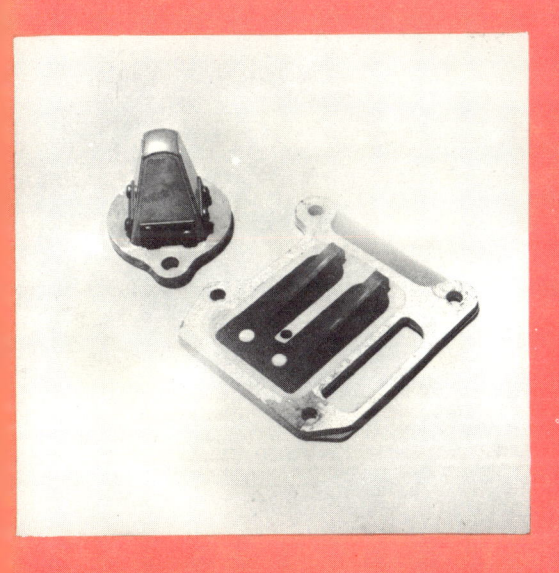

Mac reed plate is at right. Pyramidal construction of other plate gives more valve area, stuffing.

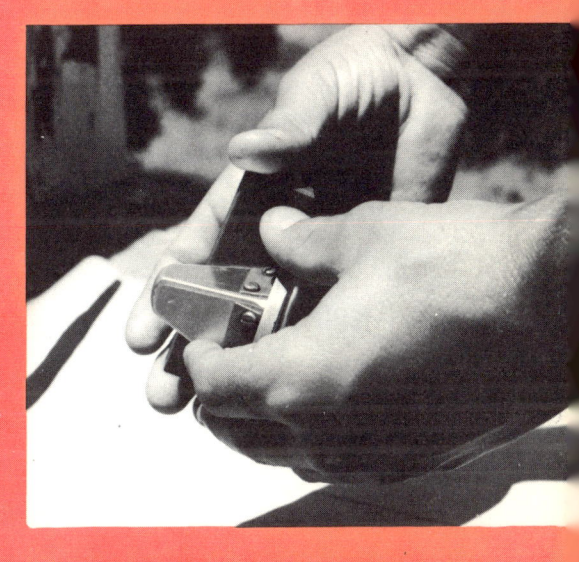

Before reeds are assembled to plate, it is worthwhile to dress plate surfaces with fine oilstone.

volume. The MC makes generous use of stuffing and the "rabbit ears" crankcase bottom is one of the nicest in the industry.

Now here's something that is scarcely known. Stuffing helps in the high-rpm range, hurts lower down. With the MC engines the dividing line is around 4500 rpm, at which speed the stuffed engine puts out just the same hp as one with a flat plate in place of the rabbit ears. Below about 4500 the unstuffed engine breathes better, pulls more strongly. An MC with a very tight stuffer and full-circle crank will lose from ten to 15 per cent hp below about 4500

but will gain that amount up at 10,000 rpm.

So, the boys who are really cagey learn to stuff the engine to suit the course. If the race is to be won on coming out of tight turns, get rid of the stuffing, use a flat plate. If it's to be won on the straights, cram in the stuffing.

Although it was primarily designed to provide greater reed-valve area, the pyramid-type reed plate, by projecting into the crankcase, also contributes to stuffing. All current designs of pyramid reed plates and their adapter manifolds for MC engines have the effect of eliminating the use of

KARTING

How pyramid reed plate fits in adapter for MC. Part-complete streamlining shown is hand work.

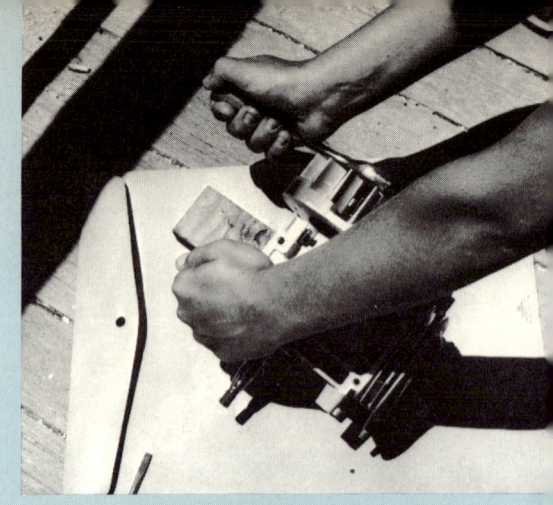

To remove flywheel nut, wedge crankshaft with a wood block. Self-locking nut takes lots of torque.

Directions are given in text for building simple flywheel puller shown in position for use, right.

Hardened crank journal and the con rod lower end serve as inner and outer needle bearing races.

Webco porting and de-burring kit. A quarter-inch electric drill should be high-speed.

Go-Power makes stuffers and adapter manifolds for McCulloch, West Bend and Power Products.

the third port. Since, when McCulloch adopted the third-port principle, they immediately began getting about 15 per cent more power from their engines, it is doubtful that the gain from greater reed area is enough to offset the loss due to cutting out the third port. At the present time Go-Power (who began the whole pyramid-reed revolution in karting, having gotten the idea from Lou Borelli) is developing an adapter for its six-reed, hexagonal pyramid which *will* utilize the MC third port. Whether it goes into production will be determined by the quality of its performance.

Bug Engineering makes a dual-carb manifold for MC's on which one carb feeds a pyramid reed assembly while the other feeds the third port. This is a lot of venturi area for a small engine to handle but there are many satisfied users of these conversions.

The MC engines' ports are round for two reasons. First, it's more economical to drill round holes in mass production than it is to shape square ones. Second, round holes provide better directional flow. A lot has been printed about chamfering and polishing MC inlet ports. DON'T TOUCH THEM! Practically anything you do to them destroys their precisely-calculated nozzle action and upsets the balance between good intake and good scavenging. More MC engines have been spoiled by people "improving" inlet ports than by any other cause.

A square hole has greater cross-sectional area than a round one of equal width and, for top output, the *exhaust* ports should be squared with a hand file. First, square the ports and thin their vertical bridges. *Do not* square the outer side of the end ports and do not file beyond the top and bottom edges of the ports. To do so will foul up the valve timing. A Webco porting and de-burring kit, plus a ¼-inch electric drill, is most helpful in this and other modifications. Be *sure* to remove all burrs, above all, any that may extend into the cylinder bore.

As soon as you open up the exhaust ports you create the possibility of the ring ends hooking against the top or bottom edges of the ports. To eliminate this possibility both rings should be pinned to prevent their rotation.

The simplest method of performing this operation is by means of a couple of phonograph needles: the cheap, tapered steel kind; not the kind that has a large main shaft, then a sudden step-down to a small point. Next, anneal the needles you are going to use by holding them with pliers and heating them well with a match flame. What you are about to do is insert the needles through the ring gaps, through the ring slots and drive them firmly into the body of the piston.

First you must determine *where* in the piston the needles should be installed. With the piston in the cylinder in correct alignment (that is, with the *closed* end of the

Crankcase stuffing, factory-style. This is Yamaha's new B-class engine. Note full-circle crankshaft.

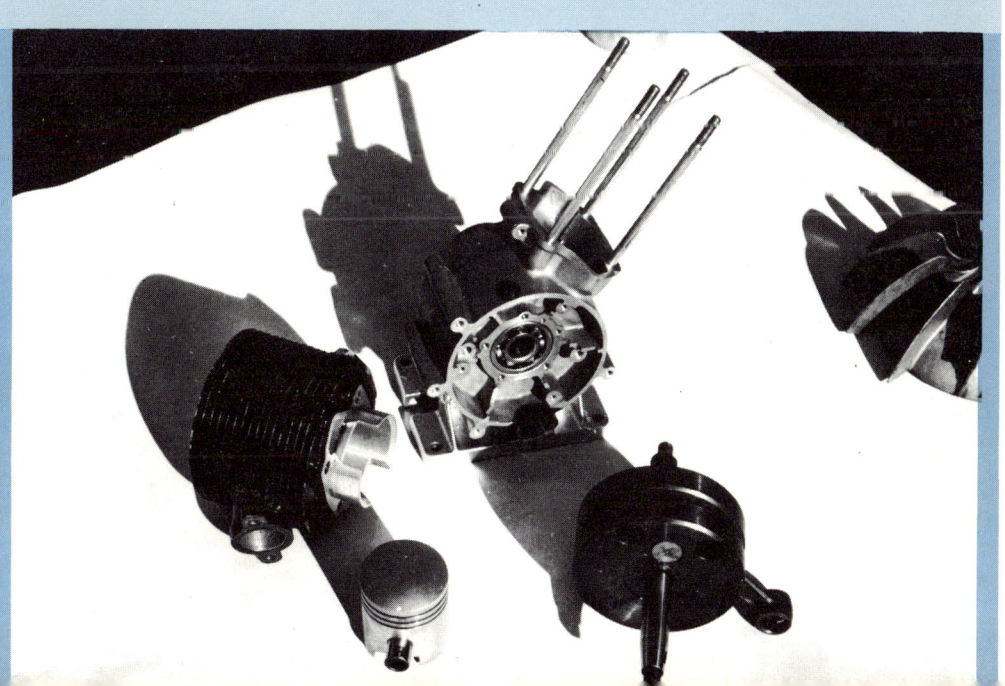

KARTING

MC-5 stock stuffer is in center; at left is MC-10 stuffer. To right of engine is Go-Power stuffer.

Go-Power pyramid-reed manifold for using MC third port will be produced only if it proves efficient.

Palmini's newest pyramid has four reeds, uses second inverted pyramid in the bottom of reed cage.

wrist pin facing the exhaust side), make pencil marks on the head of the piston at two points, as far apart as possible, where the cylinder wall is solid—is not penetrated by ports. As we said, it's largely filigree and there are only a few possible locations where piston ring ends can be counted upon not to snag against the lip of a port. With these locations determined, and using a drill bit somewhat smaller than the phono needle, drill holes in these locations through the ring grooves, sideways through the wall of the piston.

Now, with a small hammer, tap each needle deeply into the aluminum piston, making sure by center punching or delicate grinding that the needle cannot touch the cylinder wall. Now you can mount the rings on the piston with their end gaps straddling the needles. If the end gap seems tight, grind a little clearance, just making sure that you've provided enough. Go-Power has run tests on the dyno with ring gaps up to .100—that's a whole one hundred thousandths of an inch—with absolutely no change in power output. Actually, this tallies well with similar experiments with automotive engines; the time interval in which blow-by can take place through these gaps is infinitesimal.

Now for compression ratio and jacking it up. In two-strokes there are two kinds

1818

Go-Power achieves huge reed area with hexagonal pyramid and six reeds. Note the inner deflector cone

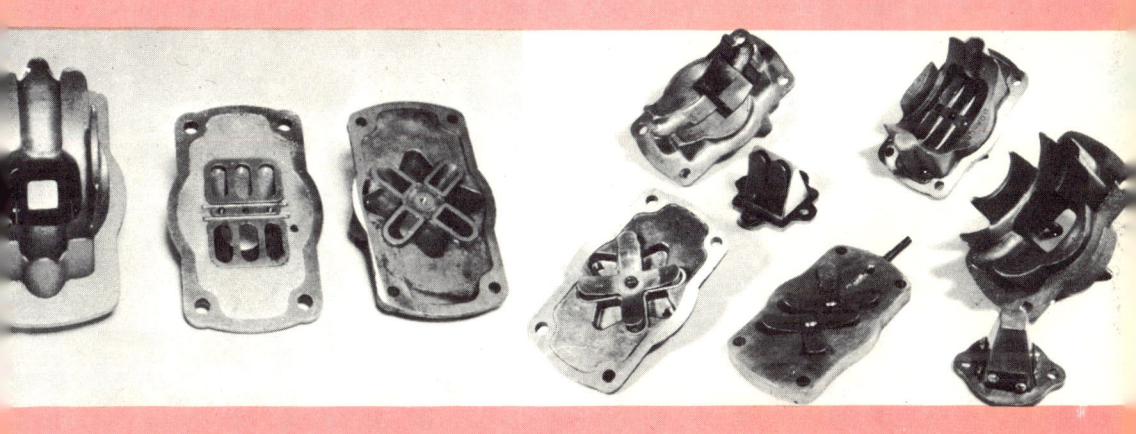

All for same West Bend engine: left, Go-Power 6 reed; center, West Bend 6 reed, with 4 reed, right.

Another example of variety. All these stuffers and reed plates fit the same late-model WB's.

of compression ratio: the familiar *measured* kind that we know from automotive practice and the *effective* kind which, in two-strokes, is determined by port timing. We will speak in terms of measured compression ratio, or c/r.

On the MC engines stock c/r is about eight to one and the aluminum head gasket is about .066 inch thick. From about .013 to .016 is the minimum clearance that most manufacturers recommend from top of piston to the opposing surface of the cylinder head. In the case of the MC-6 and MC-10 the piston pops up about .031 above the top of the cylinder. On these engines you can safely go to a .045 head gasket and still have the recommended clearance. Each reduction of .015 in gasket thickness is good for an increase of about 1.5 points of c/r.

In the case of the MC-5 you can get away with no gasket at all. The mating surfaces of cylinder and head must be lapped to form a perfect seal; suitable lapping compounds are available through hardware stores and auto-supply shops. But be careful; McCulloch has more than one die for the MC-5 cylinder casting and dimensions may vary slightly from engine to engine. Check to be sure that the at-least .013 clearance will be there when the head is torqued down. Useful for this is Plastigage, also universally available.

KARTING

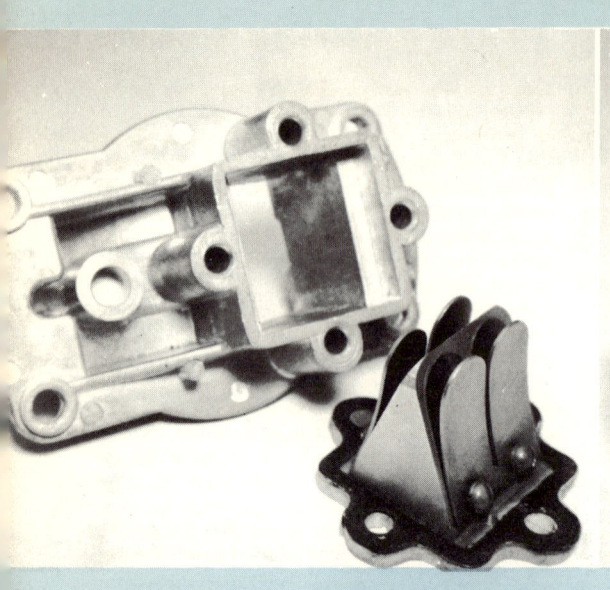

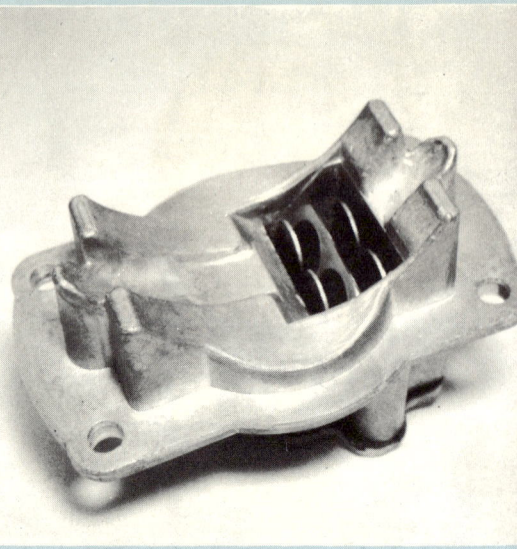

Two views of West Bend's new "V"-Power kit for souping up all of its kart engines.

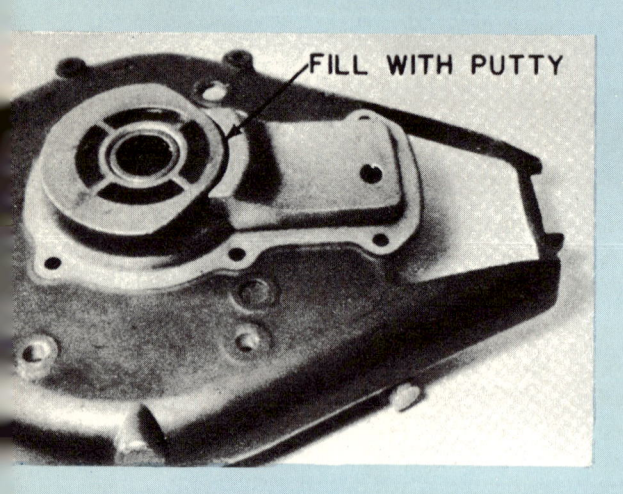

Go-Power transfer-port stuffer/deflector for WB can be faired in with Devcon putty.

FILL WITH PUTTY

This WB engine, modified by Dick McAdams shows the miracles that can be wrought with aluminum putty. Side intake port and stuffer fins are formed entirely of Devcon.

With the cylinder head off and with the piston at about top center, place a small piece of this material near the edge of the piston, where it faces the outer shoulder of the combustion chamber. Torque down the head, then rock the crank a few degrees on each side of TDC. Remove the head, measure the thickness of the Plastigage with a micrometer or, lacking that, make sure that it's thicker than a .013 feeler gauge. Jacking c/r upward is, of course, a sure-fire route to increased engine output and the sturdy little engines will take the pressure.

Now for the ancient and long-revered subject of polishing. Think like a molecule of air. You're that tiny and what do you have to go through to get from A to B? Naturally, each tiny rough spot in your path will be a mountain or wall to slow you down or stop you dead. So, naturally, you want highly polished surfaces to move over and around. Besides, so many polished racing engines have done well that it was proved long ago that polishing pays off. Or is it just that polishing and thorough, painstaking preparation have so often gone hand in hand?

Go-Power Corp. has scored a large number of firsts, but the most shattering and the one which probably will have the longest reverberations is a chapter titled, "Should You Polish For Power?" contained in the firm's definitive $2 book, "How To Hop Up Your West Bend." We quote here just one paragraph from that long chapter but it will serve to establish the point.

"The primary factor which originally led

Squaring WB ports and thinning ribs require two ¼-inch round files: one coarse and one fine file.

Before and after port reworking a WB. See how full-circle crankshaft assembly fills the case.

KARTING

The big West Bend engine, shown here, is fully modified with Go-Power goodies. The stack is not tuned, but noisy.

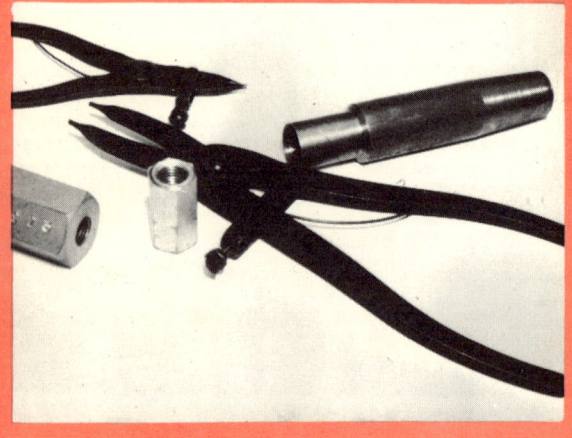

Some special tools needed for working on West Bend engines are: snap-ring pliers, knock-off nuts and seal guide.

to polishing of the engine's carburetor throat, transfer passages and exhaust ports is the widespread belief that gases travel faster and easier over a smooth surface than a rough one. This does seem logical at first, but it is not always true in actual practice. When air, water, or any gas or fluid flows through a passage, a thin boundary layer is formed along the walls. The gaseous mixture which is within this boundary layer is restrained by viscous friction with the walls and it moves at a much slower rate than does the main flow of gas. Actually, the gaseous mixture next to the passage wall surface stands absolutely still! This is true, no matter what the smoothness of the passage. Herein lies the fallacy in the polishing theory: if the air along the wall surfaces cannot move at high velocity in any case, it is obviously wasted endeavor to polish the walls."

These statements, based on mountains of aerodynamic and hydraulic evidence, have only begun to have their shattering effect on the kart-racing fraternity. They mean that, in automotive speed circles for example, literally billions of man-hours have been wasted in polishing that was pretty but futile.

There are two places where polishing pays off in a two-stroke engine: piston head and combustion chamber. As for crank and connecting rod, forget these. A forging and, even more so, a die casting has a prestressed surface that can be weakened by polishing. Stock cranks don't break; rods sometimes do, but only due to bearing failure.

Top-end performance (at the cost of the low end) can be upped two to three tenths of a hp by enlarging the carb throat to ¾ inch, a $\frac{1}{16}$-bore job best done on a lathe by a competent machinist. Jet modifications also can be made, but carb work should be entrusted to specialists; Reed Engineering is a prominent one.

About to be announced, at the time this article was prepared for publication, is a

A long-handled Allen wrench is best for torquing down the con-rod cap screws in all these engines.

WB wrist-pin circlip may be installed through the port, using a pair of small snap-ring pliers.

All these carbs fit WB. At left is Tillotson; stock float-carb is on mill; center is MC; right is Walbro Pulsycle constant fuel supply carb.

new, much-improved McCulloch carb which interchanges with the old ones. The chief shortcoming of the latter, excellent as they are, is the tendency to fall off in performance at about 10,000 rpm. The new model functions smoothly right up to 15,000 rpm. Better metering is provided throughout the range, the old sintered-metal filter is replaced by one of fine screen and the previous ball valve has been replaced by a needle valve of nylon-like material. It has bumps in its throat to guide air flow, so to bore it is to ruin it. It's a worthwhile investment in performance.

A significant percentage of carb throat area is occupied by the choke valve assembly. In some climates, such as that of Southern California, it is customary to remove the choke entirely by simply removing the one screw in the choke butterfly. This provides maximum area for air flow and the engine can be choked easily by simply placing the hand or a couple of fingers over the carb throat, first being sure to have mounted a good chain guard.

Modifications which increase an engine's output naturally cause it to run hotter. Therefore the cylinder bore should be honed .001 inch over its as-received diameter. Or, to be even safer and more precise, it should be honed to provide a clearance of .007 between piston and cylinder wall. This measurement should be based on the diameter of the bottom of the piston skirt, *not* the head.

Such a honing operation is excellent practice even when a new engine is not being modified for higher output. There are residual stresses in the major components which are a natural result of the die-casting process. So, to get a sweetly friction-free engine, run it for two or three hours in its as-received form. In engineering jargon, heat-cycle it, put it through its operating temperature range. Then tear it down and have the bore honed to clean up any out-of-true condition which almost inevitably will be present.

1823

KARTING

DIAPHRAGM CARBURETOR

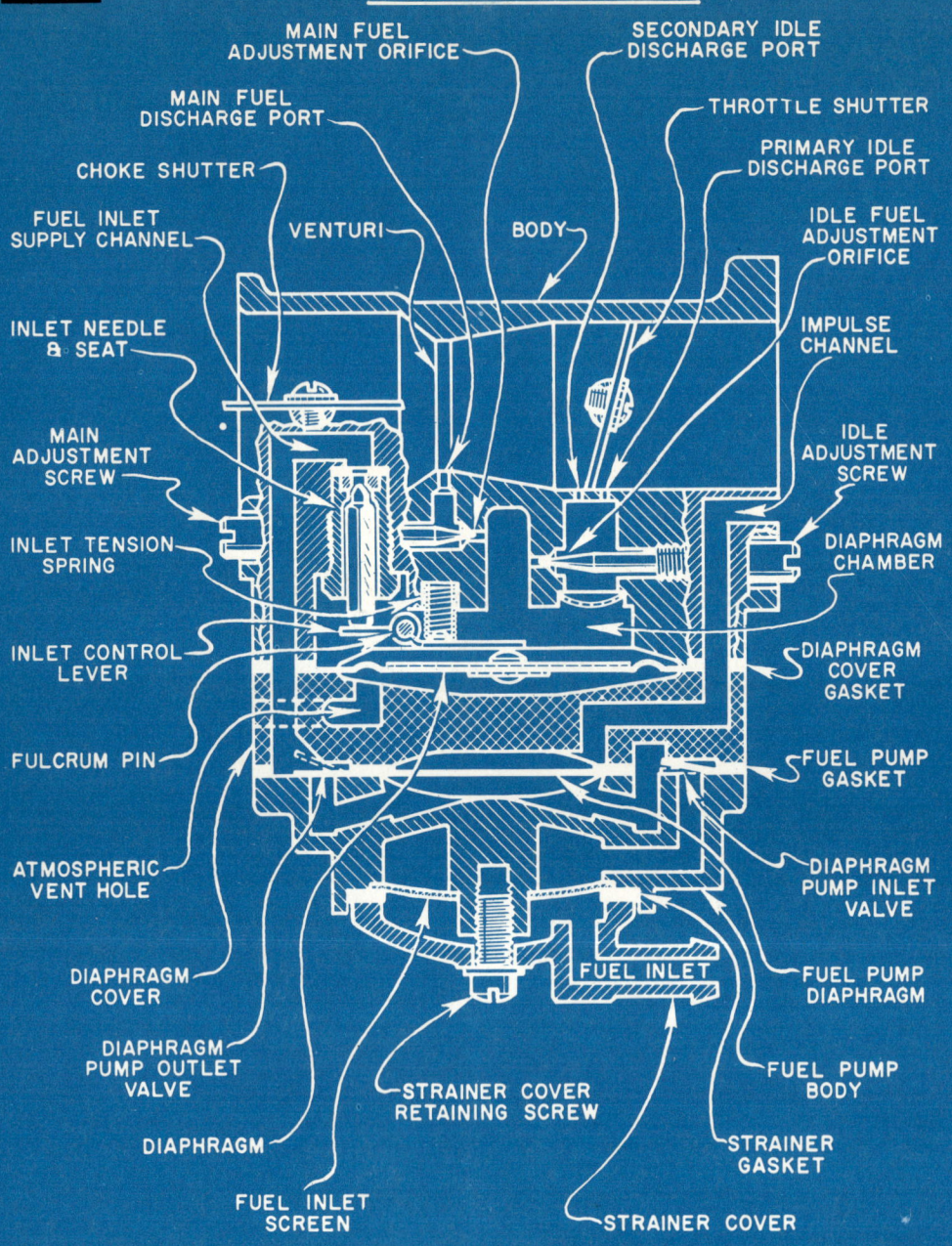

Tillotson HL Series carb is the classic of the diaphragm type. It is diagramed above and appears in photo at left.

THROTTLE SHAFT HOLE
SECONDARY IDLE PORT
PRIMARY IDLE PORT
RESERVOIR FOR LO-SPEED AND INTERMEDIATE SYSTEM
HI-SPEED ORFICE
AIR BLEED
KARTING

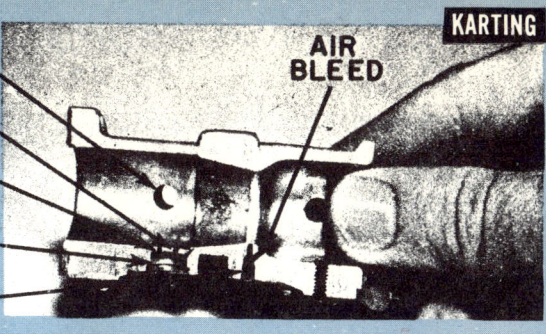

A cross-section of HL Series Tillotson carb throat showing venturi structure and jet locations.

BREAKER CAM — **SUPPORT PLATE**
COIL — **COVER SPRING**
DUST COVER
SUPPORT PLATE SCREW

WB flywheel must be removed to provide access to ignition system. Nomenclature is shown here.

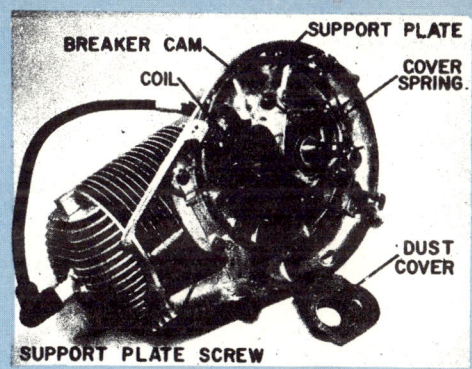

What effect does paint have on an air-cooled engine's heat-dissipating efficiency? This is another controversial subject. Some manufacturers claim that paint, or the paint that they use, has absolutely no action as a barrier to heat transfer; and they have engineering data to prove it. One German motorcycle manufacturer found that engines run remarkably cooler when the fins are coated with dull, black paint. But the public did not want to buy bikes with black engines; they wanted to see silvery aluminum. So the manufacturer was forced to leave off the paint and to enlarge the cooling fins by about 20 per cent to compensate. This is an area where much experimentation remains to be done.

Very important amounts of hp can be lost due to excessive friction between the cylinder wall and the piston piston-ring assembly. To reduce this friction loss to a minimum, after an engine has done the equivalent of a couple of weekends of racing, remove the cylinder and examine its bore for high spots. If you've performed the honing operation these will be few, if any. Also examine the piston for high spots which indicate rubbing. There are two schools of thought on what to do next. The first says to dress down the spots on the cylinder wall with fine garnet paper and do *not* touch the piston (being sure, when finished, thoroughly to wash away with solvent all traces of abrasive). The other school says don't touch the cylinder; you can never do a decent job on it by hand.

Instead, using a very fine file, dress down the high spots on the piston. We prefer the latter method, combined with honing. After this has been done it is worthwhile to tear the engine down again after another several hours of running and check the piston again for fresh high spots. The piston is the greatest single source of friction loss in an engine; give it the attention it merits.

McCulloch's entry into karting began with chain saw engines. Recognizing the great potential of the sport, in Feb. 1960 the firm introduced the designed-for-karting 4.9 cubic inch MC-5 and the 5.3 MC-10. These were immensely successful but, a few weeks before the GKCA Nationals, a competitor released a threateningly-hot Class A engine. MC retaliated immediately with a hop-up kit for the MC-5. It consists of:

Part No.	Name	Price
48730A	Tillotson carb HL93A	$18.00
48742	.017 head gasket	.35
48672	.050 head gasket	.35
55012B	.066 head gasket	.32
48695	Racing piston assy.	10.25
48744	.125 stroked crankshaft	22.00

For the MC-5 the HL-93A carb alone increases power output by five per cent. The carb, plus the .017 gasket, makes for a 20 per cent increase. The carb, .017 gasket and thin-ring piston bring a 31.5 per cent increase in output. The racing carb, piston, .066 head gasket and stroked shaft (with it,

1825

KARTING

Left: The early WB "lawnmower" ignition system at left in photo should be replaced by improved late type at right.

Above: This photograph shows the relative location of keyways in flywheel for standard and reverse-rotation WB's.

Left: West Bend makes these $2.85 shrouds for improved cooling. State the direction of rotation when placing order.

thinner gaskets cannot be used), output is upped a howling 41.5 per cent.

For the MC-10 the new piston assembly adds ten per cent to output. This, plus the .050 head gasket, adds 16 per cent. Because the MC-10's crank has ball bearings on both ends, while one of the MC-5's is a roller, the MC-5 stroker shaft will not fit the MC-10. At presstime, McCulloch was about to announce a new stroker kit for the MC-10 which should be good for an added half to three quarters hp.

Shortly after the 1960 GKCA Nationals MC introduced a new, hotter version of the MC-5, equipped with all the new goodies just described, plus a deeper-finned cylinder head with inclined rather than vertical spark plug . . . inclined away from the exhaust, at a cooler portion of the combustion chamber. The use of chain saw MC-D44 inclined-plug heads on MC kart engines has proved the superiority of this layout. The new MC-6 head will fit the MC-10, although this changeover could be more bother than it is worth since it entails other modifications, such as fabricating a new cooling shroud. With its 5.3 cubic inch displacement and price of $99.50 the MC-6 is to Stock A and B classes what the MC-10 is to Super A and B.

Any crank can be stroked for increased displacement and what is not available from manufacturers' stocks can be had from specialists. The operation is critical and far from cheap. Go-Power will stroke any McCulloch crank . . . for $50.

One of the major limitations to stroking is the point at which the piston rings start

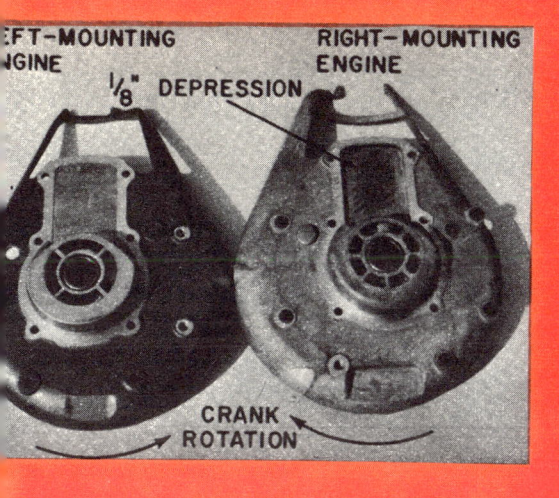

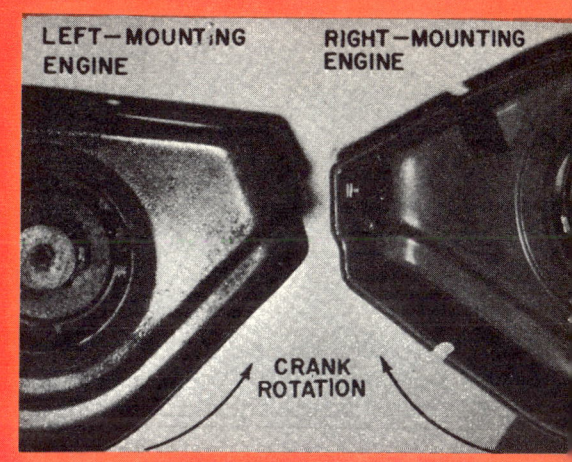

The support plates for right- and left-hand mounting WB's have entirely different construction.

Top, right: Fan housings for different-rotation West Bends also are distinctive in appearance.

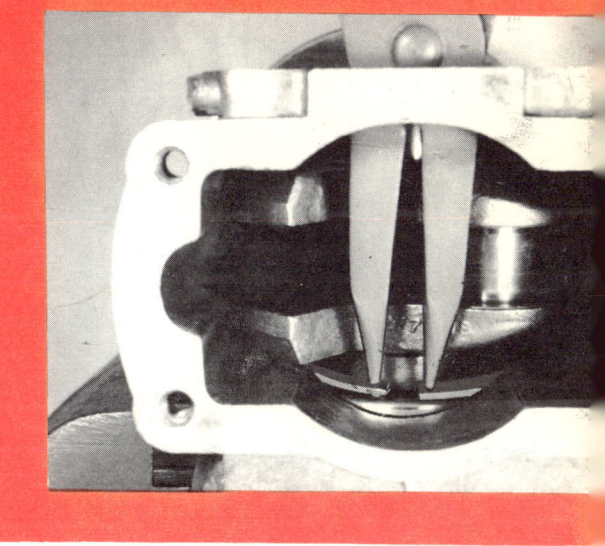

Right: Large snap-ring pliers are used to remove the main bearing circlip; shaft removal is easy.

popping out of the cylinder bore at the top of the stroke. To avoid this, the rings must be repositioned, wrist pin moved or some other compensation made. Engineered kits, such as the MC power kits just described, have these compensations built in. If you have a stock MC that you want to stroke, you can go to about .100 inch. It's at about .125, 1/8 inch, that the ring trouble sets in.

There are plenty of 1/8-inch strokers in competition and not a few 3/16-inch strokers. It is extremely likely that some of the hottest goers are running cranks with 1/4-inch strokes. The dead giveaway is the immensely-thick head gaskets some of them use.

The other means of increasing displacement, of course, is boring. The stock MC's can be bored .060 (about 1/16) with safety, and pistons to fit are readily available. To go bigger, it is necessary to bore out the stock sleeve and install a thicker sleeve which then can be bored to .080 and, in some cases, to as much as .125. First locate a source of pistons for the diameter you plan to bore to.

Gas with a 76-octane rating is adequate for stock MC engines; 100-octane white marine gas is pretty ideal. Do *not* use ethyl. McCulloch now is recommending oil no lighter than SAE 40 and that it be mixed in proportions not less than one part of oil to 12 of gas. The old recommendation was for 20 to 1. This worked for chain saws, but in kart racing, tended to cause burned piston rings. Extensive tests have shown that you're quite safe with 16 to 1. So MC recommends 12 to 1, and many of the

1827

KARTING

A groove in the WB crankcase seal collar helps in disassembly; the seal may have to be destroyed

sharpest and most successful racing people run as rich as eight to 1 . . . with no loss in hp, but with great reliability. McCulloch oil is very good. Castor oil's film strength is outstanding and many racing experts will use nothing else. Blendzall and Kart-Lube are good castor brands. Actually, all the castor in the country seems to originate from one refiner, Baker. Present-day castor is highly degummed and it offers no more problems in kart-engine maintenance than conventional mineral oil.

There is some good technical literature available from McCulloch free for the asking. It covers many important points but overlooks some vital ones such as flywheel removal.

The mechanic who has been trained never to force a piece of mechanism may be dismayed by the flywheel nut's resistance to removal. This resistance is natural because this is a self-locking nut and high torque must be used almost until the nut drops off the shaft. To keep the shaft from turning during this operation, remove the rabbit-ears crankcase bottom and insert a piece of wood of appropriate size between the crank counterweights and the 'case

After the nut has been removed the flywheel must be pulled from its tapered fit on the crankshaft and it is remarkable how difficult this fit is to break. Under no conditions must the flywheel be pried at its edges. The flywheel is drilled and tapped with ¼-20 threads on either side of the crankshaft to receive a puller, the only instrument by means of which the flywheel should be removed. Ideally, that is.

It's easy to tailor-make your own puller for this purpose. A piece of bar stock ¼ by one inch or, preferably, $\frac{5}{16}$ by one inch and 2½ inches long is the starting point. In its center, drill and tap threads for a $\frac{5}{16}$ bolt, the end of which should be pointed on a grinder. Next, drill holes for ¼-inch screws or bolts, corresponding with the puller holes in the flywheel. These holes in the puller need not be threaded if the ¼-inch screws are trimmed to proper length. Now the puller is complete. Again wedging the crank, torque down the central bolt until the flywheel comes free with a startling pop.

There *is* another way, which we describe

Go-Power converts WB 700 crank (background) for long-stroke effect in 750 bearings (foreground).

Top, r.: New bushing method of converting WB 750 to 580 or 700 crank. Tubes are for lubrication.

After you've gone all the way with rabbit ears, full-circle crank gives best stuffing gains (l.).

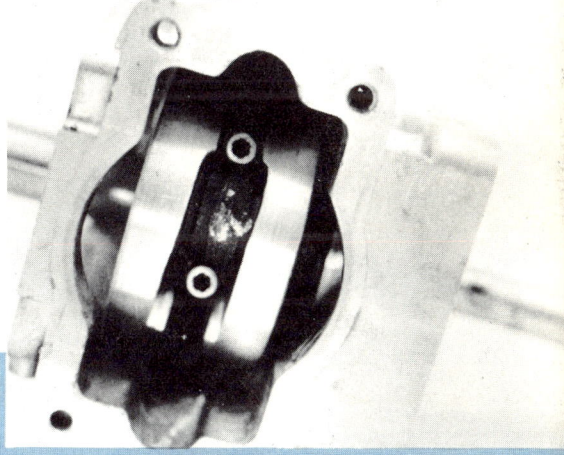

The beginning of full-circle crank conversion: the extra steel plates are clamped on, heliarced.

with reluctance. But the point is that to even begin to get at the guts of the engine the flywheel must come off. So this is what they do in the logging camps.

Take a big, disposable nut with the same threads as the flywheel nut. Screw it about halfway onto the shaft, in place of the flywheel nut. Get somebody to hold the engine, with the nut upward. Then take a hammer. A light one will never do the job—about three lbs. is right. Then you bang smartly on the nut. After enough of these impacts the flywheel pops loose. One bad blow and you've wrecked everything. But, sad to say, that's how most of these flywheels are removed; many manufacturers don't even bother with puller holes. Those flywheels that are removed with pry bars can be thrown away and probably their cranks with them. And do your best never to scratch one of these die-cast, light-alloy, high rpm flywheels. You know it takes only a scratch to set up a fracture plane in a thick sheet of glass. These flywheels are similarly sensitive.

Another closely-guarded secret of the literature is crankshaft removal, a rather

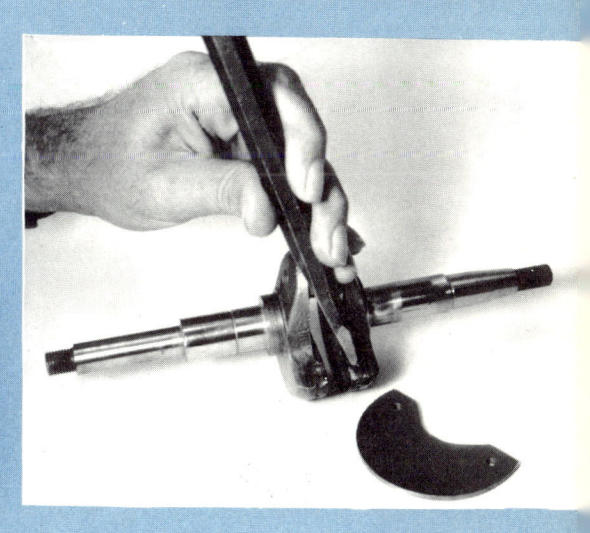

KARTING

necessary operation from time to time. Once you have the cylinder block completely stripped, the bloody crankshaft still will not come out. This is due to an interference fit between its output-side ball bearing and the block. There are fancy tools for this job, but the private mechanic needs only the household oven. Recipe: put block in oven, having disposed of wife, and heat to about 300 degrees F. Remove block, using pot holders or rags (300 is hotter than you may think) and lightly tap end of crankshaft with a soft hammer. Just like an Offy, the crank comes right out. Replace it by the same method.

Finally, there is the little matter of removing the wrist pin from the MC piston-rod assembly. Don't. The theory is that you simply heat the assembly by placing it in boiling water, on a hot plate or by means of a torch. Then, using a drift pin with two diameters to fit the ID and OD of the wrist pin, you tap it out. My own experience is that you can heat the thing like a branding iron, yet everything stays locked tight. The pin only expands and locks in the rod and you can beat the whole business to bits and the wrist pin stays put. Needless to say, this sort of assembly, this sort of attention to fit, is one of the reasons for the wonderful performance of MC engines.

The West Bend Breed

Up to this point we have dealt with the MC breed as *the* leader, in karting, which follows the loop-scavenge principle. Actually, most of the points that have been made apply to two-stroke engines in gen-

When weight-plates are heliarc-welded in position, magnesium stuffers are attached.

Below, l.: All that remains to complete this conversion is torquing in the last magnesium stuffer.

Below: Complete assembly of Go-Power's full-circle WB setup; also available for MC, PP.

eral. And that includes West Bend, *the* leader in deflector-scavenging.

Remember that it is easier to charge a two-stroke cylinder than it is to clear it of its products of combustion. This is why some high-performance two-strokes, when they are supercharged, use the blower on the exhaust side, to suck the unwanted gases out. West Bend uses (like the majority of two-stroke manufacturers) an elaborately contoured piston head to guide, by deflection, the flow of the products of combustion out of the cylinder. It has no third port in the MC sense. It's the Offy of two-strokes in being, as Wilbur Shaw once put it, a lunger and a legger, meaning its low-end torque is terrific and it can really get out and stride. It is equally reliable. In over a year of brutal dyno and track testing, Go-Power has yet to succeed in scattering one single WB engine. It's a simple engine, easier to work on than the MC. You should have, in addition to the usual home-shop tools, a few special ones:

WB Part No.	Tool
T-1081	Snap-ring pliers
T-1750	Snap-ring pliers
18091	Knock-off nut, rt. hand
T-2923	Knock-off nut, lt. hand
T-2916	Seal sleeve

The only tricky procedure in tearing down the WB engine is flywheel removal which must be done by means of hammer and knock-off nut, as previously described. WB wrist pins are retained by small snap rings or wire pin locks; they usually come

Stock Power Products AH-58 as originally introduced: improvements have been spectacular.

Below, r.: PP AH-58 with full Palmini modifications including head, tie-bars, manifold, exhaust and carb stacks, chain guard, engine mount.

Below: Cigarettes are almost as big as PP case. Imagine this wonderful device putting out 7 hp!

KARTING

Above, right, left: Exquisitely-made high compression heads for Power Products engines are manufactured by Go-Power. Note the fineness of the fins which help provide a tremendous cooling surface.

Power Products AH-58 fully Go-Power equipped (l.). Tie bars no longer are necessary to retain cylinder. Half of tiny Power Products 'case (r.) showing its relationship to Go-Power stuffer, full-circle crank.

out easily. If not, they will with a little heat applied to the piston. The crankshaft main bearings are retained by snap rings and come out easily. The engine is a delight to work on.

It responds splendidly to souping although in stock form it's a real hauler. Precisely how it responds is shown in an accompanying chart, Fig. A, the long caption of which is largely a table of contents for the already mentioned Go-Power book, "How To Hop Up Your West Bend." This is *the* definitive work on the subject, prepared in close liaison with WB factory engineers and with dyno data on the performance value of each possible modification. This wonderful, fact-packed book (which I would be proud to have written) is basic to any karting library, and indispensable to any owner of a WB engine. It

1832

KARTING

describes in detail what we will describe here briefly.

The WB responds markedly to modifications to both intake and exhaust ports. You need two ¼-inch round files, one coarse, one fine. The job takes, on the average, about an hour. As shown in Figs. B and C, the two center webs of the intake ports should be filed to a width of about $\frac{1}{16}$ inch, tapering them to a point as they enter the transfer port. Square the tops of the ports so that only a ⅛-inch radius remains at the corners or the flattened top. The most critical touch here is filing the outer edges of the outer ports. *The port must go straight into the cylinder.* Leave the bottoms of the intake ports alone; don't square them.

Rework the exhaust ports in the same manner, but square the bottoms as well as

FIG. A

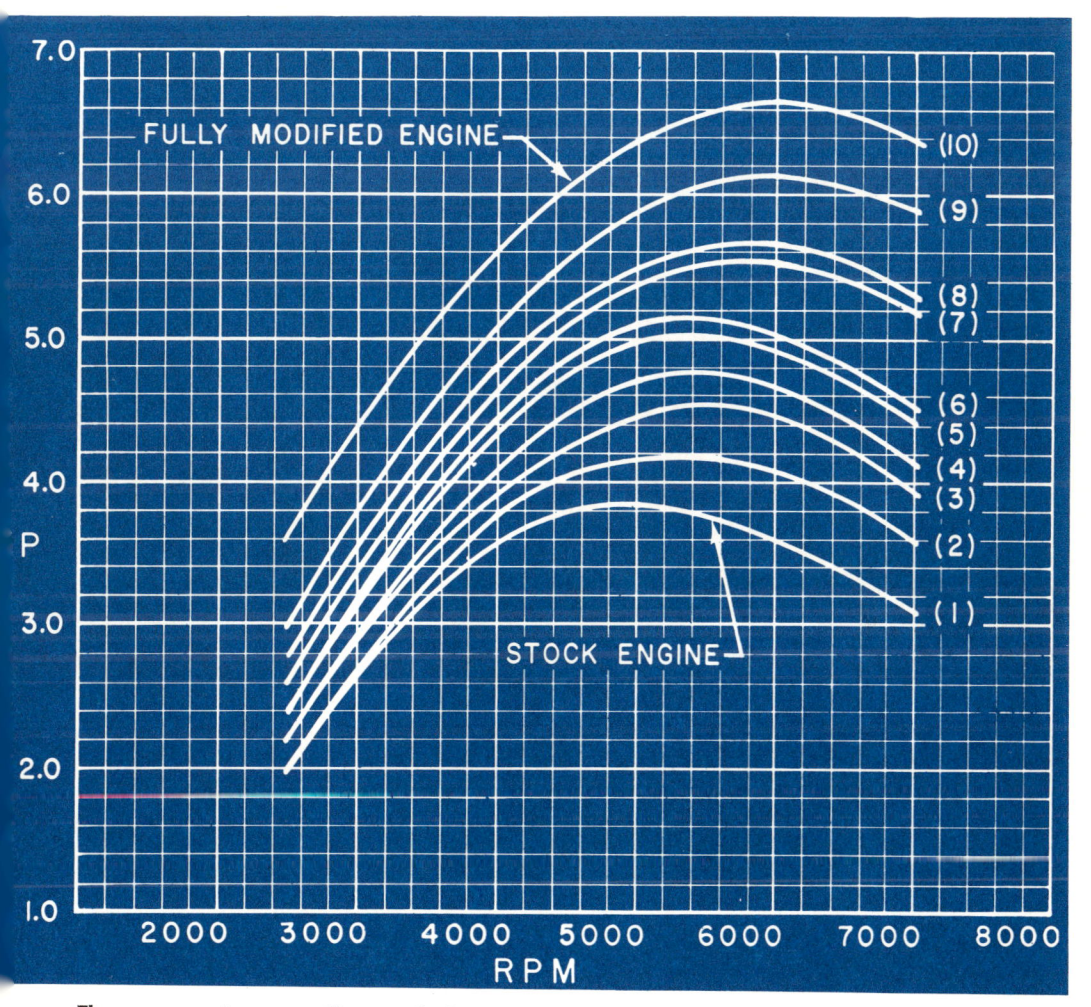

The accompanying curves illustrate the horsepower produced at various stages of West Bend engine modification. All modifications tested are explained fully in the text so that you can eliminate hit-and-miss modification—and build a top-notch racing engine even though this may be your first engine-building attempt. Readings plotted were obtained with: (1) Stock West Bend 580 with four-reed plate and stock float carb; (2) Same engine with Go-Power manifold, float carb; (3) Same as curve 2, but with MC-10 McCulloch carb; (4) Same as 3, but with modified intake ports; (5) Same as 4, but with modified exhaust ports; (6) Same as 5, but with notched piston and transfer passage; (7) Same as 6 but with Go-Power full-circle crank kit; (8) Same as 7, with welded-up and recontoured piston dome; (9) Same as 8, with stuffed piston; and (10) Same as 9, with two cans Kartane per gallon of gasoline. NOTE: An additional 10 per cent horsepower gain is available through the use of methanol-based fuels in your engine.

1833

Side view, intake ports.
- ORIGINAL
- MODIFIED

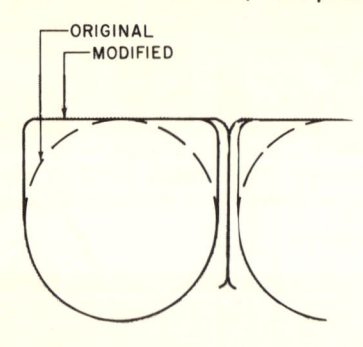

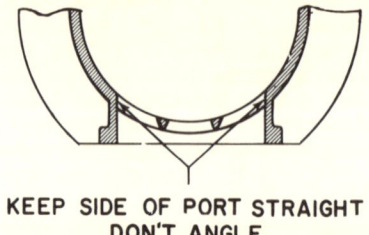

KEEP SIDE OF PORT STRAIGHT
DON'T ANGLE

Top view, intake ports. Cylinder sectioned through ports.

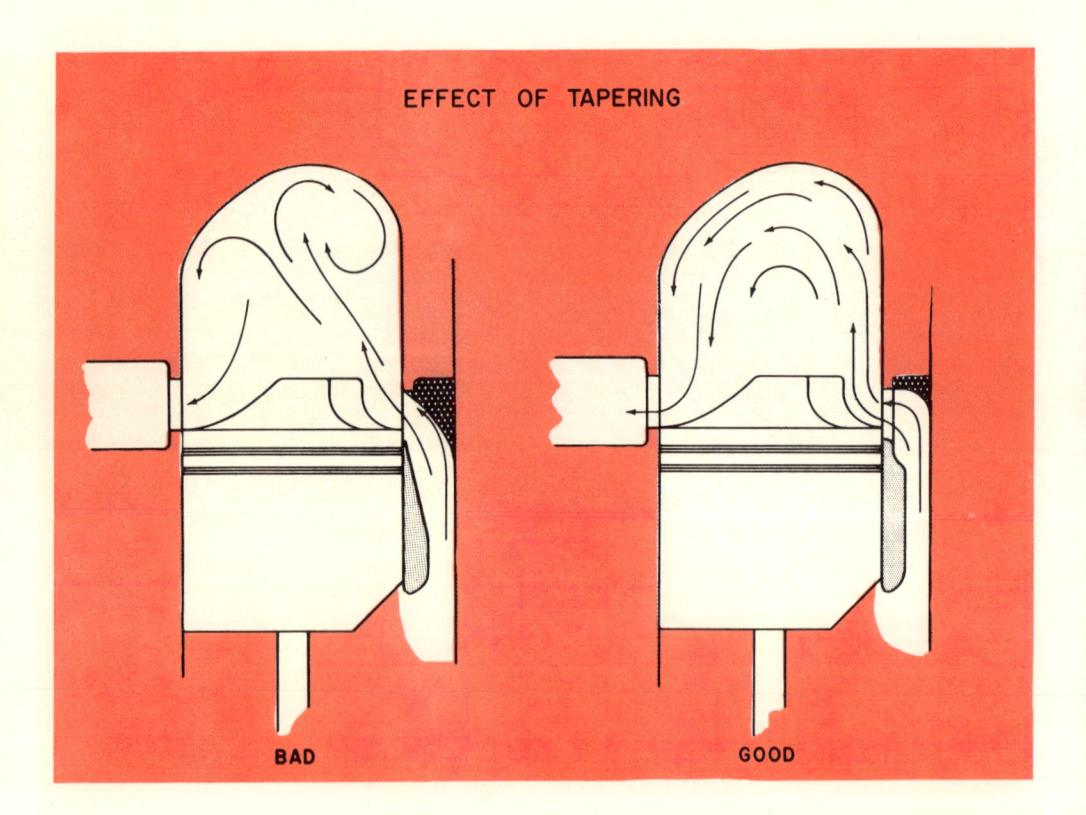

EFFECT OF TAPERING

BAD   GOOD

the tops. When finished, carefully de-burr the cylinder-wall surface to prevent piston ring hangup.

Mixture flow is improved if the lower edges of the intake ports are streamlined, but only if done correctly. The obvious way spoils scavenging, is bad (Fig. D). Fig. E illustrates the correct way. An improvement in the flow of fuel mixture from case to cylinder can be achieved by notching the cylinder/transfer-port wall and piston skirt as illustrated by Figs. F and G. The WB factory does this on its seven-inch-and-over models. It is an essential modification if a full-circle crankshaft conversion is used.

To perform this notching operation, scribe a line as shown in Fig. G, then center-punch a series of marks along a line $\frac{1}{8}$ inch below the desired edge of the notch. Drill $\frac{1}{16}$-inch pilot holes before proceeding with a row of $\frac{1}{4}$-inch holes, as the $\frac{1}{4}$-inch drill will tend to "walk," destroying the accuracy of the notch outline. After the

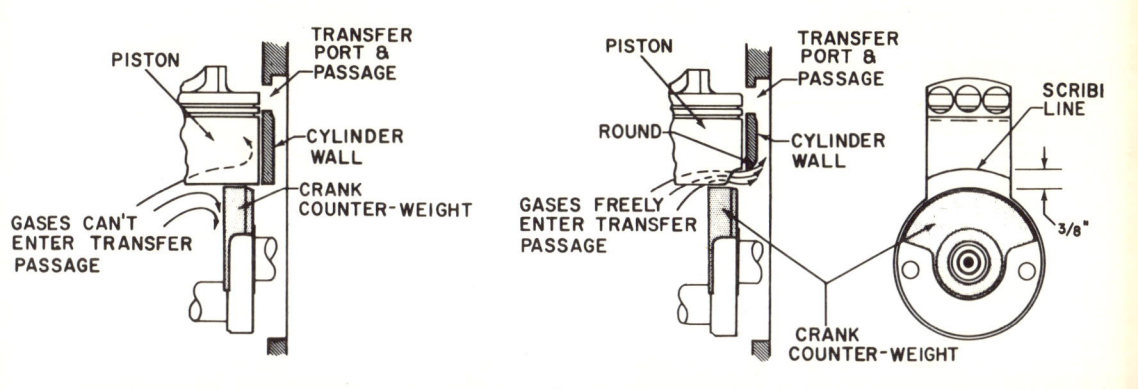

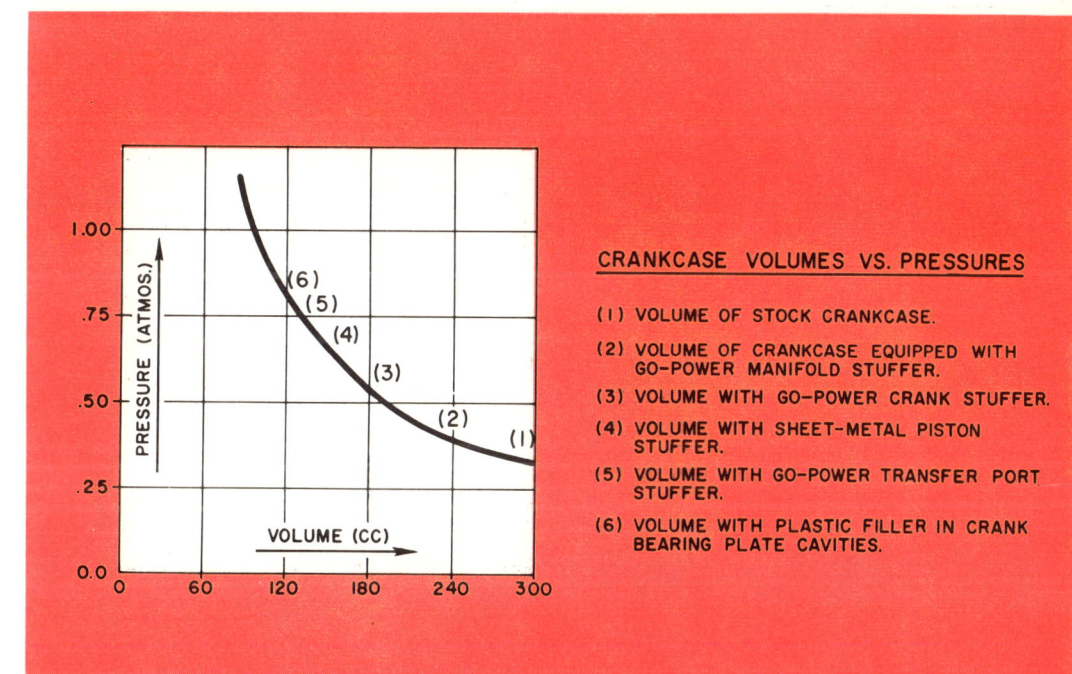

KARTING

CRANKCASE VOLUMES VS. PRESSURES

(1) VOLUME OF STOCK CRANKCASE.
(2) VOLUME OF CRANKCASE EQUIPPED WITH GO-POWER MANIFOLD STUFFER.
(3) VOLUME WITH GO-POWER CRANK STUFFER.
(4) VOLUME WITH SHEET-METAL PISTON STUFFER.
(5) VOLUME WITH GO-POWER TRANSFER PORT STUFFER.
(6) VOLUME WITH PLASTIC FILLER IN CRANK BEARING PLATE CAVITIES.

piece has been removed, file the notch edges smooth, and round off the edge which is in the transfer port, referring again to Fig. G. Make sure to eliminate all rough edges as these will spoil the piston's sealing action.

Next, a corresponding window must be cut in the piston skirt. Install piston-rod assembly and crankshaft in crankcase. Rotate crank to bring piston to bottom center. Scribe the notch outline onto the piston skirt and disassemble the various

1835

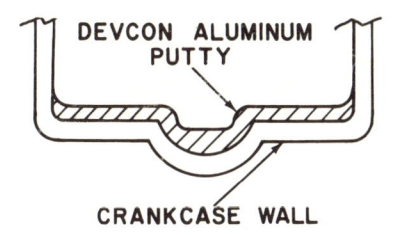

KARTING

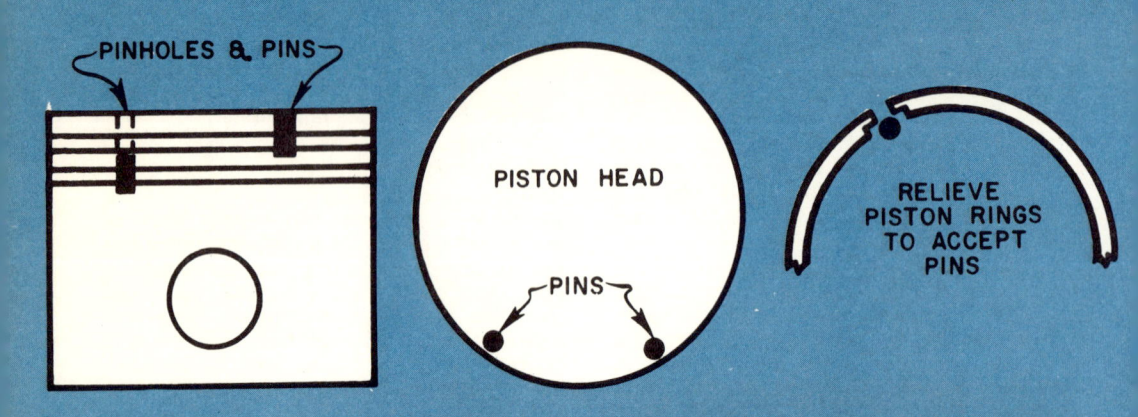

When the exhaust ports are squared for greater area, the rings should be pinned to prevent snagging.

parts which you had previously installed.

You will find that the scribed outline of the notch falls above the level of the piston-pin boss. *Do not cut the window to this height.* Instead, cut the notch the full width of the transfer port, but no higher than the web which extends across the piston just below the boss. Scribe a new line at this point. You can cut the window in the piston by drilling a series of holes along the scribed line, or you can use a coping saw Again, file smooth all rough edges.

Go-Power has reduced the stuffing of popular two-strokes to an icy, dyno-proven science. The effect of various types of WB stuffing is shown in the accompanying graph, Fig. H.

Rabbit-ear stuffers are the simplest method. They bolt directly to the stock reed plate without tearing the engine down. They reduce crankcase volume by about 1.8 cubic inches. Next comes the stuffer manifold for adapting the pyramid reed assembly to the WB. This chops the volume by about three cubic inches, and of course, it gives greater reed area. It sends the mixture straight into the crankcase instead of bending it around corners.

Next is the stuffing of nooks and crannies by means of various fillers, one of the finest of which is Devcon Aluminum Putty (from your hardware store). These fillers can be used only with gasoline fuel; alky and nitro dissolve them. Fig. I shows a typical use of Devcon.

Now you're beginning to make a really powerful pump out of your WB's lower end. Next you can go to the full-circle crank kit which cuts the crankcase volume by another 2.8 cubic inches or so. Then you can add a Go-Power transfer-port stuffer/deflector and chop another 1.6 cubic inches. Finally, you can stuff the piston for yet another whopping reduction in 'case volume. This operation is involved, time-consuming, controversial and practically a black art. We refer you to the Go-Power book for its full exposition.

Why don't manufacturers perform all these operations, saving you the trouble and giving you better performance? Because they are building you the best possible power plant at the lowest possible price. All these details we have discussed are time-consuming, critical and therefore costly. It's just like hot-rodding. Detroit provides wonderful basic iron at a practical price. If you want to put in the painstaking finish work you can convert your Chev to a Ferrari-eater. Same with kart engines.

Many, many improvements can be made in the stock WB reed assembly, all presented in detail in the Go-Power book. One of the greatest performance-per-dollar bargains ever, was introduced by the WB factory in the summer of 1960: the "V"-Power Kit. This consists of a rabbit-ear stuffer manifold and a fine, original, four-reed pyramid plate. On the WB 580 this kit yields a power increase of 25 per cent. On the Series 700 engines it gives 15 per cent more hp. All this for a price of just $5.60. Moreover, these kits do not void the factory stock-engine warranty. The rugged stock engine can take this and much more with total reliability.

The Power Products Breed

From the beginnings of karting, Power Products engines have been high-performance sleepers that have been hard to get (due to limited distribution in the karting trade) but which showed, from the beginning, a shocking potential. The sharp operators eyed the Power Products engine with anticipatory respect, while working and winning races mainly with MC's and WB's.

Power Products was very sensitive to the boom which was taking place in karting and evidently made up its mind to enter the field to compete for supremacy with a vengeance. Shortly before the 1960 GKCA Nationals a few of the brand-new, loop-scavenged, 5.80 cubic-inch PP engines found their way into the hands of certain kart-factory teams. The impact of the event would not have been noted if a new PP-equipped Echo kart had not shown up at the Azusa raceway for a few shakedown laps. Not even broken in, the new engine scorched out lap times that thrilled Echo to the same extent that they struck terror into the hearts of the competition. It was this minor event and accident that hurtled McCulloch into the hurried release of the MC-6 and the hop-up kits associated with it. Neither manufacturer will appreciate these statements of fact, but this is history as it happened.

The PP engine was a fabulous screamer . . . while it lasted. Unfortunately it didn't last long; it shook itself to bits as quickly as it spread panic. The dyno testing had been thorough but could not duplicate the testing available only in the crucible of speed. Its crankcase was a tiny work of art, about the size of a cigarette package; the designed-in stuffing was tremendous. The detachable cylinder was separated from the crankcase by means of a soft gasket. What happened was that the soft gasket, no matter how solidly torqued, continued to compress. The cylinder then would begin to rock and, once rocking, would wrench itself away from the 'case, stretching and breaking studs and eventually leaving the engine with disastrous results. This was old stuff to Bugatti, to Meyer & Drake, to many 'cycle manufacturers. By hook or crook they learned to control this problem. By careful engineering study, PP has mastered its problem in this area. Now its reliability is a match

Removal of the flywheel nut is easy if the crankshaft is wedged with wooden block against turning.

Use hammer and knockoff nut to remove flywheel, holding it so engine drops free as it comes off.

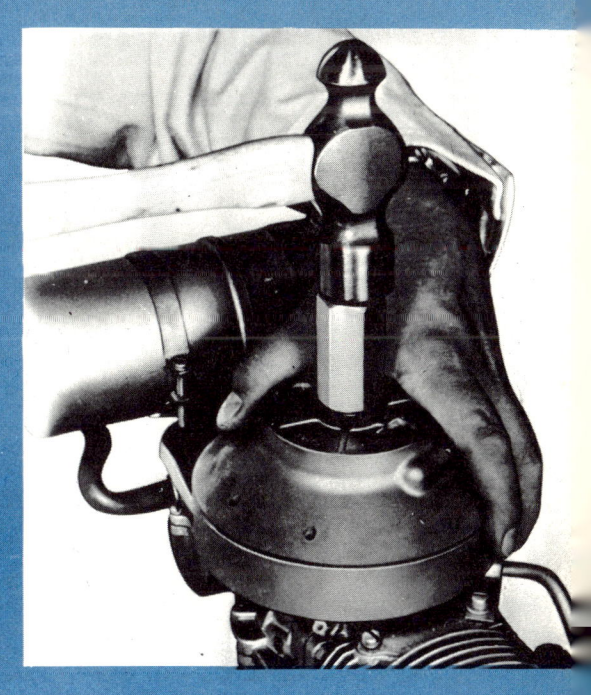

KARTING

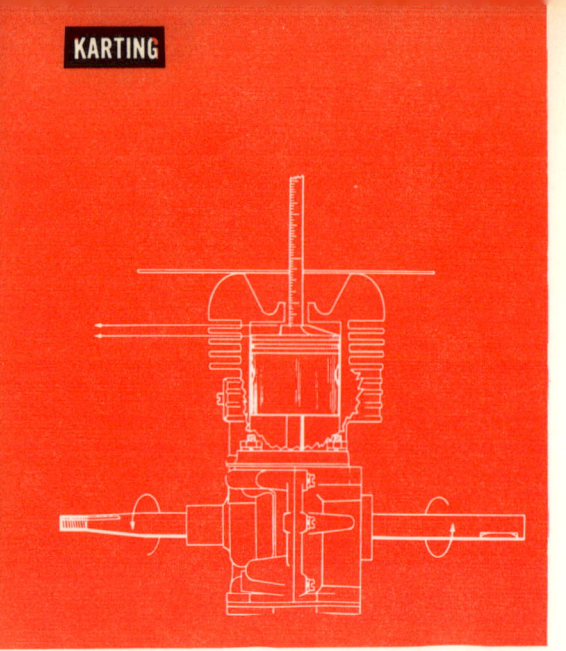

The depth-gauge method of determining piston-head clearance, and for timing all PP engines.

On any kart engine, magneto spark output can be checked by rotating flywheel with lead near plug.

Breaker points are set similar to method on automobile distributor. This is a Power Products engine.

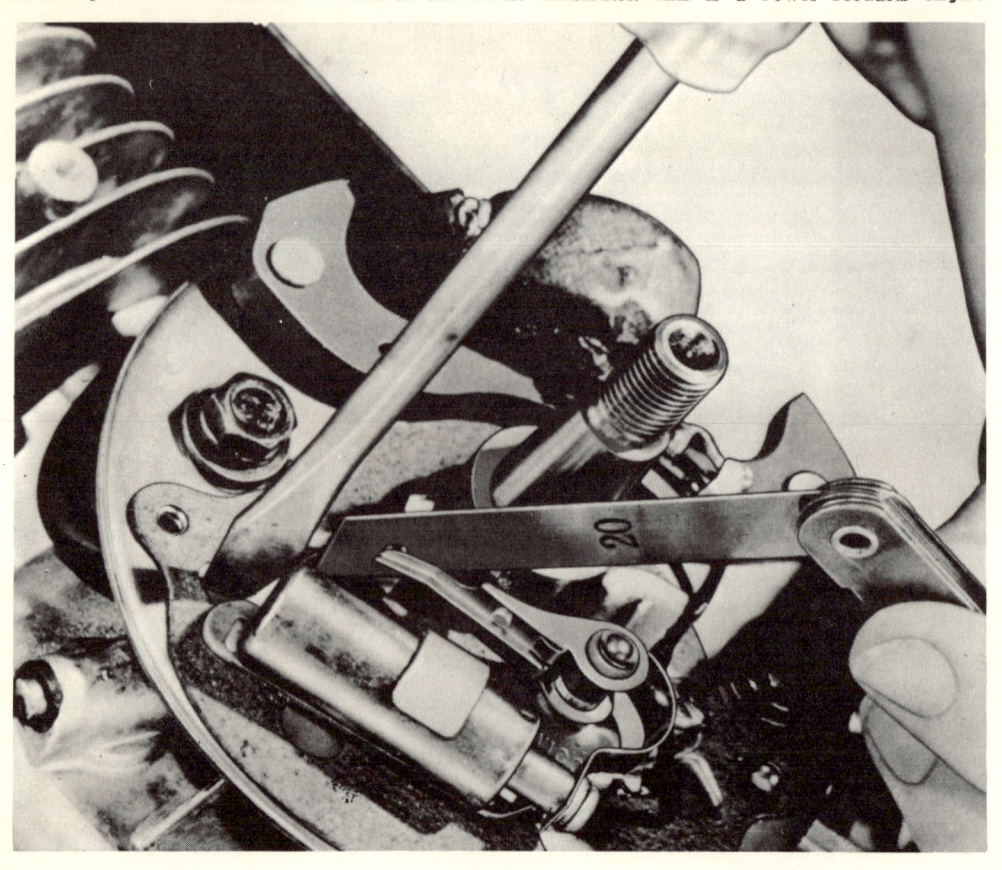

By liberal provision of small timing marks, all guesswork is taken out of timing Power Products engines.

for that of any of its competitors. This is the engine to watch and to fear in the time that lies ahead.

The PP engine has two intake ports on each side of the cylinder instead of three, as the MC does. It uses a long stroke and small bore which is to the two-cycle what an over-square bore-stroke ratio is to a four-cycle. The key difference is that this proportioning in a two-stroke permits greater valve area.

In its original form the AH-58 had a piston with a pair of .090 rings. These would begin to flutter at about 7,000 rpm and the engine would cease picking up speed. Now it has two .062 rings that permit it to wind to an easy 11,000 rpm or, with a little work, right on to 13,000.

Due to the detachable cylinder the PP engine is one of the easiest to work on. The only problem, again, is flywheel removal. There are no puller holes and you must use a knock-off nut.

In addition to the thinner-ring piston (available as a replacement from the factory and from Go-Power) the AH-58 engine has gone through a rapid series of evolutionary steps. It is now on its third crankshaft design, has a heavier 'case and cylinder, tougher heat-treated hold-down studs, different engine balance and a new cast-aluminum engine mount. The effect of all these is to smooth out the former vibration problems. All these are available as replacement parts.

A hard gasket of copper or aluminum is recommended to replace the early-used soft gasket, or the improved non-fluid gasket of later models.

The stock cylinder head uses no gasket. It is not lapped to fit but should be; use valve grinding compound for this. The PP engine benefits from upped compression ratio and the head can be milled to provide .015 inch clearance between head and top of piston. Let the machinist who does the head shaving determine this clearance. Then do the lapping job yourself.

When the PP engine is reassembled after a tear-down it is *most* important that the connecting rod be aligned in the piston with regard to perpendicularity with the crankshaft, just as in good, standard automotive practice. This applies to all kart engines, but to the PP in particular. If the rod is cocked it exposes the little needle bearings at its top end. Running more or less on the middle of these, instead of on their total length, the rod eventually will collapse a needle, after which the rest of the needles pop out, scatter through the engine and you can guess the rest.

1839

KARTING

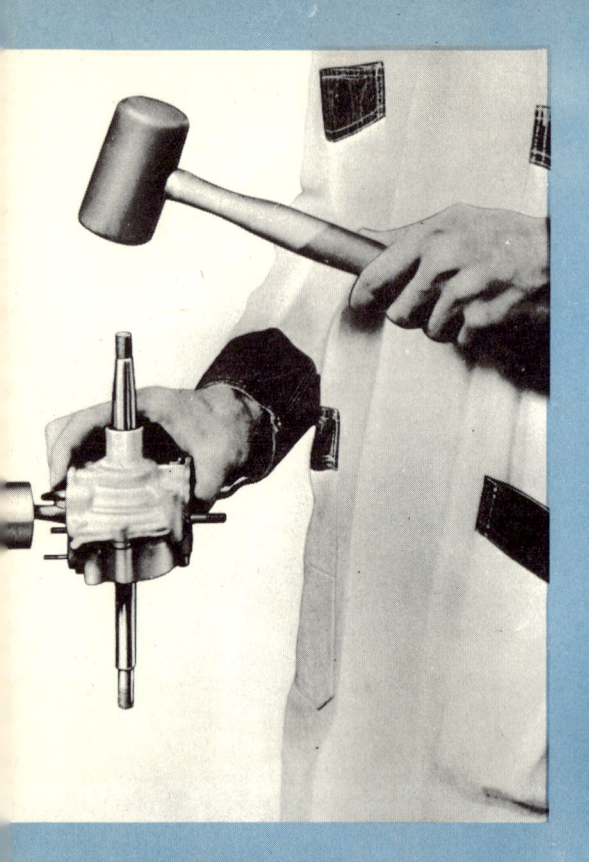

At left is correct method of separating Power Products crankcase halves, using a soft hammer.

Power Products main bearings have an interference fit with the crankcase; remove by heating 'case. Follow same procedure for installation.

Power Products has optional reed plates, but Go-Power pyramids should be used on special racing engines.

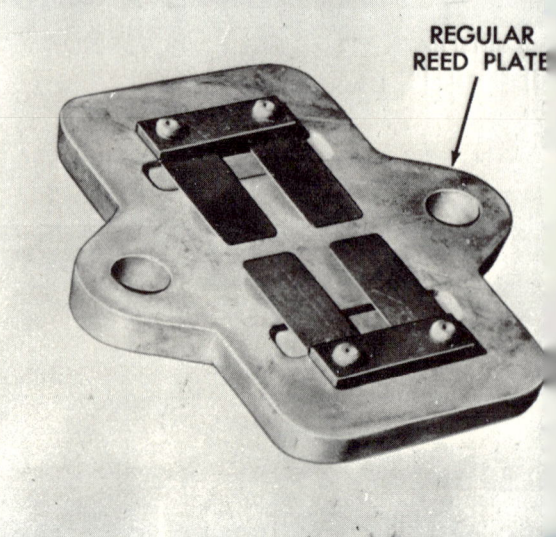

HIGH SPEED REED PLATE

REGULAR REED PLATE

At right is cutaway of West Bend air-cooled, ball and roller bearing two-stroke. Notice the position of the piston.

The PP benefits from having its piston scalloped about $\frac{1}{16}$ inch, following the angle of the intake ports carefully. Also, it is very worthwhile to square the exhaust ports, leaving small radii in the corners, as described for West Bend. The PP has three exhaust ports; unlike the three-port MC's it's OK to square up the outer corners as well as the inner ones.

The PP carb is excellent, has a ¾-inch throat. Many tuners will install a larger-throated carb, say an MC, and lose performance. Throat size is not necessarily a criterion that can be counted on for greater output. These Tillotsons all look identical externally but are vastly different internally. Unless they are calibrated for a given engine's characteristics they cannot enable it to wind freely. The PP stock carb seems to be very well calibrated to the engine.

The stock reed assembly is not a match for the engine's breathing capabilities. When specifically setting up an engine for racing, Go-Power's stuffer manifold and pyramid reed setup can be used to add as much as one hp. The same speed equipment firm makes special fine-finned cylinder heads for this engine, plus a full-circle crank conversion which, contrary to all theory, makes the engine run even more smoothly than when in stock balance.

Not long ago I saw Bob Palmini as he was leaving the Agoura, Calif., Raceway. He was as excited as though he'd just struck oil in his back yard. Pointing to the kart he'd just loaded on his truck he said, "That Power Products engine! We came in third in a field of 28 McCullochs and we're just beginning to get the hang of it! It's smooth as silk. Man, it's the comer." •

KITCHENS

The curved "island," originally suggested by kitchen consultant Harold Diamond, A.I.A., was made to fit the individual cooking tops. Eating area in family room, is behind the two built-in Thermador ovens.

KITCHEN
planning

You will buy most of your kitchen equipment, but you must still plan their placement. Here are some ideas.

ACCORDING to reputable statistics, more time is spent in the kitchen than any other room, which in itself is reason enough for you to give your kitchen planning and layout the utmost in careful consideration. However, there is a second good reason, the fact that a kitchen represents a greater initial monetary investment than any other single room.

In the home you build, your kitchen will incorporate the features that you feel will serve your family best. The type appliances you buy, their location, the design and color and brand of your cabinets are family decisions you will make. Our kitchen plan serves our family well, and is shown with the hope that it will impart an idea or two you can adapt.

The width of our kitchen was dictated by the area that remained after the basement stairs were partitioned off from the kitchen area; the exact length was determined by the space that remained in the "center core" after the entrance hall and main bath were located. We wanted ready access to a bath and also the bedrooms without walking through the living-dining room. We also wanted a sheltered passage to the garage, access to the basement, the outside screened, porch and terrace. In addition, we decided the kitchen should be in front of the house, near the main entrance, and the rear of the home, which faces south, designed with plenty of glass to take full advantage of the sun during the winter and the beautiful view of the Atlantic Ocean all year round.

We also stipulated our family room, which is located just off the kitchen and actually may be considered a part of the kitchen, should serve as a family eating area; the kitchen was to be a "machine shop," easy, efficient and compact. Our appliance requirements called for six burners, a griddle (to make the griddle cakes I always enjoyed most as a boy), two built-in ovens, a ten cubic foot refrigerator, a dishwasher, adequate working space and cabi-

KITCHENS

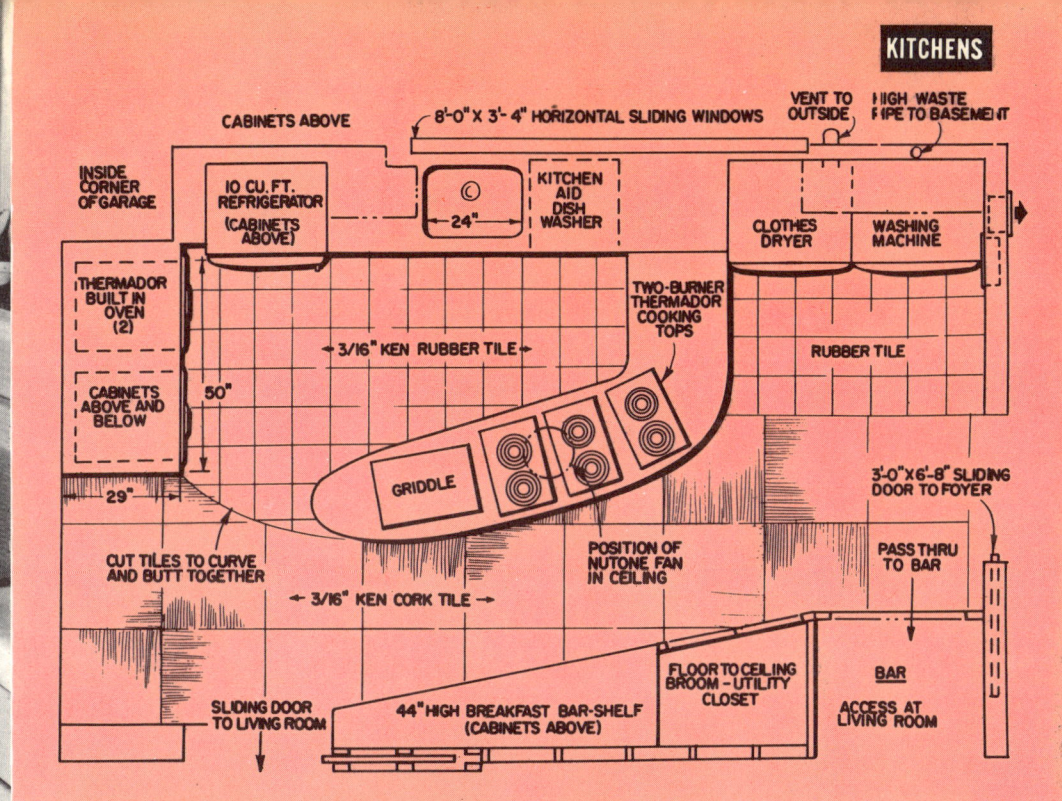

Separate clothes washer and dryer are located in far corner of kitchen; dishwasher is under counter next to sink. An exhaust fan is located in the ceiling directly above the 6-burner cooking top.

1843

KITCHENS

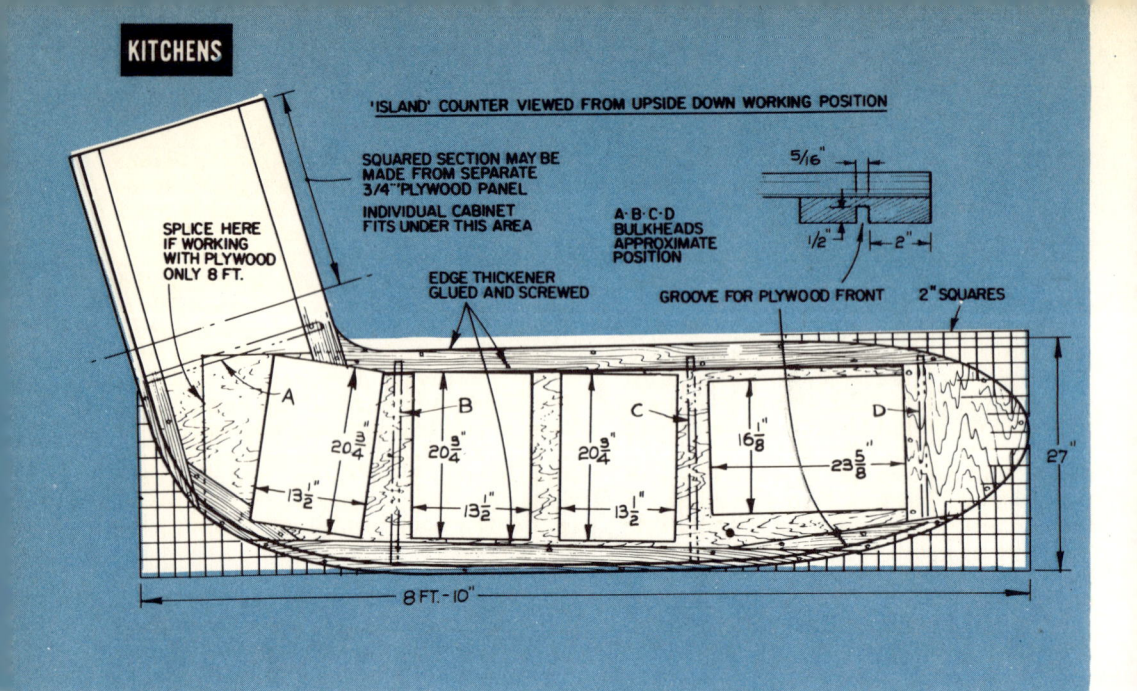

'ISLAND' COUNTER VIEWED FROM UPSIDE DOWN WORKING POSITION

SQUARED SECTION MAY BE MADE FROM SEPARATE 3/4" PLYWOOD PANEL
INDIVIDUAL CABINET FITS UNDER THIS AREA
SPLICE HERE IF WORKING WITH PLYWOOD ONLY 8 FT.
A·B·C·D BULKHEADS APPROXIMATE POSITION
EDGE THICKENER GLUED AND SCREWED
GROOVE FOR PLYWOOD FRONT
2" SQUARES

nets all carefully arranged within a few steps of each other.

We also felt automatic washing and drying equipment should be located in the kitchen proper, within easy reach of the main bathroom, but far enough away from the bedrooms and living-dining area so the noise all machines make would not be objectionable.

More than 50 percent of your kitchen costs will be represented by your appliances, which still provides you with a good opportunity to save on the cabinets. If you prefer to make your own you will find "knock down" units readily available. If you plan to buy your cabinets, shop for them like you would an automobile; the price fluxuations are usually as great!

Installing kitchen cabinets is a business in itself and you will have little difficulty receiving quotations from a half dozen different cabinet shops. Few shops make their own cabinets, most merely adapt mass produced units to your layout. However, the counter top is usually custom made to your specifications.

Cabinet prices vary greatly, depending upon the materials and the workmanship. Wooden cabinets as a rule cost more than metal units. A common method of estimating the cost of "custom" cabinets is to figure $2.50 to $3.00 per lineal inch of wall length containing base cabinets and upper storage cabinets. Thus, if you have an eight-foot wall of upper and lower cabinets you probably will receive quotations in the neighborhood of $240-$290. Some shops may quote slightly less and others may double the price. You will find the price varies considerably with the type and shape—and the salesman. A good check against what cabinets cost can be gained by comparing the prices of units advertised by the national mail order firms.

Making A Curved Base Cabinet

The rather unusual free-form base cabinet that curves out into our kitchen actually encircles the work area. The top was designed to accommodate a griddle, three separate cooking top units and allow space for food preparation. The electrical equipment occupies the upper fourteen inches of the cabinet while the remaining space is used for utensil storage.

You can make a similar cabinet to fit the cooking tops you choose. The curved edge is not as difficult to make as you might initially

KITCHENS

believe; the curve is cut with a keyhole saw or power jig saw and, after a framework is made from 1x2s, the front is covered with ¼-inch plywood. We used Philippine mahogany because the theme of the entire home was to have as much natural wood visible as practical.

When making a free-form cabinet, first lay out the position of the cooking tops and your adjacent work area on a large piece of wrapping paper. Use as many straight lines as possible but blend in curves where necessary to control the direction and the design. Cut out the full size template and then actually position it in a marked off area the size of your intended kitchen. This will give you the opportunity to change your mind should you want extra space at any point.

After you have your final curve section, duplicate two narrow strips having the same curve, one to be used for the bottom of the frames and the other glued to the underside edge of the top section to make the edge a full 1½ inches thick. Normal counter top height is 36 inches, so cut the vertical braces accordingly to obtain this total height. You will note the underside of the top at a point along the curved section is routed out to fit the ¼-inch thick plywood front which curves easily to fit this slot. The bottom is glued and nailed to the base, which is eventually attached to the floor with 3-inch lag screws passing through the sub-flooring into the floor joists. Screws at each end and in the center of the front and back pieces will hold the cabinet secure.

In an "island" type base cabinet of this type, the electric line runs from the basement ceiling up through the cabinet. Have the electrical connections made after the

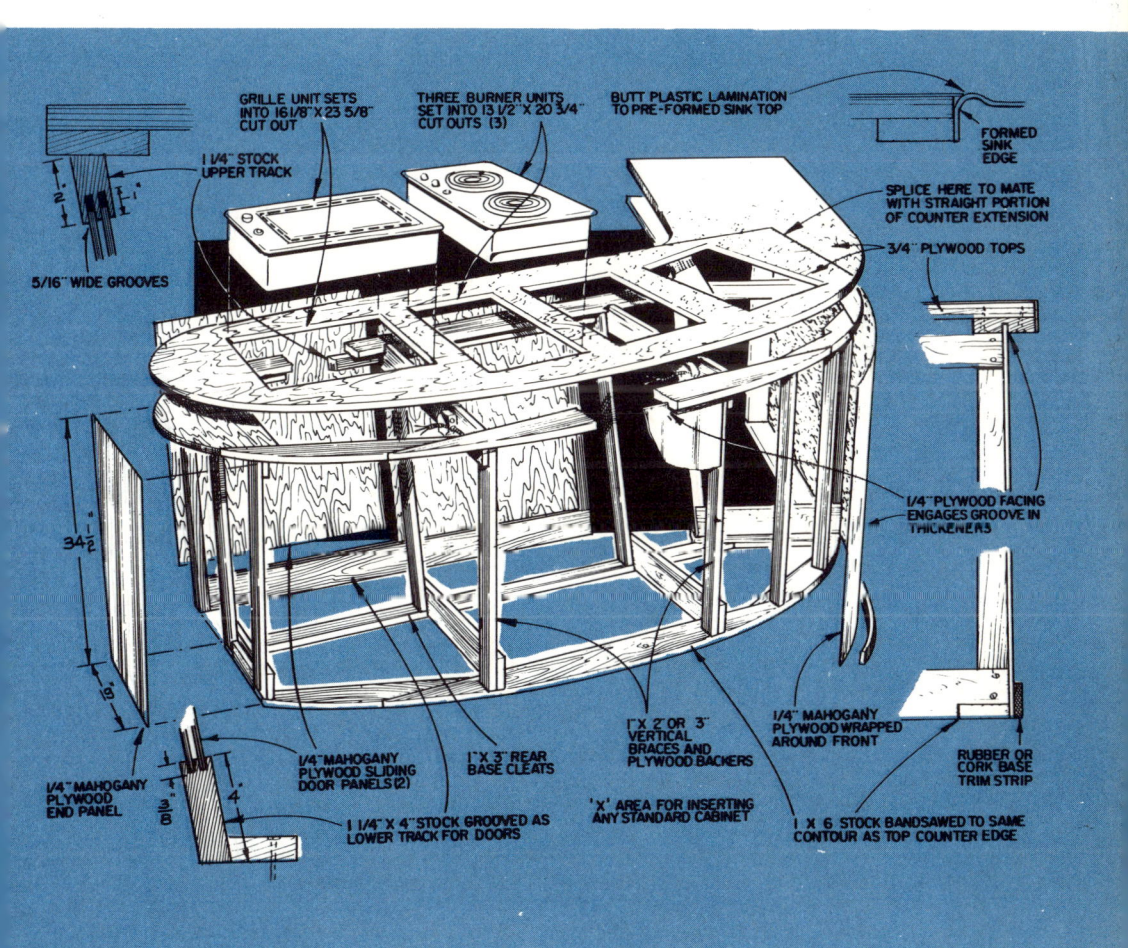

1845

KITCHENS

Textolite Monotop was used for the straight counter top. Trace sink outline and then rough-cut to size.

After cut out panel is mounted on the wooden stringers caulking is applied around the edge.

cabinet is permanently mounted on the floor.

The interior space below the burners is partitioned off. Two sliding doors, also made from ¼-inch mahogany plywood, slide in 5/16-inch slots. Depth of the slots in the base piece is ⅜ inch while two slots in the upper section's two grooves are one-inch deep to make possible lifting up the doors for easy removal. The doors will glide easily if you lubricate the bottom of each with graphite.

The top of the cabinet and the 1½-inch thick edge is covered with a plastic laminate adhered with a contact cement. First cement a strip of laminate to the edge and then trim so it is flush with the top. You can do this with a belt sander or a carbide tipped edging attachment designed especially for plastic laminate work and used on a router or other high-speed hand tool.

After the side strip is in place laminate the top in the same manner. Then seal the exposed wood with an approved sealer and apply a few coats of a good grade varnish.

Making a Custom Counter Top

We did not make our straight base cabinets but we did prefabricate the counter top to fit the base cabinets. We chose a molded plastic laminate top 3/16 inch thick that is mounted on three wooden stringers which help make the top very rigid.

Before you make your counter top you must, of course, first determine the length and plan the position of the sink, if that area has a sink. Molded tops come in 6-foot length, so you will be required to join the two pieces together. We chose area where the sink was to be placed as the ideal spot

Ceiling ventilation fan is a variable speed Nutone located over the cooking area. Air is pushed through ceiling duct.

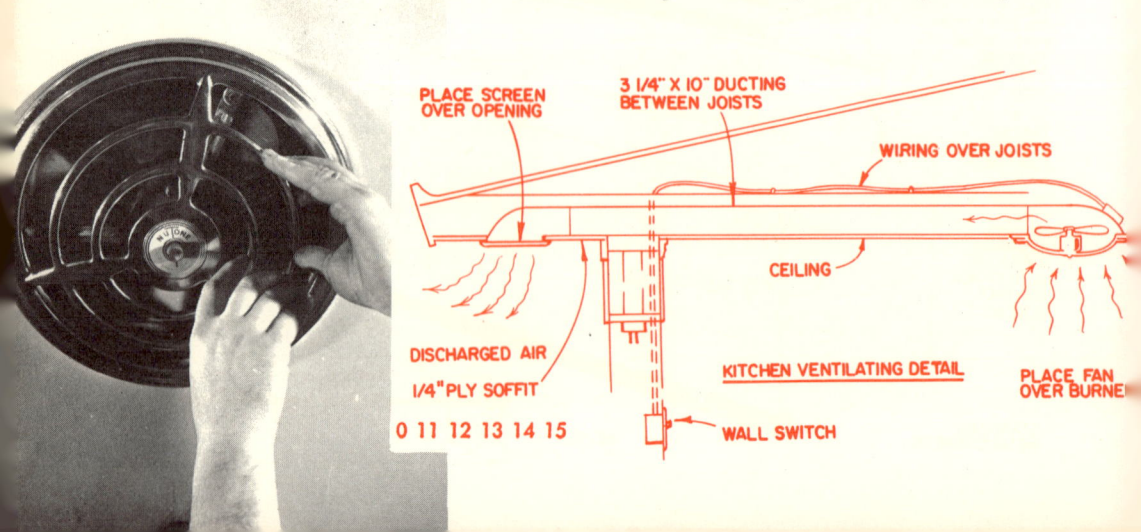

PLACE SCREEN OVER OPENING

3 1/4" X 10" DUCTING BETWEEN JOISTS

WIRING OVER JOISTS

CEILING

DISCHARGED AIR

1/4" PLY SOFFIT

KITCHEN VENTILATING DETAIL

PLACE FAN OVER BURNER

WALL SWITCH

KITCHENS

Use a gray caulking and set the stainless steel rim (cost: about 5 dollars) into the caulking.

Press the rim down so the caulking is squeezed out the sides and bottom. Sink is then set in place.

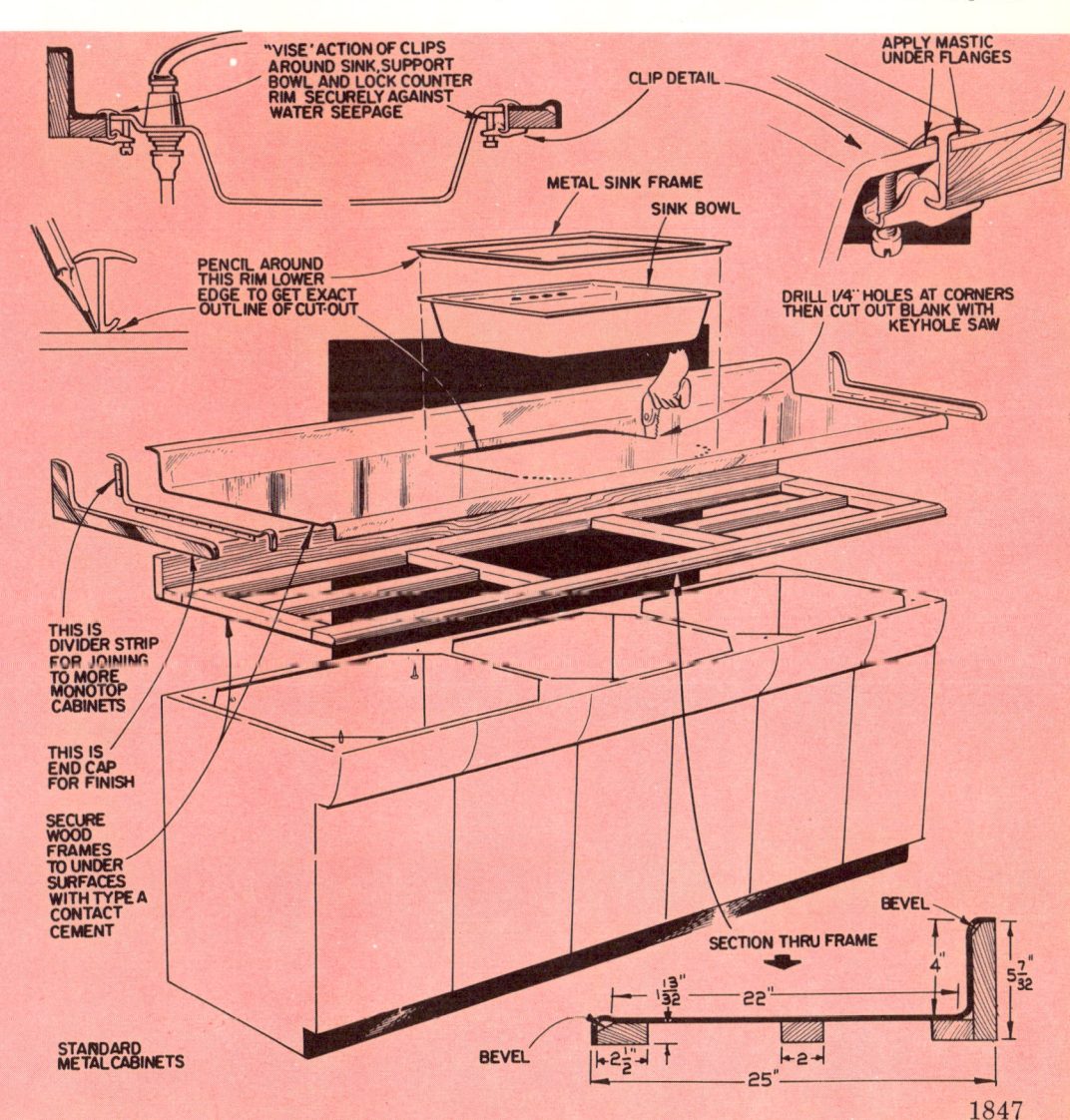

"VISE" ACTION OF CLIPS AROUND SINK, SUPPORT BOWL AND LOCK COUNTER RIM SECURELY AGAINST WATER SEEPAGE

CLIP DETAIL

APPLY MASTIC UNDER FLANGES

METAL SINK FRAME

SINK BOWL

PENCIL AROUND THIS RIM LOWER EDGE TO GET EXACT OUTLINE OF CUT-OUT

DRILL 1/4" HOLES AT CORNERS THEN CUT OUT BLANK WITH KEYHOLE SAW

THIS IS DIVIDER STRIP FOR JOINING TO MORE MONOTOP CABINETS

THIS IS END CAP FOR FINISH

SECURE WOOD FRAMES TO UNDER SURFACES WITH TYPE A CONTACT CEMENT

STANDARD METAL CABINETS

BEVEL

SECTION THRU FRAME

BEVEL

$1\frac{13}{32}$" 22" 4" $5\frac{7}{32}$"

$2\frac{1}{2}$" 2"

25"

1847

KITCHENS

Floor-to-ceiling utility closet houses all cleaning equipment. A pass-through to a bar serves the living and dining area. Floor area near sink and washer is rubber tile; rest of kitchen is cork.

KITCHENS

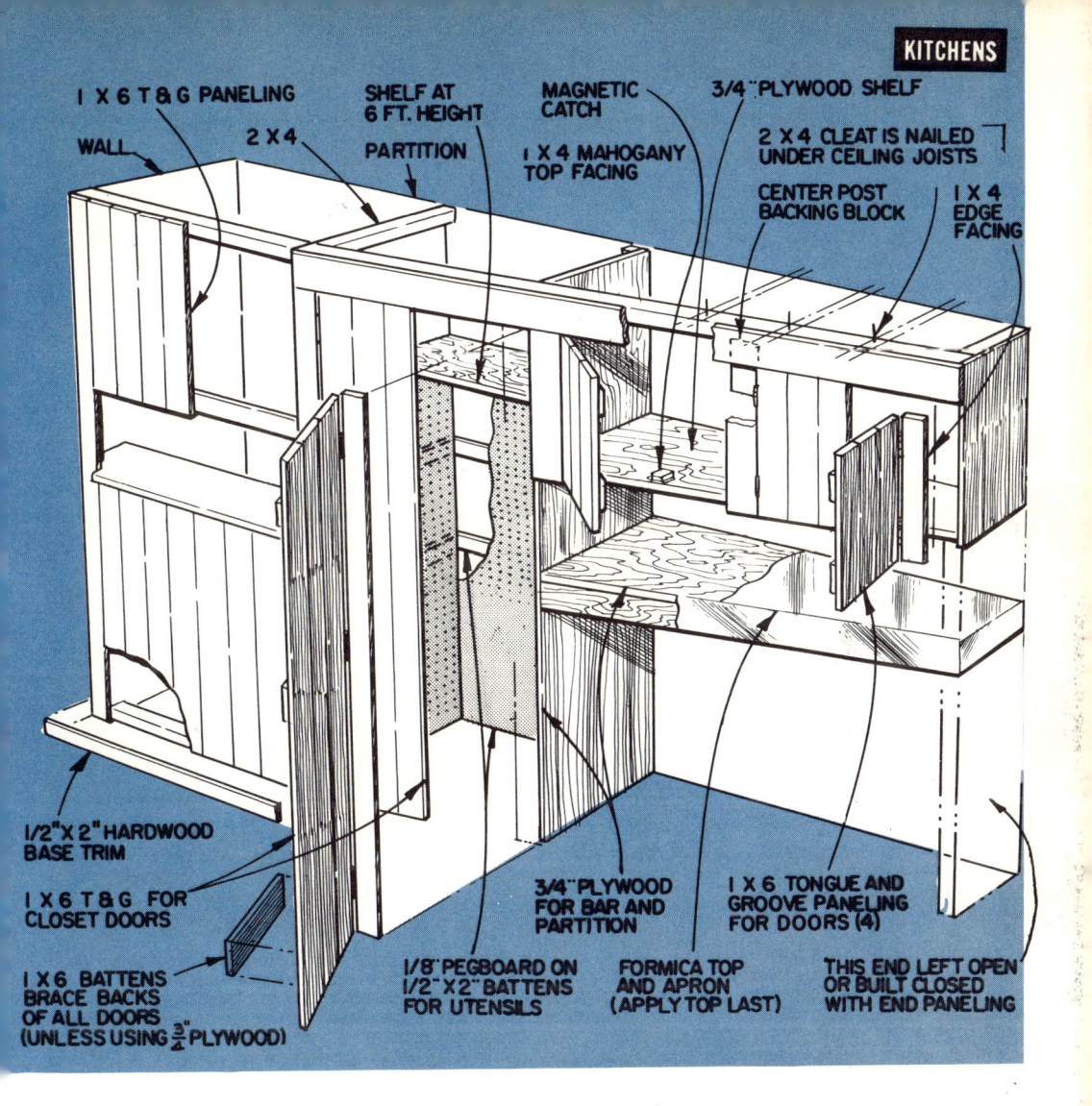

Labels on diagram:
- 1 X 6 T & G PANELING
- WALL
- 2 X 4
- SHELF AT 6 FT. HEIGHT
- PARTITION
- MAGNETIC CATCH
- 1 X 4 MAHOGANY TOP FACING
- 3/4" PLYWOOD SHELF
- 2 X 4 CLEAT IS NAILED UNDER CEILING JOISTS
- CENTER POST BACKING BLOCK
- 1 X 4 EDGE FACING
- 1/2" X 2" HARDWOOD BASE TRIM
- 1 X 6 T & G FOR CLOSET DOORS
- 1 X 6 BATTENS BRACE BACKS OF ALL DOORS (UNLESS USING 3/4" PLYWOOD)
- 3/4" PLYWOOD FOR BAR AND PARTITION
- 1/8" PEGBOARD ON 1/2" X 2" BATTENS FOR UTENSILS
- FORMICA TOP AND APRON (APPLY TOP LAST)
- 1 X 6 TONGUE AND GROOVE PANELING FOR DOORS (4)
- THIS END LEFT OPEN OR BUILT CLOSED WITH END PANELING

to join two sections together. In this manner only the end and base section of the joint are noticeable.

We used a stainless steel sink which was very easy to install. A special stainless steel trim holds the sink secure and watertight to the top. Trace the outline of the rim on the surface of the molded top and cut out, using a portable electric saw equipped with a fine tooth blade to prevent chipping of the plastic. A fine-toothed hand saw can also be used for the job but you will find the $\frac{3}{16}$-inch thick plastic tough to work. After the corners are filed round, mount plastic panel in place on the strips of kiln dried lumber as per the drawing. The edges can then be laminated and the counter top attached to the base cabinets. Finally, the stainless steel rim is inserted into the opening after the edges have been liberally coated with caulking. The sink should also be mounted at the same time because it, too, is set in caulking.

The wall area opposite the sink was devoted to a floor-to-ceiling utility broom closet and a small breakfast bar that has cabinet space located directly above. The breakfast bar was made in much the same manner as the center island.

The doors of the cabinet, however, were made from solid ¾-inch thick mahogany and consist of individual strips of 1x6-inch tongue-and-groove V-joint boards screwed and glued to battens located on the back of each door.

The interior of the utility closet is covered with ⅛-inch pegboard on which mops, brooms, dustpans, a vacuum cleaner and other common household cleaning items are hung. •

KITCHENS

A MODEL KITCHEN

By Bill Baker

Space-saving appliances, functional built-ins and modern wooden cabinets are featured in this remodeled kitchen.

WHETHER you build your kitchen from scratch or modernize the one you have, careful planning is more important for the kitchen than for any other room in your house.

The remodeling project shown on these pages was executed in a $19,000 home which, of course, had a kitchen. The existing kitchen, however, did not suit the requirements of the housewife who spends most of her time in the kitchen.

During redesigning of this area, function and glamour were added section by section. Where the serve-through breakfast counter is now located, for instance, a wall and door leading to the adjacent dining room served little function; part of the wall next to the door was cut away to make room for the breakfast bar installation.

Start construction of the bar by laying out the top, as shown in the drawing. The top is made of ¾-inch Duraply, later covered with white Micarta. The inside, or kitchen side, of the bar is covered with V-plank Nakora paneling; the outside, or dining room, part of the bar is faced with walnut paneling, finished to fit in with the surrounding decor. All parts of the counter are assembled with glue and 6d or 8d box nails. When covering with Micarta apply contact cement to the apron and install the plastic to this part first; then cover the top. Use a paper slipsheet to line up the Micarta with the edge and press down firmly. A pressure roller will be helpful to roll down the plastic and to adhere it to the cement. The inside edge of the bar is also covered with Micarta, after the unit is installed.

The ceiling above the counter should be brought down, as shown in the photos, to give the proper height between it and the counter top and to allow for installation of the overhead cabinet.

The wedge-shaped upper cabinet is made entirely of ¾-inch Duraply. Install the top and bottom of cabinet to the wall and ceiling, fastening it securely. Solid, ¾x3-inch wood frame is used to hold the sliding doors. Install it between the top and bottom Duraply cabinet, allowing it to extend 2 inches beyond the edge of the cabinet These wood strips have $\frac{5}{16}$-inch wide grooves, ¼ inch apart, starting ½ inch in from the front edge; the bottom grooves are ¼ inch, the top grooves are ½ inch deep. This allows the two ¼-inch strip Acrylite sliding doors to be lifted into the grooves without difficulty. If desired, a light fixture, such as the Globe in-

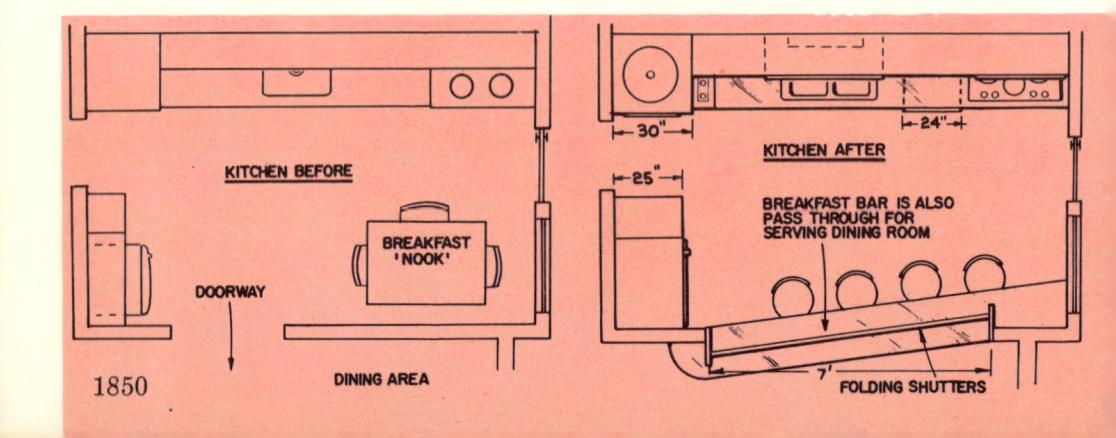

KITCHEN BEFORE
DOORWAY
BREAKFAST "NOOK"
DINING AREA

KITCHEN AFTER
BREAKFAST BAR IS ALSO PASS THROUGH FOR SERVING DINING ROOM
FOLDING SHUTTERS

1850

KITCHENS

FINISHED kitchen is shown above. At right is original kitchen before any remodeling started. Drawings at bottom of opposite page show floor plan in before and after views. Note breakfast counter of the new kitchen.

stallation used in this project, may be attached to the upper inside corner of the cabinet. This makes for striking effect with the light shining through the Abaca straw pattern of the sliding doors.

After completion of this over-the-counter cabinet, its bottom, side and the wall above it may be covered with 1x1-inch mosaic tiles, as shown in the photos.

The dining room side of the breakfast counter is completely closed off with prefabricated louver doors. They are mounted in line with the walnut plywood overhang. Hardware used is Stanley No. 2987 for four bifold doors; the two extra doors, one mounted on each side of the bifold units, are added on with piano hinges. Louvers may be painted in the color of your choice to fit the surrounding area.

Bar-type, upholstered stools on the kitchen side of the counter add the final touch to this useful installation.

The oven cabinet was the next proj-

1851

KITCHENS

REFRIGERATOR installation and breakfast counter are visible in photo, above left. At right is the old free-standing unit. Note complete enclosure of the new Hotpoint 12-cu. ft. built-in.

BREAKFAST counter, above left, visible from outside dining area, shows louvered doors and Micarta-topped counter. Old wall, right, was partially broken through to extend area.

ect. Here, in spite of the wall oven, everything else was out of date. A few additions, such as the Lazy Susan shelf arrangement for the top section and the laundry chute, made all the difference. The chute installed below the oven leads directly into the basement laundry room below.

Nakora plywood was used for the face of the oven cabinet. It was completed in the workshop first, with the doors hinged on and even the touch latches, mounted on blocks, glued to the inside of the face. The ¾-inch panel was then installed, making sure that all parts fitted square and plumb. The Lazy Susan assembly is covered with two 20-inch diameter discs made from ¾-inch plywood, centering on a 1-inch diameter pipe. It moves freely inside the top cabinet and is extremely useful for the storage of small items.

To make the laundry chute, cut a hole of the desired size through the cabinet bottom, the subflooring and flooring of the kitchen, until you have an opening clear through to the basement. The chute itself can be made from galvan-

KITCHENS

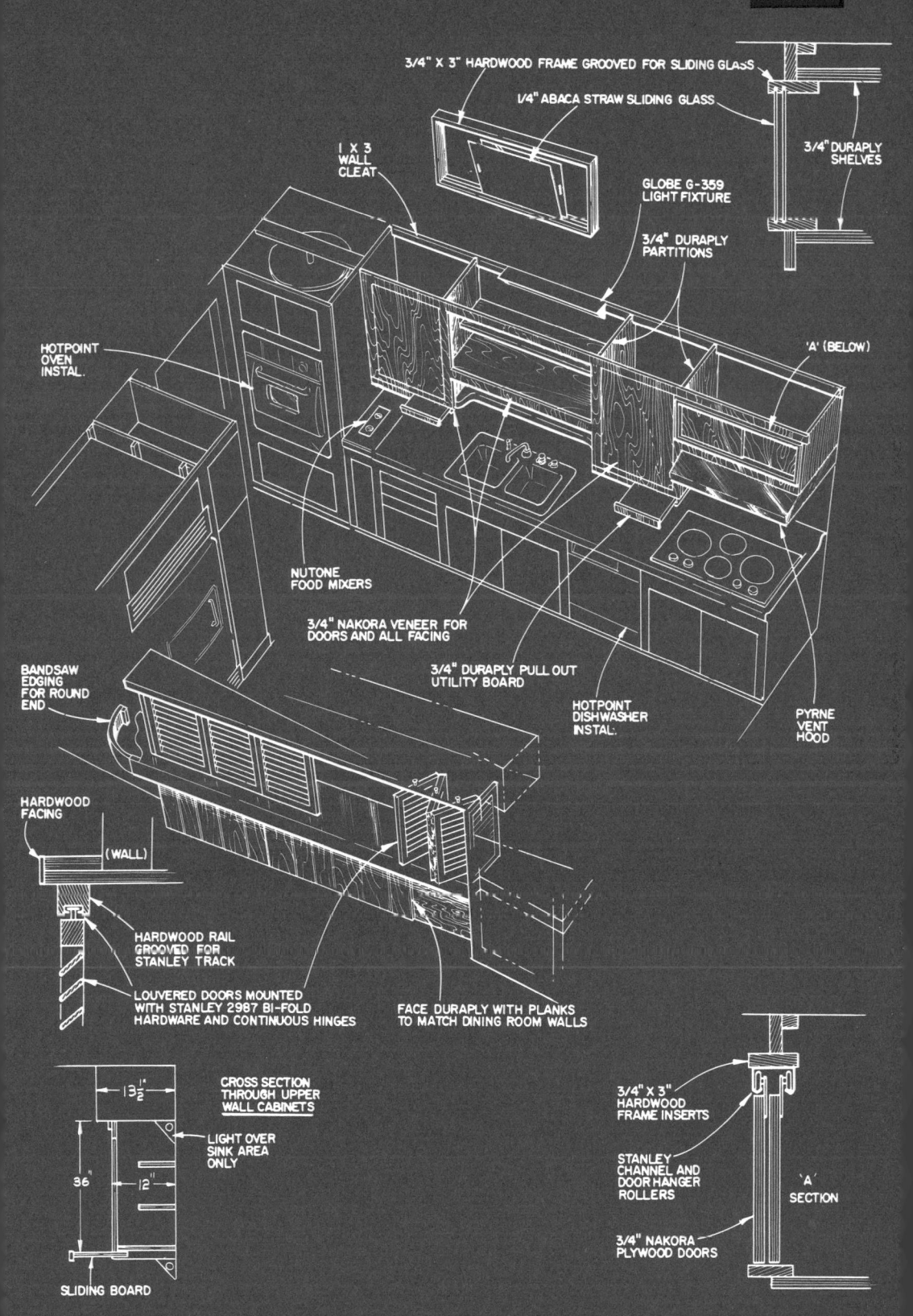

KITCHENS

CEILING beam is lowered with 2x4's to give the correct height between it and counter.

THE NEW FRAME is now covered with plywood panels and made flush with the wall.

COUNTER overhead cabinet is mounted in position by nailing bottom to ceiling beam.

TRIANGULAR dining room overhang, made of ¾-inch walnut plywood, is attached.

SOLID wood frame, ¾x3-in., is used on the inside; it contains grooves for doors.

COUNTER top is made of ¾-in. Duraply, is later covered with the white Micarta.

KITCHENS

BOTTOM counter is assembled with glue and nails. Drawing, page 36, shows details.

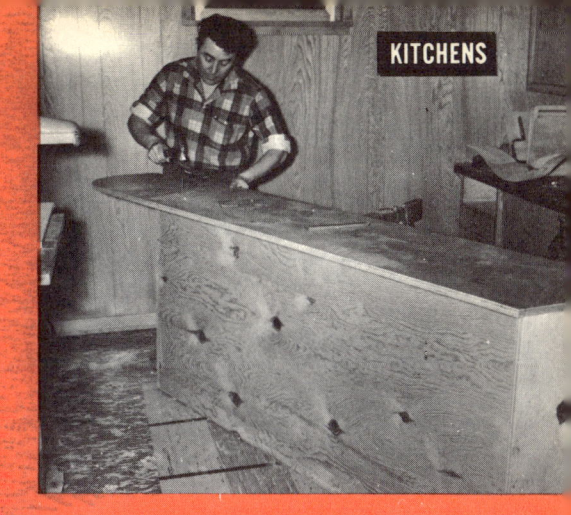

NAILS and glue attach the previously cut out counter top to the bottom assembly.

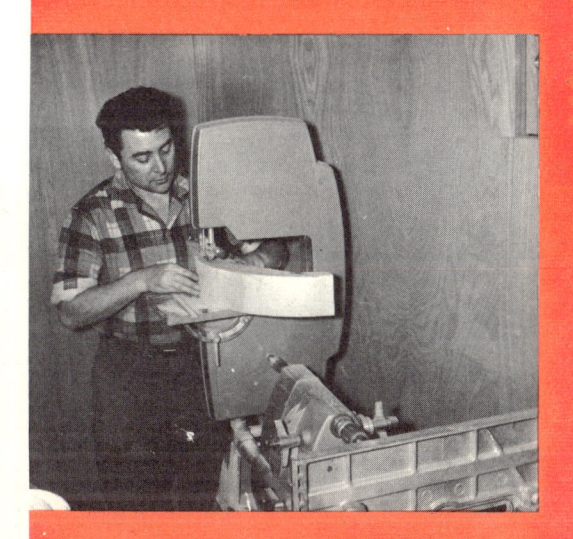

APRON for breakfast top is made of glued-up solid wood boards, cut on a band saw.

CLAMPS are used when gluing the rounded side apron to the Duraply counter top.

WHITE Micarta covers the surface. The apron is covered first, then the counter.

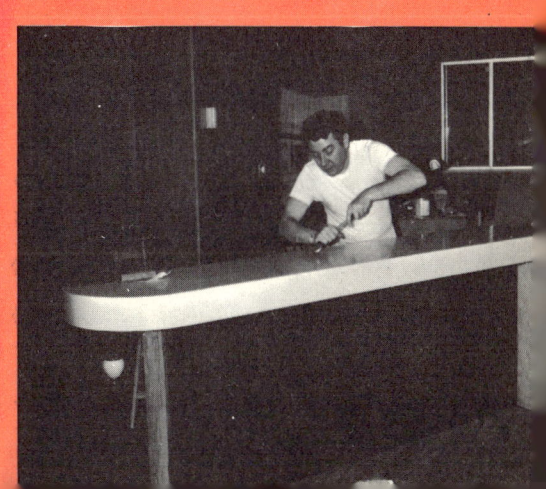

USING CEMENT and paper slip sheets, firmly press plastic in position and roll down.

KITCHENS

ized sheet metal or some other suitable material; it attaches to the cabinet bottom cutout, as shown in drawing, and is supported in the basement with brackets; it may even be connected directly to a clothes hamper. The length and location of the chute is, naturally, determined by your own special requirements.

The old kitchen counter was made of plastic material with a large number of metal moldings which allowed water to penetrate. Top and bottom cabinets did not offer anything in the way of organized storage, nor were they attractive to the eye. Major remodeling here consisted of organizing the new upper cabinets into functional sections for the storage of groceries, china, etc. Shelves are now adjustable—a very important item in a kitchen. Doors are mounted on continuous hinges, held flush with the face of the cabinet. Instead of using conventional handles, doors are now equipped with touch latches; a light touch on the door opens it without the bother of fussing with clumsy handles—a convenient feature when the housewife's hands are full.

All cabinet fronts and doors are made of ¾-inch plywood with ¾-inch Duraply shelves and partitions. The Nakora plywood is rich looking, giving the cabinets a clean-cut appearance which is usually found in the more expensive homes. At the bottom of the upper cabinets small sliding doors are placed to be used for handy storage or bread boards, etc. These ¾-inch Duraply boards are covered with Micarta and slide by means of channeled edges in the board, riding in aluminum or angle

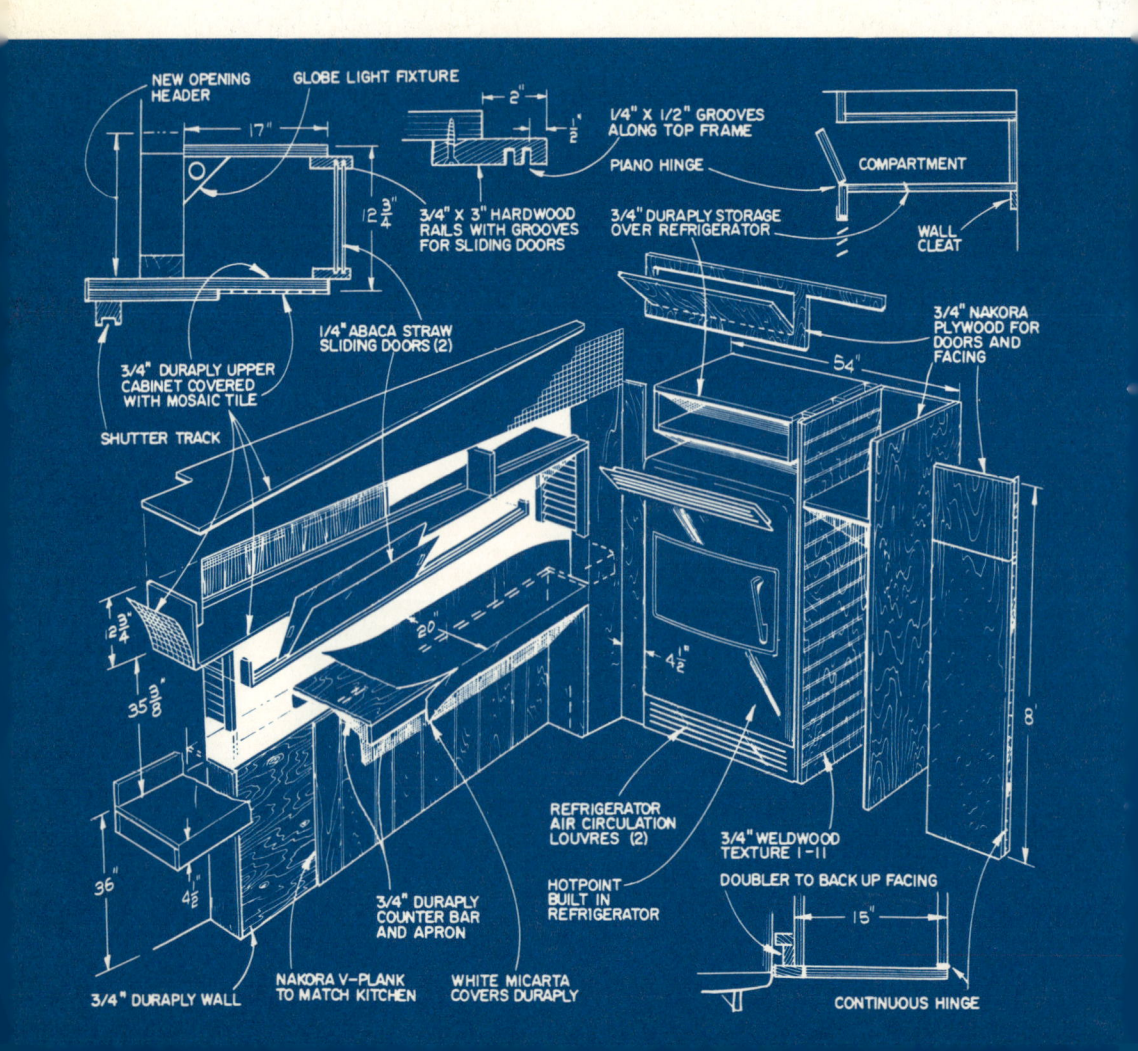

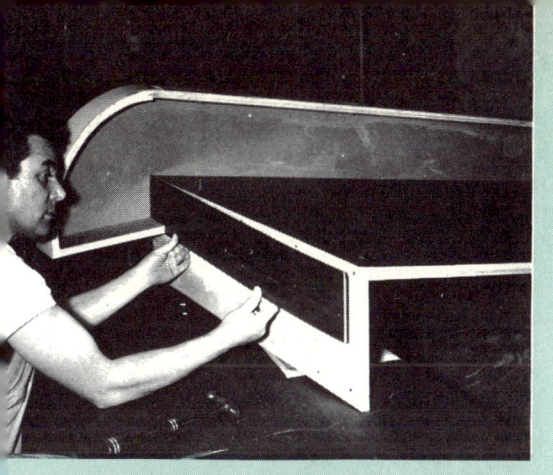

KITCHENS

V-PLANK paneling is used for covering the bottom; match decor of the surrounding area.

SCREWS attach the counter to wall. Space them evenly and fasten through the apron.

BOTTOM portion of breakfast counter is mounted to studs, making all parts plumb.

AFTER installation of unit cover the inside edge with Micarta, using a pressure roller.

iron guides, according to preference.

The center cabinet has a solid wood frame and contains similar Acrylite sliding doors as the opposite wall over-the-breakfast counter cabinet. In this portion of the unit glass shelves are used and a light is installed in the upper back corner. Here, again, the light shining through the patterned sliding doors makes for a striking effect. Under the top cabinets—one at each side of the center unit—are also the same Globe fixtures to light up the sink counter top area below.

The old bottom kitchen cabinets were entirely removed and replaced with new and better designed units. One high, narrow section at the left stores large trays, utensils, etc., for the oven; it also contains a meat cutting board. Drawers are installed in the next section; they were moved from their old position to make room for the Hotpoint dishwasher. The new plastic molded drawers contain Dekalux partitions, extremely suitable for storage of silverware. The large bottom drawer, made of ¾-inch plywood, rolls out on an 18-inch slide, lifting out easily for cleaning. Dimensions for the drawer space depend upon the type of plastic drawers used. For further information about the above write to Bakelite Corp., New York City, New York.

Counter cabinets are made in three parts, all of which are basically con-

KITCHENS

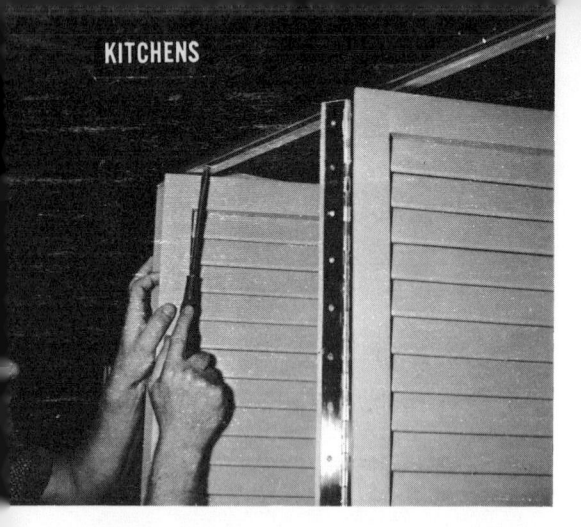

MOUNT louver doors with Stanley bifold hardware. Fasten to walnut-ply overhang.

MOSAIC tiles are attached to the designated surfaces. Tiles come on adhesive sheets.

TROWEL is used to apply Miracle cement to outside surfaces of the overhang cabinet.

structed in the same manner, as shown in the photos and drawings. It is advisable to use ¾-inch waterproof Duraply for the cabinet bottoms.

The sink cabinets are mounted to the wall with screws going into the studs. Back-mounting strips have to be placed between the top strips and cabinet bottom to coincide with the wall studs When installing the cabinets make sure that they are completely square, level and plumb. Mount the dishwasher and, finally, the doors.

The kitchen counter is a premolded Micarta Unitop which needs no metal moldings, thus making it easy to clean. This counter is screwed through the top mounting strip of the base cabinets. Due to the fact that Unitops are only available in up to 10-foot lengths, and since the counter top shown is eleven feet long, an extra foot was cut out of ¾-inch Duraply and covered with mosaic tile. However, before this section was covered with the tiles a NuTone Food Center was installed.

Cutouts for the sink and electric hot plate were made after the top had been fitted but before permanent installation. The sink and faucets, also, should be installed and properly caulked into the top before mounting same to the cabinets. A single lever Gyro water faucet and stainless steel sink with garbage disposal unit make for a functional and well organized working area.

The third, or refrigerator, wall comes next. The old type free-standing dust-catcher was replaced with a built-in 12 cubic-foot Hotpoint unit. This, together with utility cabinets surrounding the new built-in, has not only added to the decor and cleanliness of the kitchen but has also utilized all available space. Here, the side cabinets are made of ⅝-inch plywood, grooved 4 inches on center, to allow for installation of sliding trays, shelves and drawers. The outside of the refrigerator cabinets is covered with prefinished Nakora V-plank panels, matching the rest of the kitchen cabinets, when finished.

Doors for the refrigerator cabinets are again mounted on continuous hinges and operate by means of touch latches. The upper cabinet, containing a wide lid opening, is especially useful for the storage of large objects. Made of ¾-inch

KITCHENS

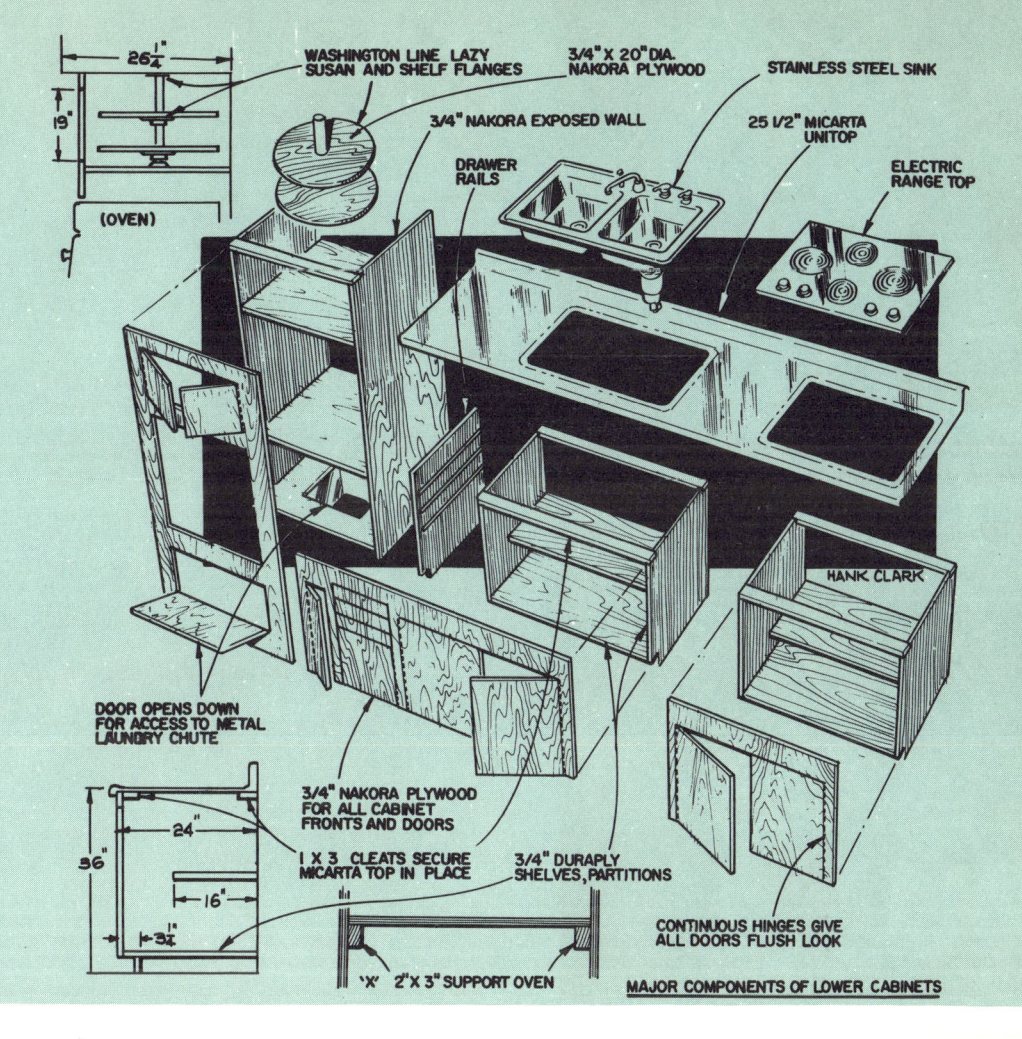

Diagram labels:
- (OVEN) 26¼" × 19"
- WASHINGTON LINE LAZY SUSAN AND SHELF FLANGES
- 3/4" × 20" DIA. NAKORA PLYWOOD
- STAINLESS STEEL SINK
- 3/4" NAKORA EXPOSED WALL
- 25 1/2" MICARTA UNITOP
- DRAWER RAILS
- ELECTRIC RANGE TOP
- HANK CLARK
- DOOR OPENS DOWN FOR ACCESS TO METAL LAUNDRY CHUTE
- 3/4" NAKORA PLYWOOD FOR ALL CABINET FRONTS AND DOORS
- 1 × 3 CLEATS SECURE MICARTA TOP IN PLACE
- 3/4" DURAPLY SHELVES, PARTITIONS
- CONTINUOUS HINGES GIVE ALL DOORS FLUSH LOOK
- 'X' 2" × 3" SUPPORT OVEN
- 24", 36", 16", 3½"

MAJOR COMPONENTS OF LOWER CABINETS

OVEN unit at the left end of kitchen now gets a new face, plumb with cabinet wall.

LAZY SUSAN unit goes into upper part of oven cabinet. Electric oven is a Hotpoint.

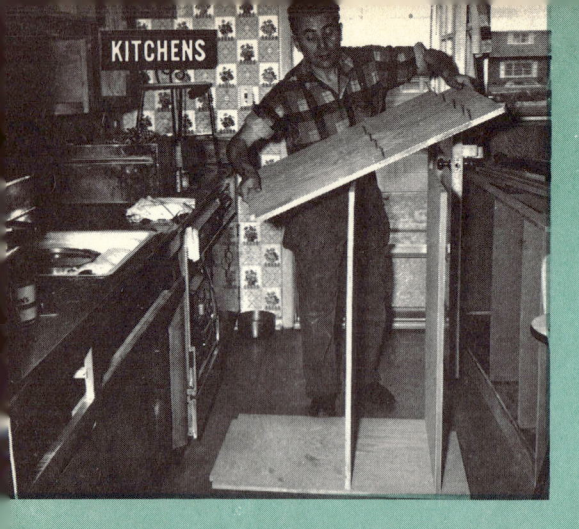

WORK counter cabinet is made of ¾-in. Nakora plywood. See sketch.

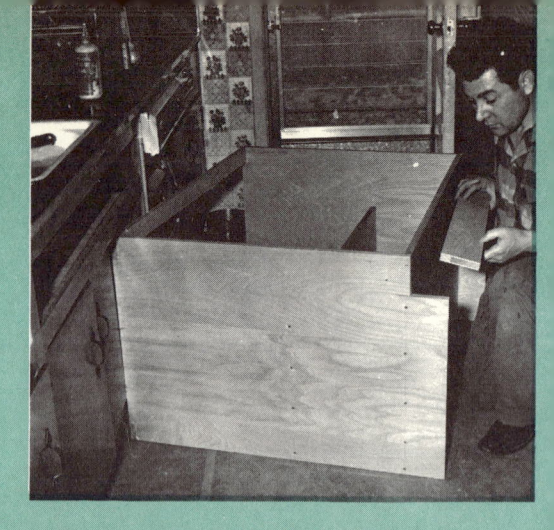

NAILS and glue are used for assembly of cabinets. Shelves are made from Duraply.

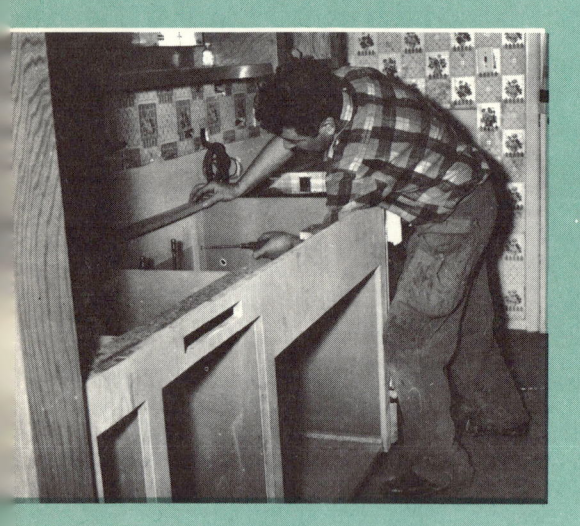

CABINET section is mounted to wall with screws into studs. Install rear wood strip.

SLIDING doors, in straw pattern, are cut from ¼-in. Acrylite, fit into frame groove.

FRAME is inserted into opening over sink cabinet. It should extend 2 inches outward.

WOODEN sliding doors go into cabinet over the stove. Mount after installing hardware.

KITCHENS

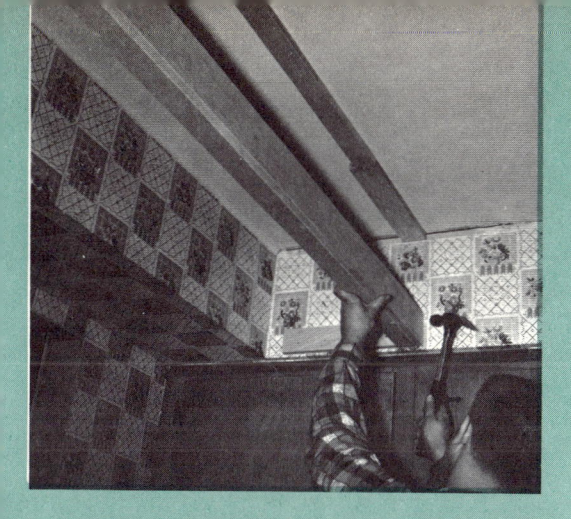

DROP ceiling must be widened to meet the depth of the built-in refrigerator installation.

CEILING is dropped with long 1x3-in. firing strips and sufficient number of cross strips.

COVER the new drop ceiling with sheets of ¼-in. Duraply, using glue and short nails.

STORAGE cabinet goes alongside the refrigerator built-in. See drawing.

METAL refrigerator installation frame is mounted to side cabinet with wood screws.

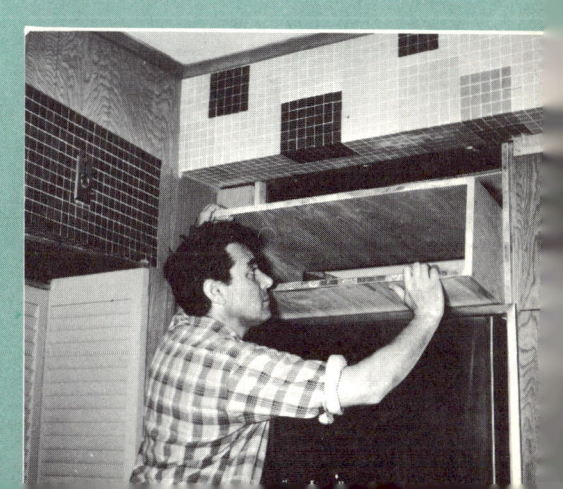

INSTALL the cabinet atop the refrigerator by screwing into side cabinet and ceiling.

KITCHENS

REFRIGERATOR overhead cabinet gets a face frame. The lower half is for ventilation.

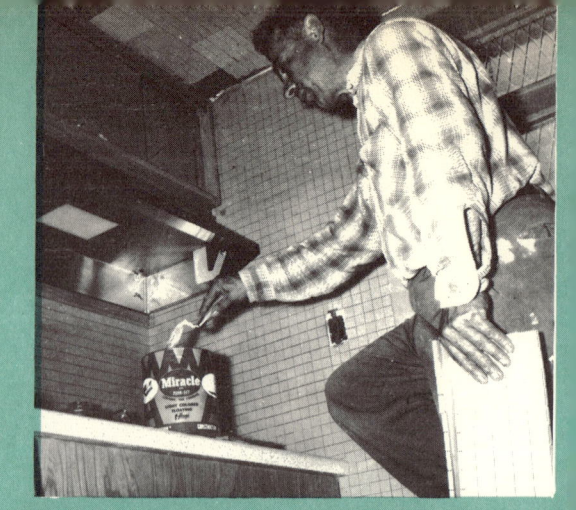

MOSAIC tiles are applied to walls and part of the drop ceiling in a colorful pattern.

RETRACTABLE bread tray is one of many details found in this well-designed kitchen.

CLOTHES CHUTE under oven installation is placed so clothes fall into basement below.

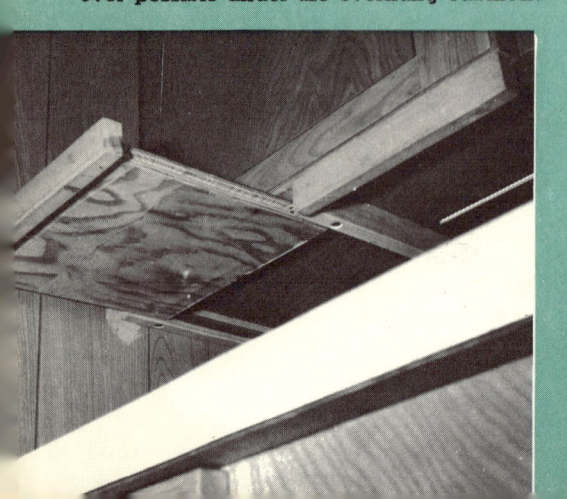

HANDY pull-out trays are installed wherever possible under the overhang cabinets.

CLOSEUP of stainless steel sink shows the garbage disposal unit and Micarta Unitop.

KITCHENS

BEFORE AND AFTER. The finished kitchen, as shown at right, won the Medallion Award of the Live Better Electrically Institute.

pine, it is mounted between the side cabinet and strips installed against the wall. For installation of the necessary vents and for the refrigerator itself, the manufacturer supplies a complete plan with instructions.

One of the final touches on the sink wall was the installation of a stove vent hood. This unit, by Pryne, is made of stainless steel and contains a light fixture as well as a three-speed fan.

Before finishing the floors, all the drop ceilings were covered with 1x1-inch mosaic tiles which were mounted in a random color arrangement, using six different colors. These tiles come attached to a paper sheet and are thus easily mounted. Use special tile adhesive for installation, following the manufacturer's instructions. Mosaic tiles add a colorful and decorative touch to the whole kitchen area and are easily maintained and kept clean.

The floors were first sealed with flooring felt paper, then covered with vinyl tiles. Brass inlays were used in the tiles, arranged in a pleasing pattern to break the monotony of the speckled flooring.

Some of the final touches, giving a real luxurious feeling to the kitchen, are a Bogen intercom system installed on the wall and a NuTone mixer built right into the sink counter top. •

KITCHENS

Built-In Oven, Range & Hood

Here is how you can update your kitchen cooking center.

EVEN if you are not inclined to do your own electrical installations (and on jobs like this it makes good sense to rely on a pro for that phase of the operation), you can save considerable money by doing your own cabinet work for housing the units.

Between the drawings shown here and the instructional material which you will get with the range and oven you buy, you should have no trouble doing a most satisfactory job. The instruction sheets will tell you the exact size of the opening you need for the cooking units. They will recommend practical heights-above-floor, tell you whether insulation is required around the oven, give detailed information on how to install the units, and offer suggestions for best placement of control panels in the case of surface ranges. The latter is important for it determines whether you must provide a cutout in the front of the cabinet work for the panel or whether you need an opening in the wall. Most people prefer

The controls for both the range and oven are placed high and away from the reach of children.

KITCHENS

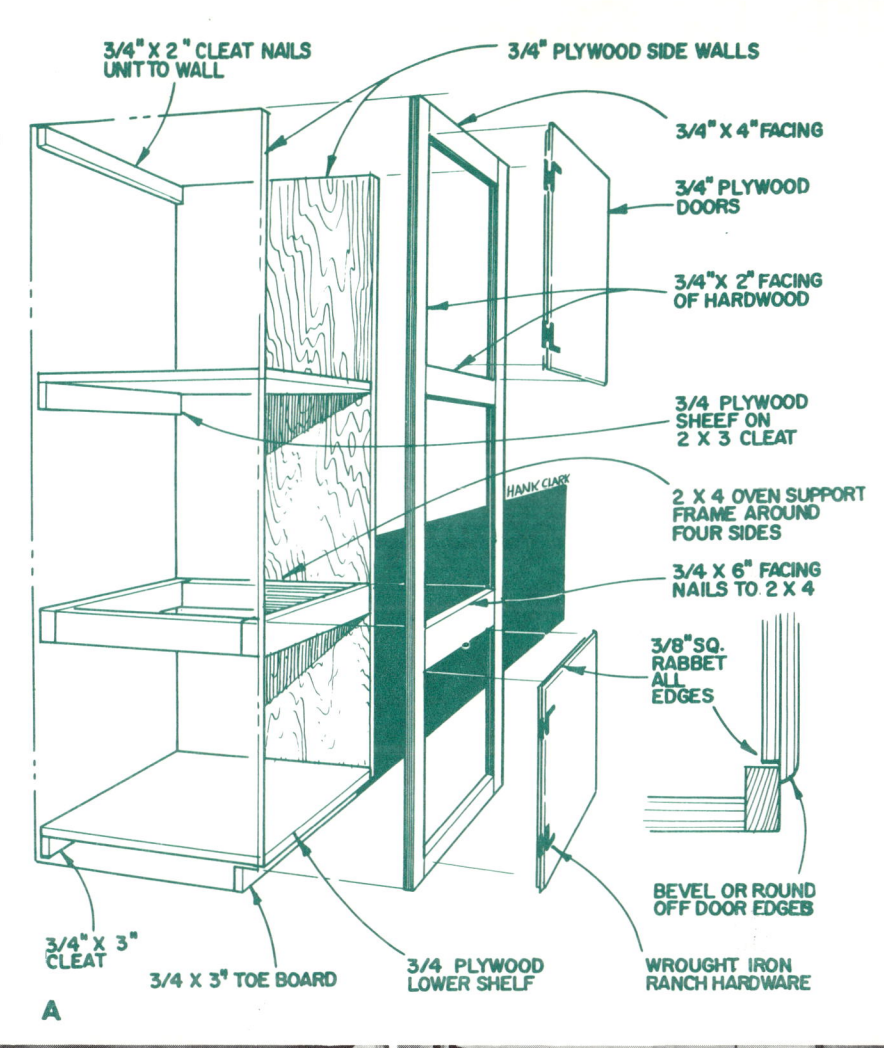

Diagram labels:
- 3/4" X 2" CLEAT NAILS UNIT TO WALL
- 3/4" PLYWOOD SIDE WALLS
- 3/4" X 4" FACING
- 3/4" PLYWOOD DOORS
- 3/4" X 2" FACING OF HARDWOOD
- 3/4 PLYWOOD SHELF ON 2 X 3 CLEAT
- 2 X 4 OVEN SUPPORT FRAME AROUND FOUR SIDES
- 3/4 X 6" FACING NAILS TO 2 X 4
- 3/8" SQ. RABBET ALL EDGES
- BEVEL OR ROUND OFF DOOR EDGES
- WROUGHT IRON RANCH HARDWARE
- 3/4" X 3" CLEAT
- 3/4 X 3" TOE BOARD
- 3/4 PLYWOOD LOWER SHELF

A

There is storage space next to exhaust flue.   Waist level is most convenient oven height.

1865

KITCHENS

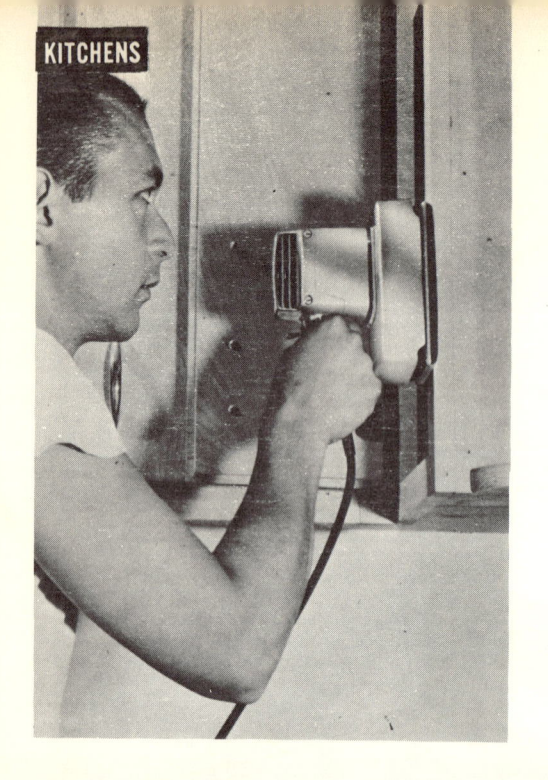

Electric sander is also used for a buffed finish.

an installation for the panel on the wall and just short of shoulder height. This makes it very convenient for the cook and puts the buttons out of reach of the little guys.

Be sure to read very carefully the instructions that come with the units. It's important that openings and cut-outs be made exactly as called for.

One easy method of doing the job, one that will not make it difficult for the electrician to get where he must go, is to make the basic framework for the cabinets, sized for where they must fit, and have these all ready to push into place before any electrical work is done. Then, if you can stand by while the electrician works (bringing his lines through the walls, etc.) you can place the framework and actually mount the range and oven before adding the final pieces to the cabinets.

On the oven cabinet, for example. You can cut the two main vertical pieces (sides of the cabinet) and join them with the 2x4 frame on which the oven rests plus the bottom shelf. This is strong enough to hold the oven while you work around it to finish the job. This is also true of the sur-

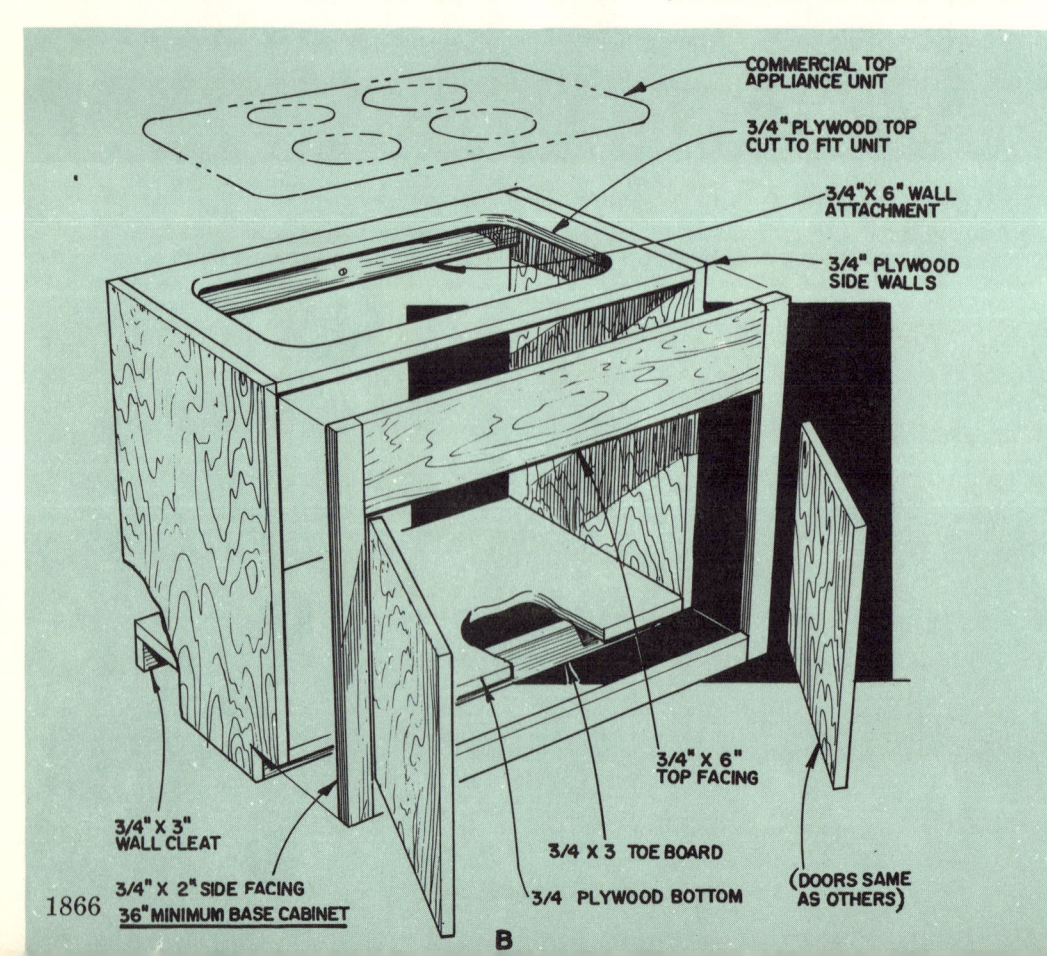

COMMERCIAL TOP APPLIANCE UNIT
3/4" PLYWOOD TOP CUT TO FIT UNIT
3/4" X 6" WALL ATTACHMENT
3/4" PLYWOOD SIDE WALLS
3/4" X 6" TOP FACING
(DOORS SAME AS OTHERS)
3/4 PLYWOOD BOTTOM
3/4 X 3 TOE BOARD
3/4" X 2" SIDE FACING
36" MINIMUM BASE CABINET
3/4" X 3" WALL CLEAT

B

face unit. Make the two sides, connect them with the bottom shelf and the cutout top for the range, and you have a structure strong enough to hold the surface range while you finish the cabinet work. This makes it possible for the electrician to work freely and to complete his end of the job without interference.

Once you've gone this far, it's a simple matter to add additional shelves, then the front framing members and finally, the doors.

If you have sound walls to work against the cabinets do not have to have backs; the walls can provide this. Ample rigidity is provided by locating wall studs and tying the new units to the walls by toenailing and/or with cleats.

There are a few things to remember if you are remodeling and the new work must match existing cabinetry. Toe space dimensions should be picked off from cabinets already in use. Include thickness of tiles or other countercover material when determining what the total height of the cabinet for the new surface range must be. New doors must be level with doors on existing cabinets. • *By R. J. DeCristoforo*

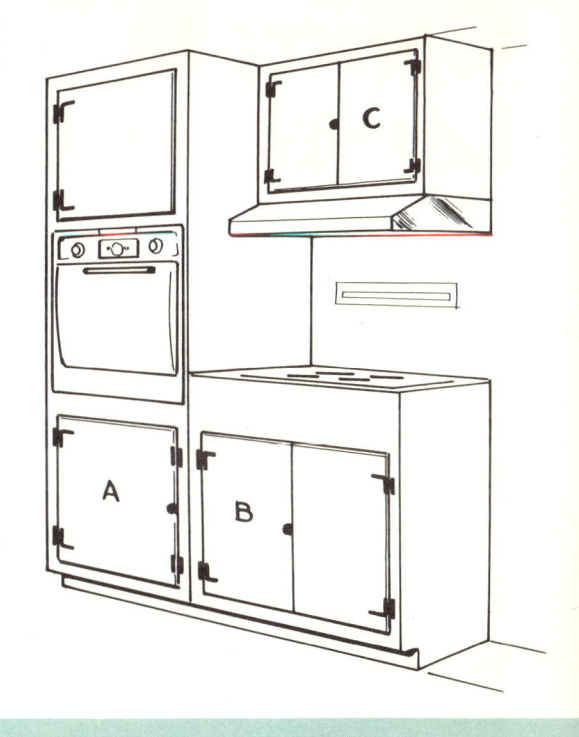

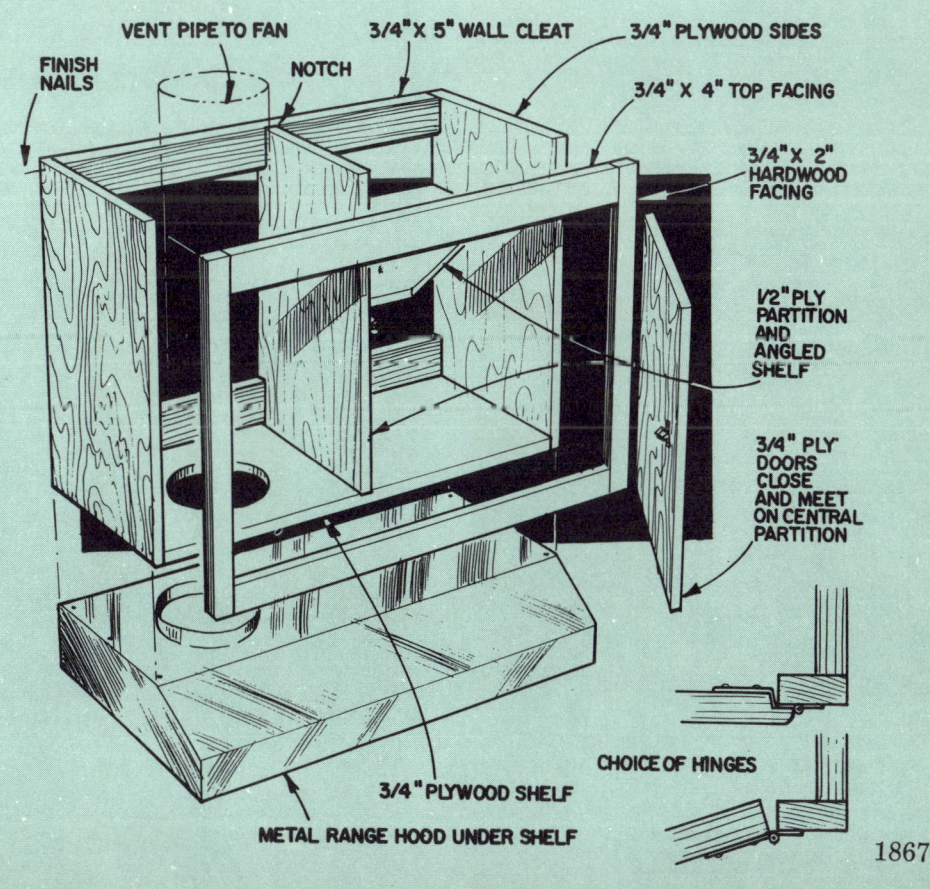

LAMP POST

Concrete Lamp Post

by George Daniels

Make it in a couple of hours with 2 bags of ready-mixed cement

Post has coat of white cement paint, fluted corners formed by quarter round. Won't chip easily.

YOU CAN make this concrete lawn lamppost in an hour or two with two bags of ready-mixed concrete (gravel mix). The form in which the post is cast is made from ordinary 8-inch sheathing with stock ¼-round molding (½ or ⅝ inch) at the corners.

The post shown in the photos is 5 inches square and 8 feet from end to end. In use, the lower two feet are underground. A length of conduit (you can use ordinary pipe) runs through the center of the post from top to bottom to carry the wire to the lamp and to serve as reinforcement for the concrete. Wiring underground is waterproof plastic coated. Where codes demand it, conduit may be run all the way from post to house.

To make the form, begin by attaching the ¼-round molding strips. Two strips are attached to the bottom of the form, one strip to each of the sides, as shown in the drawing. If you're using sheathing attach the side pieces to the bottom so that grooved edges are in contact with the bottom, tongues up, as shown. (You can, of course, use square-edged stock, but it's usually a little higher priced.) The molding strips are nailed in place with copper or other rustproof lath nails. Common nails (2 or 2½-inch) are used to fasten the sides to the bottom and the central cross brace to the upper edges of the sides. Use the same nails to attach the ends to the form.

Leave all nail heads slightly above the surface so you can pull them easily when you want to take the form apart to remove the post. If the form is to be used for more than one casting it will be best to use form nails, as these can be driven up tight and may still be removed easily.

You can mix the concrete in a mortar box if you have one or in a garden cart or even on a sheet of hardboard. Mix the material dry first, then add water according to the instructions. If your form shows any gaps at seams (as when lumber is badly warped) simply chink them with folded scraps of tarpaper. If the concrete is properly mixed it's not likely to ooze through minor cracks.

Before filling the form slip the pipe or conduit through the holes in the end pieces Be sure these are mounted so that the pipe or conduit is held centered in the form.

Use a shovel to transfer the concrete from the mixing bed or cart to the form. Don't worry if you spill a little as the two bags (usually 80 lbs. apiece) provide a little extra anyway.

When the form is filled tap it along both

LAMP POST

Following dimensions in diagram, assemble mold for post. Use rust-proof lath nails.

Check spacing of molding strips with ruler. Must be parallel or sides won't be straight.

Fit parts of form together for trial assembly before nailing. Minor gaps may be filled with paper wads before form filled with concrete.

Turn form upside down to assemble, nail thru bottom into lower edges of side members. Be sure sides are snug against molding strips of bottom. Leave nail heads above wood surface for easy pulling later, or use form nails.

Check open side of mold for accuracy, then nail small piece of wood across mold to keep the sides in place when form is filled with cement.

LAMP POST

End pieces of form have holes centered so conduit will be in center of post. If lamp attaches to conduit end directly or with fittings, leave enough of conduit protruding, with threads if necessary. If the conduit fits loosely, put tarpaper in gaps.

Use short 1x2 cut to fit between sides of form to act as screed board. Slide along upper edges of quarter-round moldings to smooth off concrete at molding level. Keep small trowel handy for this.

Grass clippings or rags may be used on top of concrete to hold moisture after it sets. Sprinkle the rags or grass until well soaked and keep them damp for several days to give concrete strength.

Screwdriver and hammer are used to take form apart. Time: 5 minutes. Completed post is at right.

Plastic-covered underground wire is stiff, easy to lead through center pipe or conduit. Dig center of post hole deeper to form rounded bottom so wire won't be kinked against end of the post. Post weighs 200 lbs., so move it in wheelbarrow.

LAMP POST

sides with a hammer to make sure it is worked solidly down to the bottom without voids. If tapping lowers the surface below the top of the upper molding strips add a little more concrete to bring the level up. To smooth and square off the upper surface slide a short screed board along the molding strips, pushing excess concrete ahead of it, and smoothing the surface as it goes along. Use a trowel to smooth off any roughened areas.

When the concrete has set cover it with dry grass or old rags and soak it thoroughly with water from the garden hose (with nozzle adjusted to spray) or with a sprinkling can. Keep it damp for several days to assure high strength.

As the concrete may stick to any rough or checked areas of the wood it's a good idea to coat all inner surfaces of the form with oil or grease before filling with concrete. You can use ordinary engine oil (preferably about a No. 40) for this.

To remove the post from the form tip the form over on its side and pull the nails projecting from the bottom. Tap off the end pieces at the same time. Then simply lift the form parts off the post. That's all there is to it.

Roll the post over to see if there are any pitted or rough areas. If there are just trowel a little cement into them for a smooth surface. Do this while concrete is still "green."

Standard lamps may usually be mounted on the conduit. If you're using an antique lamp or a custom made one it's a simple matter to adapt the top of the post to take it. In many cases a layer of fresh cement may be troweled on the top of the post and the lamp pressed down into it for firm anchorage when the cement sets.

For a paint finish the post should be allowed to season for several months before finishing, although several modern types may be applied after a few days. •

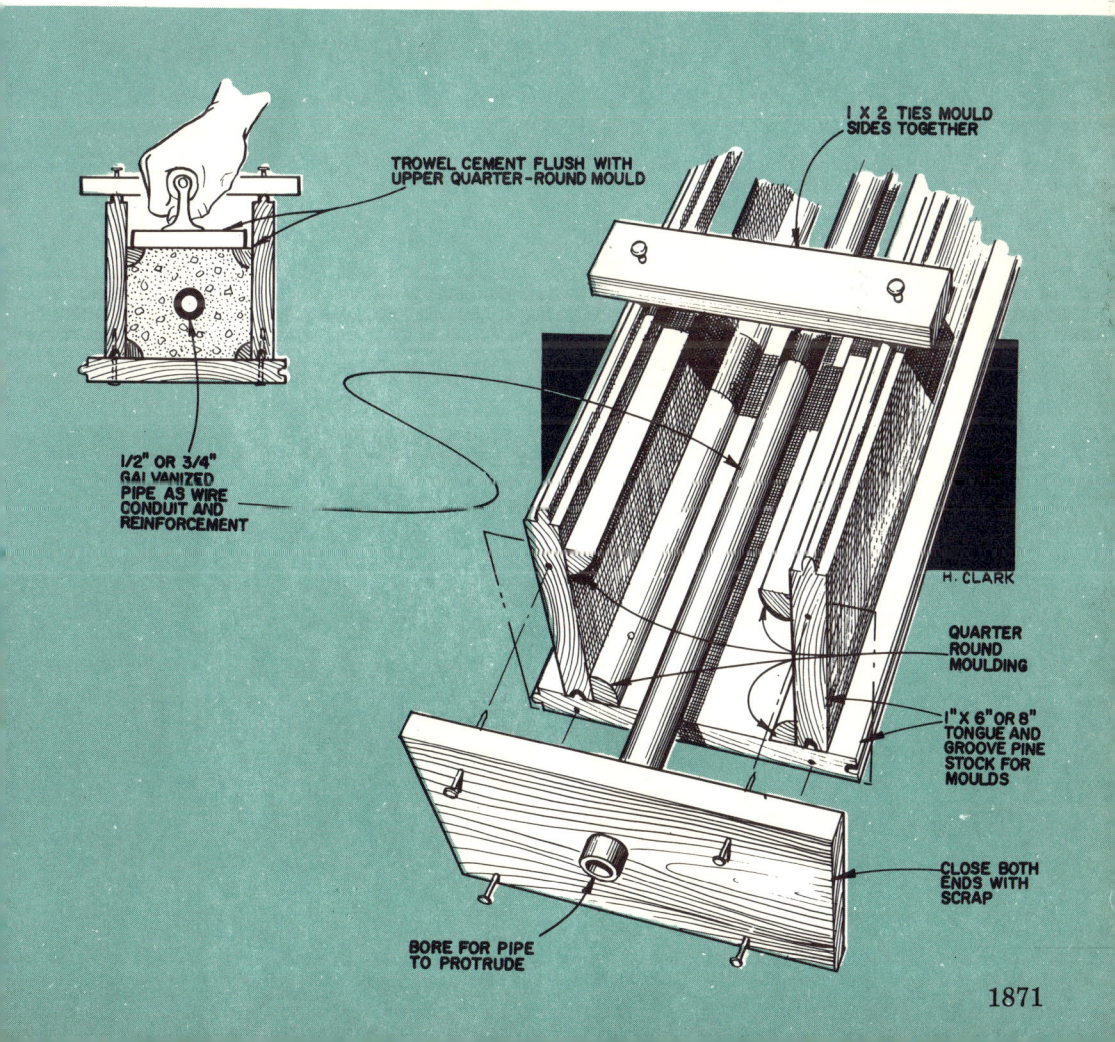

1871

LAMPS

Hanging Lamp

by Jackson Hand

This one plugs in easily, beats installation costs, looks like a million.

HANGING lamps have caught the homeowner's fancy because of their design, illuminating performance, and low cost. They are expensive, however, if you have a fixture-box wired in the ceiling. Such wiring can cost $25 and up.

The teardrop cluster shown here solves this problem, providing at the same time the raise-and-lower feature so popular in today's lamps. You can use the idea with any hanging lamp.

Buy enough rubber-covered (or plastic) two-wire cord to reach from the nearest outlet to the ceiling—across the ceiling to the point where the lamp should hang—plus about four feet for slack. This cord is now available in white—inconspicuous against a white ceiling—or in several accent colors

LAMPS

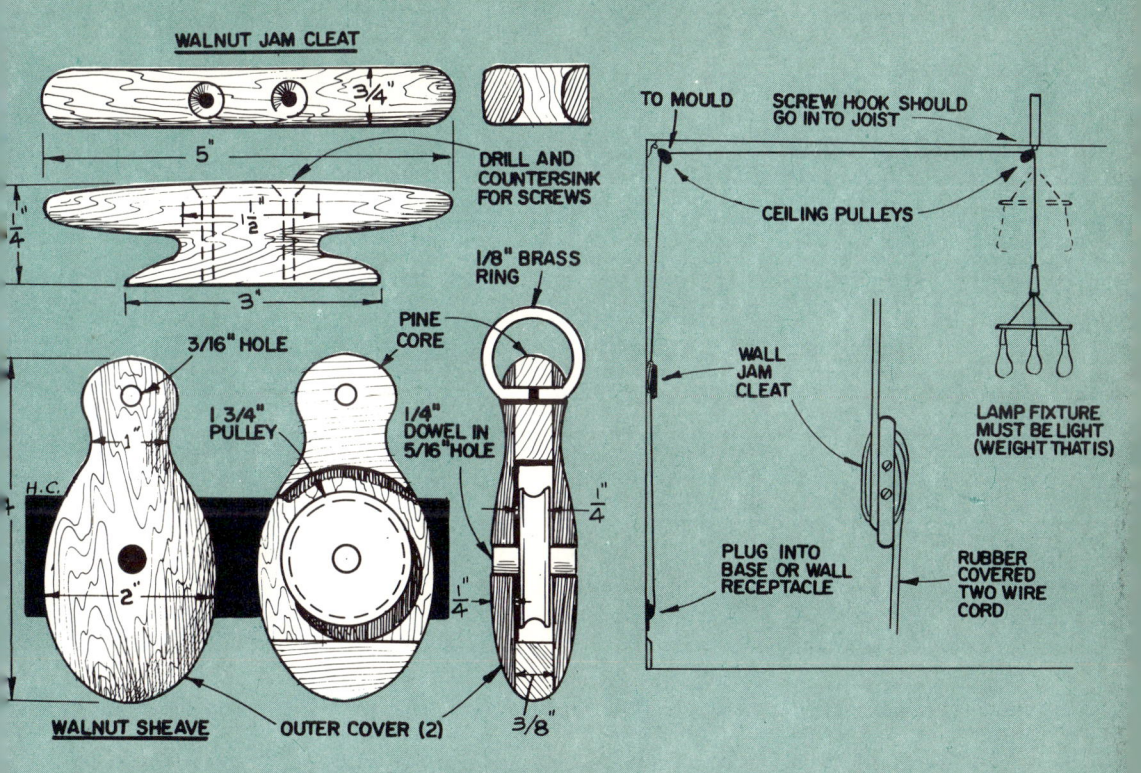

TO MAKE PULLEY: (1) turn or cut out wheel, insert ¼-inch shaft (2) drill 5/16-inch holes for shaft in walnut pieces about 2 x 4 x ¼ inches (3) cut pieces of walnut ⅜ inch thick for cross-core at top and bottom (4) assemble and glue unit in rough form with grain vertical on faces, crossbands at right angles (5) cut out rough shape with saw, round with surform tool, then sand (6) open a brass curtain ring and squeeze it shut through hole. Strength of pulley comes from the cross lamination of the wood. Diagrams give various construction details.

which you may prefer. Wire one end of the cord to the lamp; the other end gets a two-prong plug, after it is strung through a pair of pulleys.

Also buy—or make—a pair of pulleys. You can find attractive metal or plastic ones at hardware, drapery, or marine outfitting shops. Those shown here were made of walnut, to complement the walnut parts of the lamp. Of walnut also is the "jam cleat" in the wall—another item you can purchase in plastic or metal if you prefer. The lamp cord is set loosely around the cleat, holding the lamp at the desired height.

Accompanying sketches show how the jam cleat and the walnut pulleys were made, two fairly simple jobs of whittling.

You can fasten the pulley at the top of the wall, of course, into the cap member of the framing, by means of a screw eye. The ceiling pulley should go on a screw eye into a joist. If the lamp must hang in a spot which falls between joists, bridge between them with a firmly nailed wooden member.

Your job will look best if you go straight up the wall from the outlet to the first pulley, then accommodate any necessary angle as the cord crosses the ceiling.

After the pulleys are up, string the cord through them and fasten on the plug. A "line switch" or "feed through" switch gives you control, if the outlet is not on a regular switch. On or off, higher or lower, as you please. •

1873

LAMPS

Child's Lamp

by Dick Howe

Using alphabet blocks, it's as easy as ABC to build it

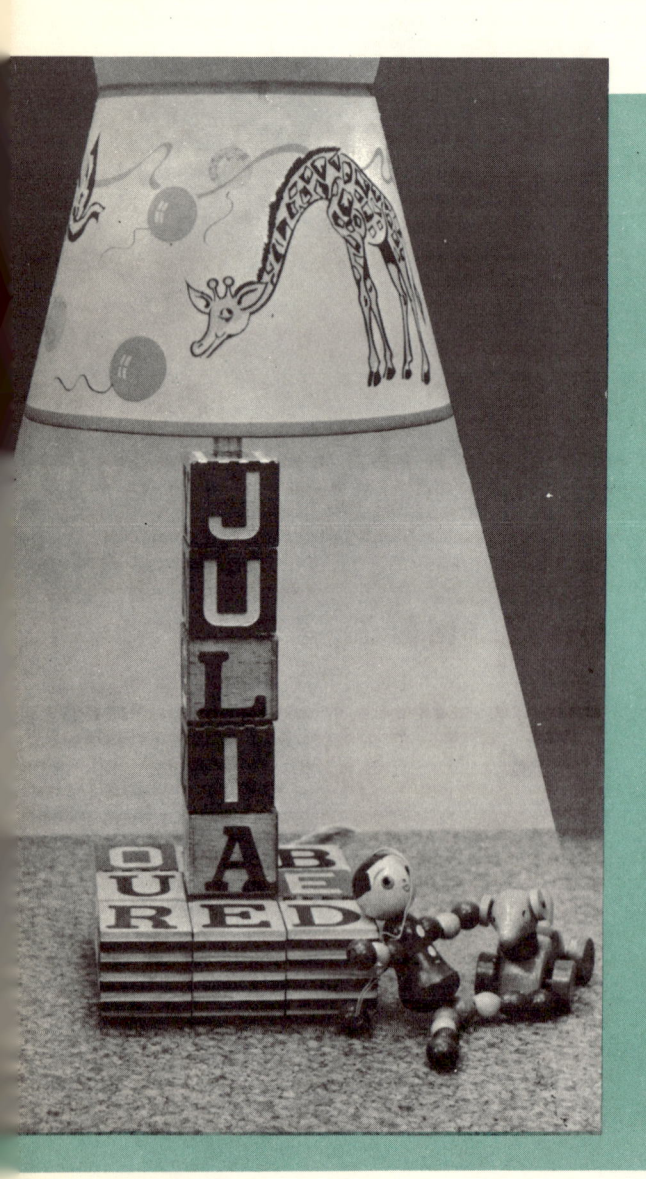

Mark blocks with ruler to find center before boring holes with a ⅜-inch drill.

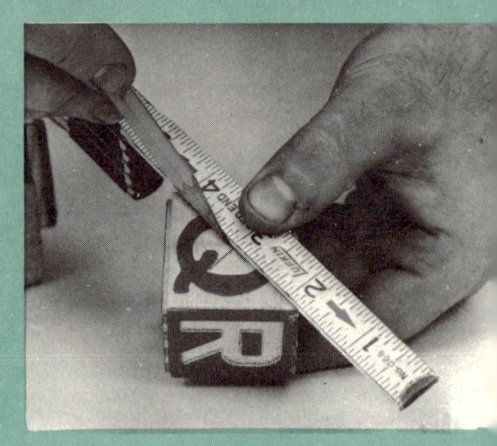

Base blocks are glued together and then bound tightly with twine until glue dries.

1874

LAMPS

WOULD you like to delight your child with a personalized lamp that not only illuminates his room, but instructs him as well? You can, and it's as easy as ABC to build. It's also cheerful looking because of the alphabet blocks that compose the lamp. And you'll undoubtedly want to build it to spell out your youngster's name.

Begin construction by marking the centers of the lamp post blocks. Drill ⅜-inch holes through the blocks, and then stack them on a length of ⅜-inch threaded pipe, as shown in the diagram here. Line up the letters to form the desired name or design before tightening the assembly with nuts threaded over the pipe ends.

Glue the remaining blocks together around the bottom block of the post, and bind them together with cord until the glue dries.

Now thread the lamp wire through the post pipe and connect it to the light fixture, which you've bought at the dime store. Screw the fixture into place, put in a bulb, cap it with an amusing shade, and there's the lamp to put a song in the heart of any child! •

Lamp base consists of eight blocks glued together around sides of bottom post block.

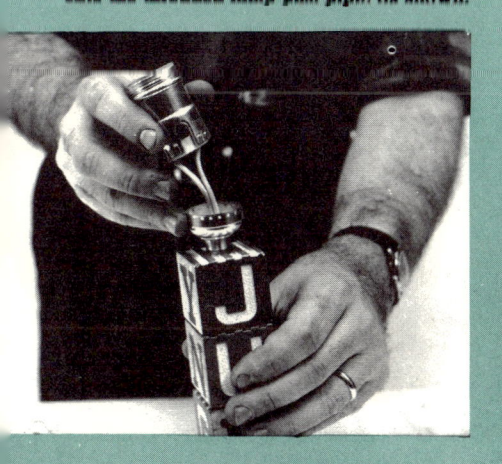

Diagram below shows construction of child's lamp. As you can see, the construction is very simple.

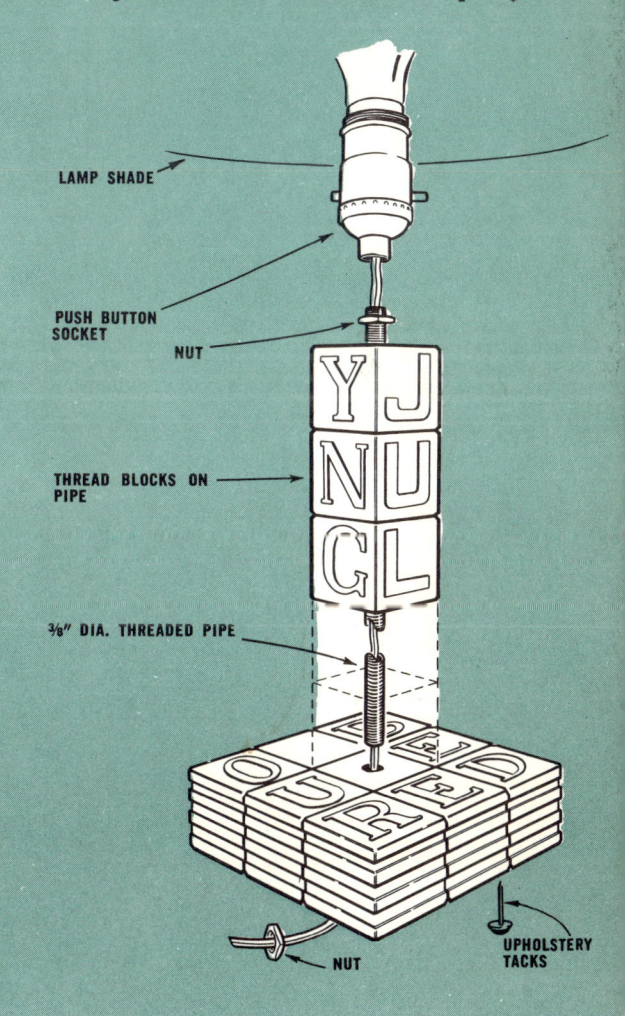

Light fixture is wired and then turned onto the threaded lamp post pipe, as shown.

1875

LAUNDRY CART

Laundry Cart and Cabinet

This rolling, double-compartment cart rounds up the laundry and then fits neatly out of the way.

HEAVY, unwieldy laundry hampers and the straining and tugging that go with them just aren't necessary. Here's a laundry cart that you wheel from room to room and has convenient separator bins for white and colored clothes. When the wash is out of the way, merely fit the cart into its "garage" under the sink counter.

Establish dimensions that will suit the sink that you wish to install; this, of course, is further decided by the size of the kitchen space available.

Because a sink cabinet can't help but take an occasional dousing and is always subject to moisture, use a plywood that is made with 100% waterproof glue. As in the preceding project, an exterior grade of Douglas Fir Plywood was used

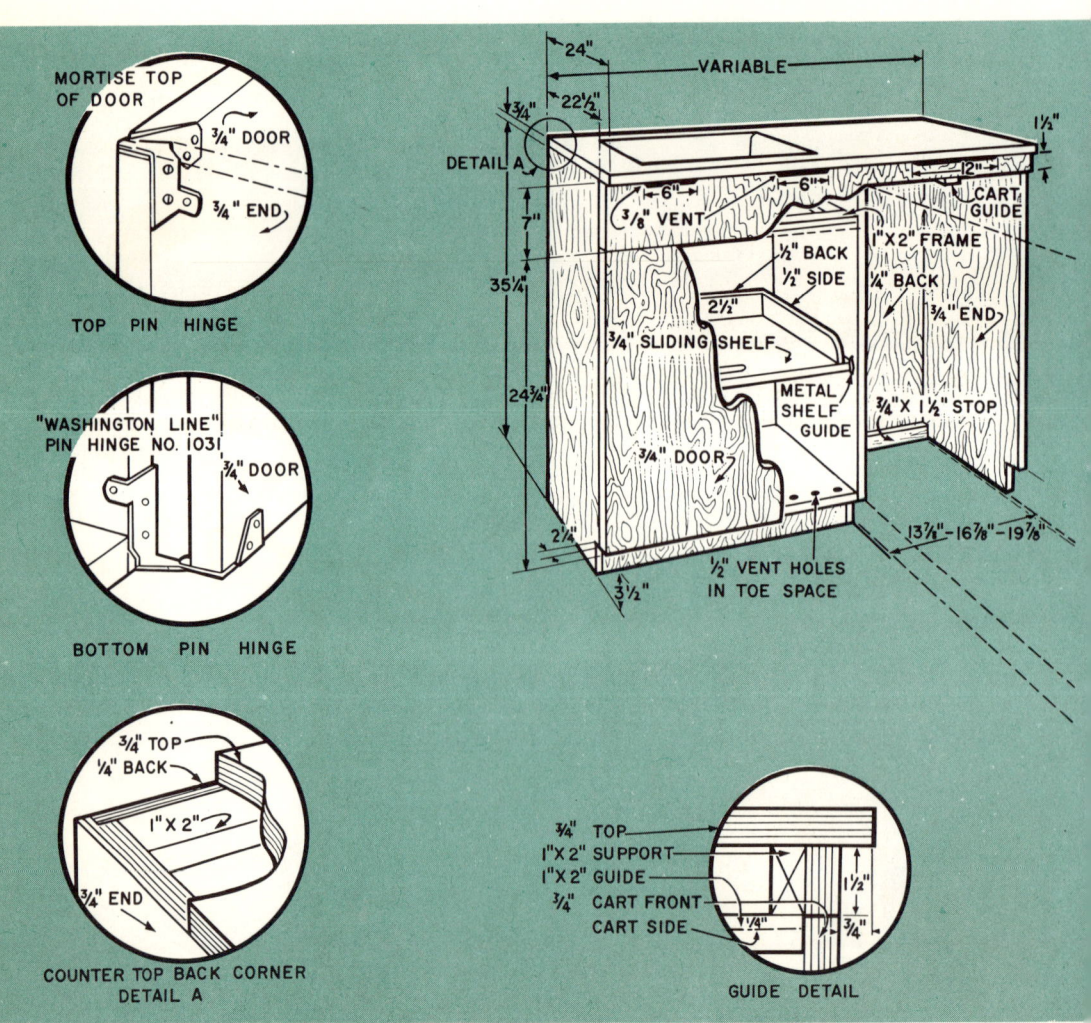

1876

LAUNDRY CART

here. All joints should be made with a waterproof glue, and 6- or 8-penny finishing nails.

Cut all structural panels and frames to size. Sand all the edges and check the parts for fit. Note that vent holes are cut in the toe-space portion of the base, as well as in the cart bottom.

Attach the bottom shelf to the base and the ledger strips. The ends, back, face and framing members are the next parts to be assembled.

After fastening on the top, apply a counter surfacing material (preferably a plastic laminate like Formica or Micarta). Band the edges, and install the sink.

Move the sink and cabinet into place. If the floor is uneven, level the base so that the cabinet stands solid. Then cut, fit and hang the door.

Sand and prime all door edges thoroughly, and be sure to finish both the inner and outer faces alike. Edges must be sealed, and it's a good idea to prime-paint other surfaces.

To make the laundry cart, follow the same procedure, referring to the accompanying illustration. Cut the parts to size, sand the edges and check for fit.

Either cut dadoes in the cart side panels or attach ½-in. wood strips to form slots, to hold the removable ½-in. divider in the cart. Glue and nail the bottom to the toe-piece. Then fasten the sides and ends in place.

Apply a finish, then make and install a sliding shelf for the cabinet. •

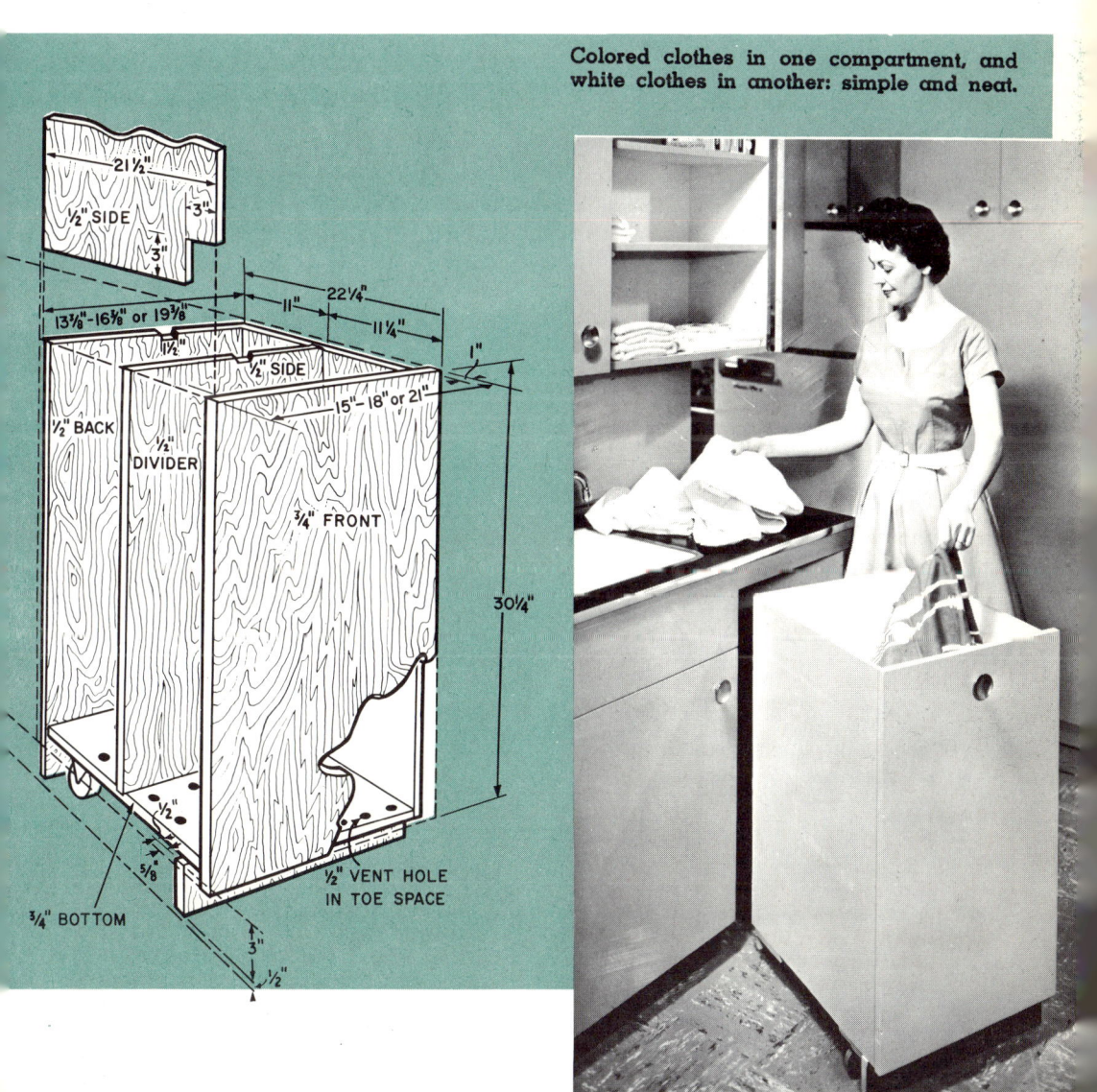

Colored clothes in one compartment, and white clothes in another: simple and neat.

LAVATORY

Built-In Lavatory

Basic dimensions can be altered to suit the individual layout, but construction remains the same.

NOTHING dresses up a bathroom more than to replace that old hanging wall sink with a built-in Pullman sink. Beautiful and luxurious, the Pullman sink adds class to the bath, hides unsightly plumbing, provides additional table work space for shaving and cosmetic accessories, and converts an otherwise unusable area into valuable storage space for linens, towels, cleaning compounds and accessories. Even a comparatively small bathroom can be given that mark of distinction with the addition of a Pullman sink. The sink shown in the photos was installed in a small 6x6 foot bathroom and instead of making the room more crowded, it actually made the room seem larger by permitting the removal of some bulky linen storage cabinets.

The Pullman sink shown in the photos is simple to build and will fit into the corner of a small bathroom. The dimensions given, however, can be altered and the basic design changed to meet any individual requirements. Main features of the Pullman sink shown are sliding doors and a Formica table top. A partition inside separates the sink and plumbing area and provides a shelved section for linen storage. The sliding doors are fitted with rollers and slide smoothly on corresponding tracks. If for any reason, an emergency plumbing job is required, the sliding doors will lift out in a jiffy, the shelves ditto, and the partition removed by loosening a few screws, thereby permitting free access to the entire area under the sink and eliminating the need for working in cramped quarters.

The sink used is a 20x17-inch, built-in type lavatory and comes with a stainless steel ring and special clamps and bolts for installing it into the counter top.

The sink shown is 33½ inches high, 42¾ inches wide and 20 inches deep. The counter top which is cut from ¾-inch plywood, overlaps the cabinet dimensions slightly on its two exposed sides, being 44 inches wide by 21½ inches deep.

The first step in making the sink is to build the frame which is made of lengths of ¾x1¼-inch wood. Draw a horizontal line along the wall 32¾ inches from the floor. Use a level to make sure the sink counter will be level. Nail a 42-inch length of ¾x1¼-inch wood to the wall, its top edge even with the line on the wall. Next, complete the frame as shown, making sure that the top crosspieces are perfectly level and parallel to each other. After the frame is finished, the counter top can be cut from ¾-inch plywood. Use the stainless steel sink ring as a template for marking out the hole in which the sink will fit, positioning it so that sufficient margin is allowed all around the hole to allow enough room for clamping the sink in place. Directions given with the sink and sink ring specify the amount of margin required for the particular sink used. Cut this hole out with a keyhole saw and make sure the sink ring drops snugly into it before proceeding

LAVATORY

further. Some play is permissible.

Next, fasten the counter top firmly to the top of the sink cabinet frame, either with brads or flathead wood screws, making sure that its back and side edges are pressed flush against the wall.

Next, a front base plate of 3/4x3½-inch wood is nailed to the floor along the leading edge of the cabinet. This plate will hold the tracks for the rolling doors and must be perfectly level and parallel with the cross frame above it. If the floor is not level, it will be necessary to shim up one end to make it level. A simple way to determine the required thickness of the shim is to lay the level on the plate and then slip a number of thin cardboard sheets or file cards under the low end until the plate is raised to a level position. The cards are then removed and their collective thickness measured to arrive at the right thickness for the shim. Don't worry about any air-space showing under the plate after it has been shimmed up. This will eventually

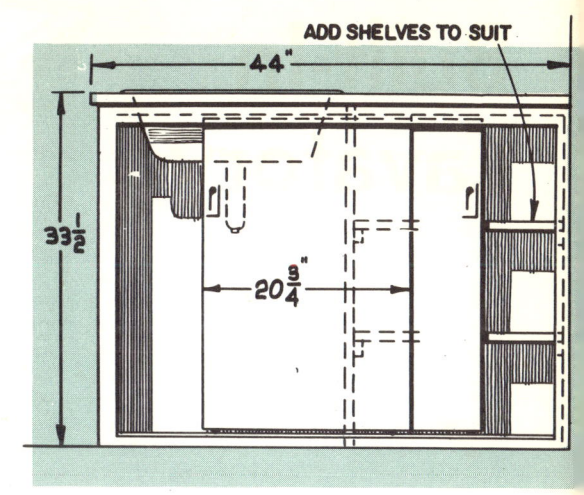

Counter height is standard, but storage and shelf arrangement can be laid out to suit.

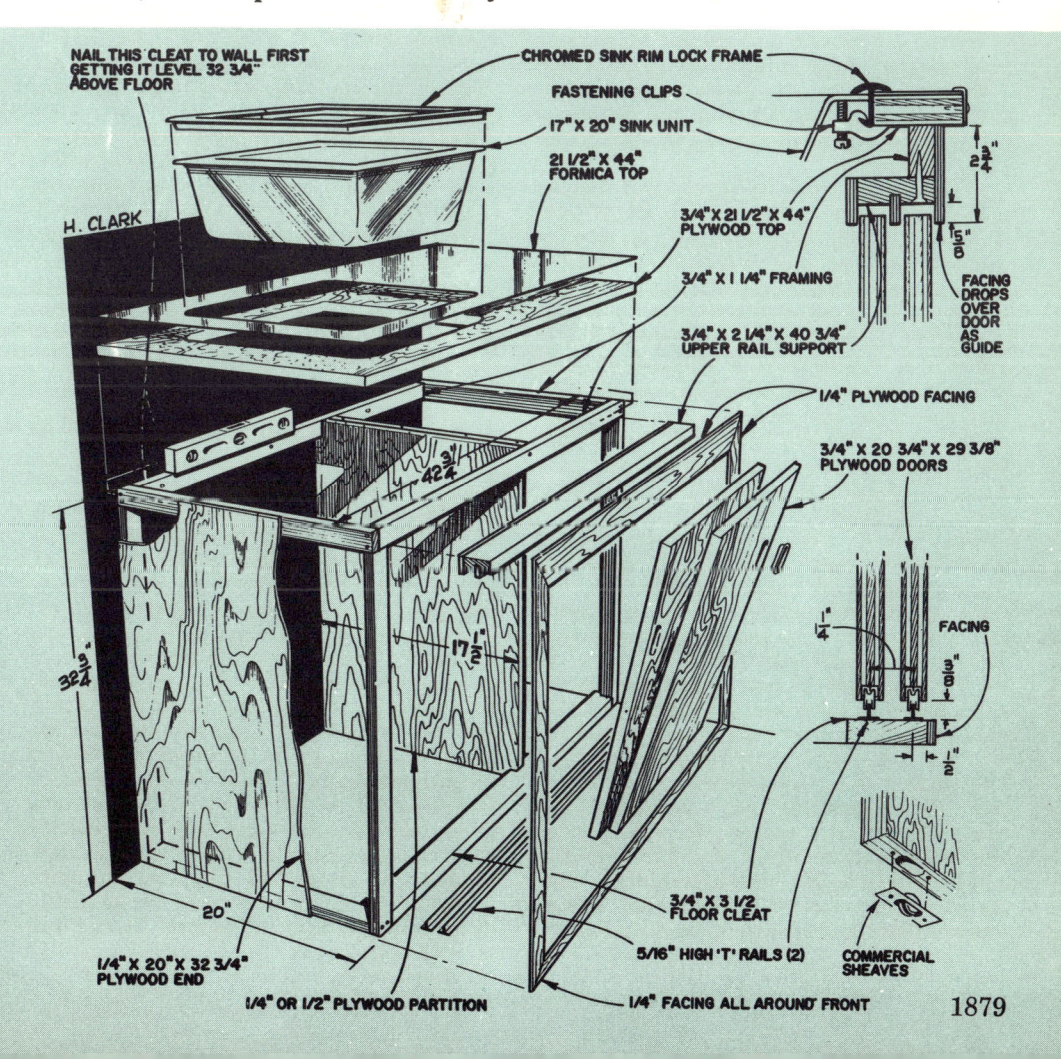

1879

LAVATORY

be hidden and the plate braced by a ¼-inch plywood trim strip nailed along the edge of the base plate.

Next, using a keyhole saw with a metal cutting blade, cut a sheet of Formica to the approximate dimensions of the sink counter top, allowing a slight margin around the edges for later filing to a flush fit. Allow the same slight margin when cutting the hole out for the sink section. Then apply contact bond cement to the back of the Formica, spreading it with an old brush or a saw-toothed spreader made for the purpose. Lay the Formica aside to dry and repeat the cementing process on the sink counter top after first sanding it clean down to bare wood. The cement should be allowed to dry for about 20 minutes, or until a piece of paper, pressed lightly onto the cemented surface, can be pulled away without it sticking or taking cement with it. When this test can be made successfully, you are ready to join the Formica to the counter top. However, because the Formica will bond instantly to the cemented counter top on contact and cannot be removed or shifted once placed, particular care should be taken to position the Formica accurately on the counter top before allowing the cemented surfaces to contact each other.

This is best done by laying two sheets of wrapping paper, their inside edges overlapping each other slightly, on the cemented counter top so that they cover the top completely. Then, lay the Formica on top of the paper and shift it around until you can feel through the paper that the Formica is correctly positioned over the counter top. Now, pressing firmly down on one end of the Formica to keep it from shifting, lift the other end enough to permit removal of the sheet of newspaper under that end of the plastic laminate. After removing that sheet, the Formica on that side of the counter top can be pressed down and permanently bonded to the top. Next, lift the other end of the Formica, remove the remaining sheet of newspaper from under it, and let the laminate drop and bond to the rest of the counter top. Using a rolling pin press the laminate down firmly all over, then file down the projecting edges of the laminate all around the table top and inside the rim of the hole cut-out until it is flush with the wood edges.

Now, following the directions that come with the sink, attach it to the steel sink ring and drop it into place in the counter top, fastening the clamps and bolts as directed in the instructions. Hook up the plumbing and the sink can be used, if needed, while the rest of the cabinet is completed.

The next step is to make an upper track guide for the tops of the doors to slide in. The channels for this guide are formed with parallel strips of ¼-inch plywood fastened to a length of 2¼-inch wide by ¾-inch thick wood. The wood strip should be 40¾ inches long. Down the complete length along its exact center, cut a groove ¼ inch wide by ¼ inch deep. Into this groove, fit and glue a ⅞-inch wide strip of ¼-inch thick plywood. Along one edge of the strip, nail another strip of ¼-inch plywood that measures 1½ inches wide.

Always be sure frame is square and level.

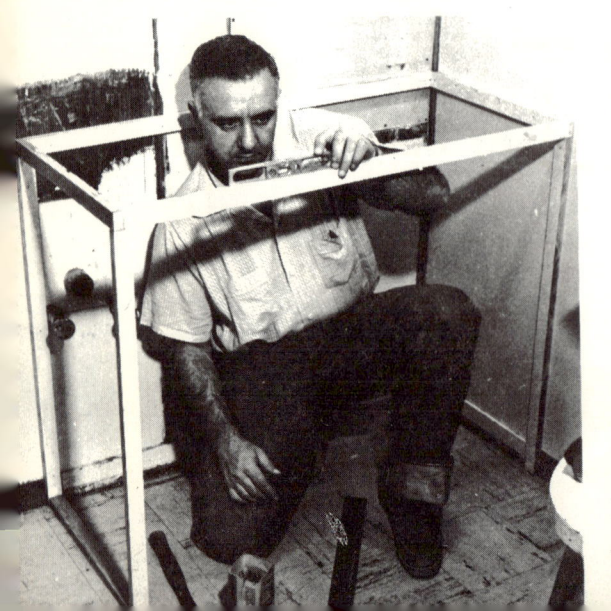

Make sink cut-out with fine toothed saw.

Both plywood strips should then extend exactly ⅝ of an inch above the face of the wood base and form one channel guide for the rear sliding door. The plywood strip needed to form the other channel guide will also serve as front trim for the cabinet and is not added until after the channel strip is attached to the cabinet frame.

The channel strip is attached with flathead wood screws to the underside of the top crosspiece of the cabinet frame. The edge having no plywood channel strip should be flush with the edge of the crosspiece with the channeled section of the guide extending in under the counter top and paralleling the base plate on the floor under it. After it is fastened securely in place, face the side of the cabinet with a 32¾x20-inch panel of ¼-inch plywood. Next, face the front of the cabinet with a frame of ¼-inch plywood trim all around, mitering the corners. The trim on the sides and along the bottom should come flush with the edges of the cabinet frame, but the trim along the top should be 2¾ inches wide so that it extends downward ⅝ inch beyond the frame and forms the grooved channel for the outer sliding door.

Make the doors of ¾-inch plywood, each measuring 20¾ inches wide by 29⅜ inches high. Fit them with sliding door hardware, wheels and track which can be bought at most hardware and building supply stores. The track used with the sink shown is a "T" track with a $\frac{5}{16}$-inch high rail. The wheels which ride on this track are set into holes cut out in the bottom edges of the doors. They are spaced an inch from each end and two wheels are used per door. For handles, oblong recessed finger grips can be gouged out of the door faces at points near their edges that is most convenient for the user. A choice of brass or chromed handle insets are also available if desired.

Two tracks should be fastened to the cabinet base plate, next, running them parallel to each other and centering each directly under its corresponding grooved channel above.

The doors are then set into place by first slipping the top end into the upper channel as far as it will go, then swinging the bottom end in and dropping it down so that the wheels rest on the track. A ¼-inch free space in the channels above the door tops allows for this insertion process.

The inside of the cabinet is then completed with a plywood partition, ½ inch or ¾ inch plywood will do, set in as close to the sink section as possible and held in place with cleats at the top and bottom which are fastened permanently to the partition, but held to the underside of the sink counter and to the floor with flathead wood screws. Cleats on the side of this partition with corresponding cleats on the opposite wall, will then serve to hold the shelves.

Finally, finish off the edge of the sink counter with aluminum or chromed metal trim, and along the edges that lie flush against the wall, nail lengths of metal cove trim. However, before fastening any of the metal trim down, squeeze some caulking compound into the area under it to provide a waterproof seal under the molding. •

By Louis Hochman

Contact cement is applied with spreader. Paper slip-sheet is used in positioning.

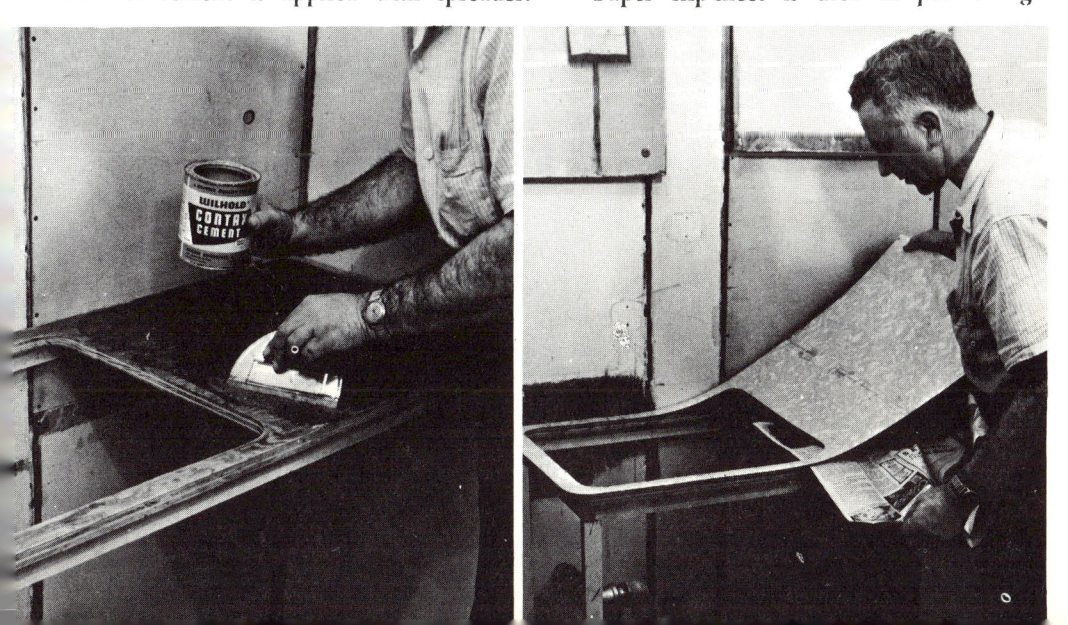

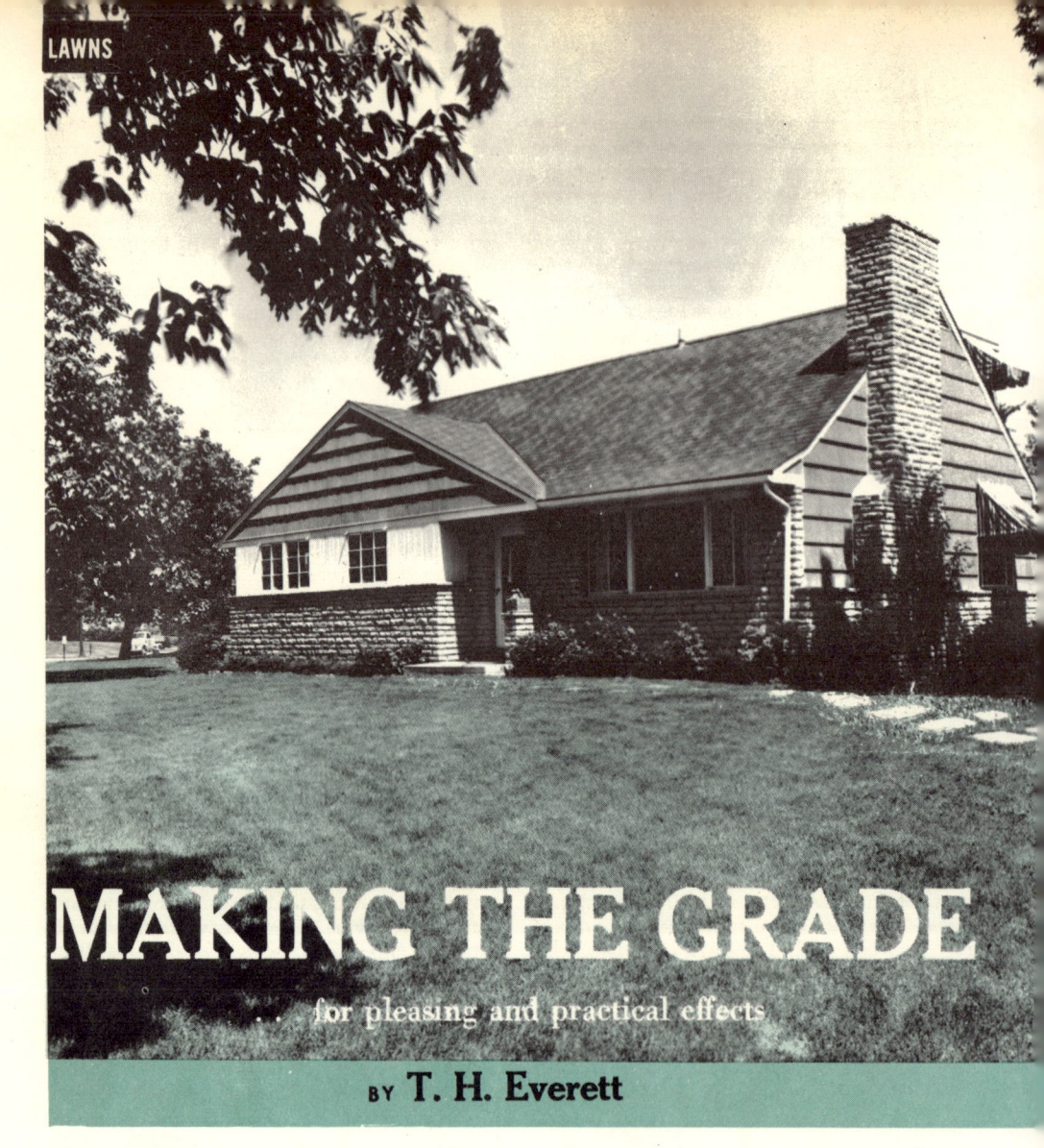

MAKING THE GRADE
...for pleasing and practical effects

BY T. H. Everett

BEFORE making a lawn or garden consider carefully, and modify if desirable, the contours of the ground. The surface grade is of immense importance in establishing a feeling that the garden is in harmony with its surroundings, that it fits the landscape. This appearance of rightness, of belonging, cannot be attained if grades are wrong.

Many beginners assume that a lawn should be flat and their efforts at grading are directed toward attaining this end. If the location is too steep for this they are likely to attempt a series of flat or nearly flat terraces separated by banks, walls or other devices marking severe changes of grade. That is, they are likely to do this if their pocketbooks permit.

This is all wrong. Level areas of lawn have their useful place in many garden plans but to assume that the more level the turf is, the better, is sheer nonsense. Unless there is good need for a lawn to be flat, every effort should be made to have it otherwise. A perfectly level lawn often indictates lack of imagination.

Flatness is a restrictive landscape feature. It calls for formal or semiformal plantings. It does not permit the easy use of the beautiful and seemingly casual informal planting that goes so splendidly with gentle slopes and flowing contours.

Poorly landscaped, a flat lot can be a horror. Straight lines of paths and plantings cross it without apparent purpose or, worse still, meaningless, silly curves may

LAWNS

O. M. Scott and Sons Co.

A good way to get even grades on slopes or level ground is to sight along T-shaped pieces of wood with cross pieces at right angles with uprights.

be introduced to produce "artistic" effects.

This is not to say that perfectly level panels of well-kept turf are not grand when well located or that flat terraces in the immediate vicinity of the house and at "overlooks," for example, are not in good taste. I merely emphasize that they should be accepted only after careful thought and that in many places contours are preferable. Not any old contours, of course, but those that are practical as well as pleasing. Too-steep grades present their own difficulties and contoured ground, badly landscaped, can be pretty awful, too; but it is harder to do a bad job of landscaping it.

If your lot is not level, develop it in such a way that its natural grades are retained wherever feasible and let any necessary modifications be in keeping with them. Don't buck Nature, work with her.

The surface to aim for should roll or flow in smooth, pleasing slopes that merge imperceptibly without sudden changes of grade or direction. But be practical about it. Arrange the grades so that they present no very special difficulties, as, for example, extraordinary steep ones may do. Let the lawn slope gently away from the house for at least 10 or 12 feet so that surface water drains away (a matter of particular importance when the ground is frozen). Where paths must go arrange minor valleys or, alternatively, let the paths follow natural depressions.

These recommendations are not to be

1883

LAWNS

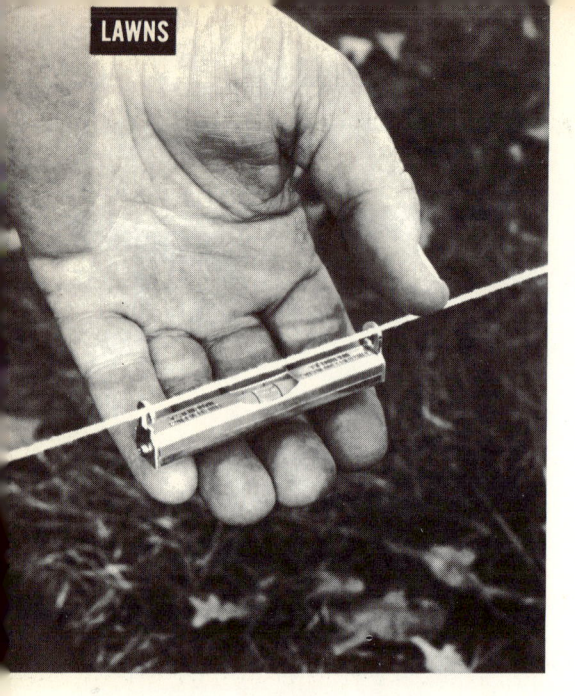

Line or string level is inexpensive instrument for determining levels. Bubble is centered when level.

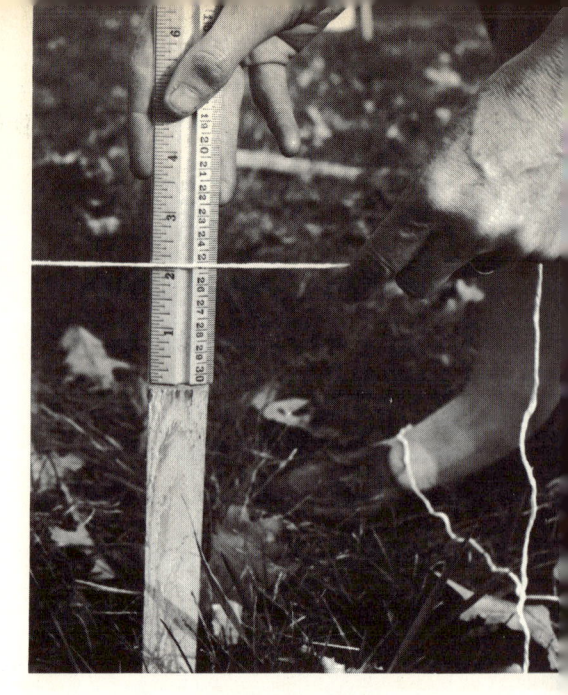

As one operator determines if bubble in line is centered, the other raises or lowers end of string.

taken to preclude the possibility of having paths leading to high points of vantage; the thing to remember is that they should follow the apparently easiest way to their objectives. Curves or turns made without obvious reason or a hill climbed when an easier way is apparent are bad. Functionalism in landscape grading brings its own beauty as it does in so many forms of art.

If your lot is flat don't regard it as impossible. In flat country it is natural that it should be this way and a perfectly level garden in a naturally flat-land region never looks out of place, as such gardens may do when artificially created in hilly or rolling country.

But added interest can often be given to a level lot by contouring it slightly. The effect must not be extreme. Err by doing little rather than much. No hills or scooped-out depressions, obviously the work of the bulldozer, but the gentlest of rises and barely perceptible hollows, the latter always with outlets so that surface water doesn't collect.

By having the higher land where you will plant trees and tall shrubbery and the lower where free sweeps of lawn and low-growing plants are to be, you will accentuate and improve the effect.

When grading operations are finished there should be an even layer of good topsoil overlying the subsoil. It should be a minimum six inches thick and better eight or more. This even distribution cannot be attained by having a bulldozer, scoop or other implement or tool move the surface soil only. If this is all that is done when

When grades are too severe, lawn is scalped or partly scalped at area "a" or left too tall at area "b."

1884

LAWNS

Grading operations should begin by establishing levels from base of a building or other fixed point.

When using line level without an assistant, weight ends of line and hang them over ends of stakes.

the grading is completed the topsoil will be disproportionately thin in the hollows and thick at the elevations.

To avoid this, strip the topsoil first. Pile it either nearby or where change of grade is to be made. Then grade the subsoil to the desired contours but six inches or more (depending upon the depth of topsoil to be put back over it) below the finish grade.

Topsoil is valuable. Save all you have. It is worth going to considerable trouble to do this. If your house has a cellar you may find topsoil under subsoil against the house or nearby. This is where the builder dumped excavation material on the ground without first stripping the topsoil. It is a common practice. In your grading operations take care to correct this and bring all available topsoil to the surface.

Grades can sometimes be established by eye alone. Where natural rolling effects are the objective, this is often the best way. In critical areas, for example near the house and where the surface is to be reasonably level but drainage in a particular direction must be assured, more precise methods are needed. The eye, unaided, can be very deceiving.

You can establish the grades for a garden of moderate extent with simple tools. If the area is large and distances of more than a hundred feet are involved, it may be desirable to have grade stakes set by someone skilled in the use of a surveyor's level or a transit, although this is not always necessary. To grade without a surveyor's level or a transit (both costly instruments) proceed as follows:

When changes of grade are smoothly curved, as areas "c" and "d," mower cuts grass to even heights.

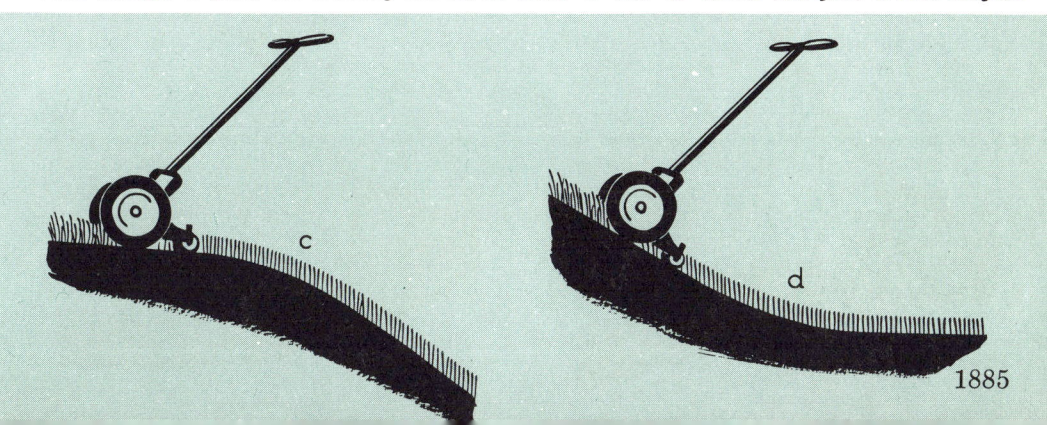

1885

LAWNS

Leveling the ground with a straightedge and a mason's level is a simple and accurate procedure.

Bubble in a small glass tube in center of mason's level indicates whether the straightedge is level.

Take a line (or string) level (obtainable from a hardware store for less than a dollar), a length of mason's twine, a wooden mallet (or a hammer and piece of board) and a number of stout stakes of lengths that allow their tops to stick six inches above finish grade after being driven a foot or so into the ground. Mark each stake clearly, six inches from its top, with a horizontal pencil mark. Begin at some established feature such as the front door step, the sidewalk or road or the base of a large, well placed tree and drive one of the stakes into the ground until the pencil mark is at the level you want the finish grade to be. If you use a hammer for driving the stake hold a board on top of the stake when you strike it to prevent splitting.

Ten to twenty feet away, along the line of the grade you are establishing, drive another stake with its pencilled line (as nearly as you can judge) as much lower or higher than the pencil mark on the first as you wish the fall or rise to be. If you wish a perfectly level grade, set stakes with their pencil marks level with each other.

Now determine exactly the relative levels of the marks by holding the mason's line fairly taut (it need not be stretched tightly) between the stakes, touching the top of each. If you are working alone you can wind the line around a nail set in the top of each stake or weight its end and hang it over the top of the stake, otherwise have someone assist you by holding the line. Hook the level on at the center of the line. Its bubble indicates which stake, if either, is higher than the other. By raising or lowering one end of the line until the bubble rests at the center of glass containing it, you determine any difference in grade that exists between tops of the stakes. This is the same as the difference in grades between the pencil marks. Raise or lower the second stake until the pencil mark is set where you want the finish grade of the lawn to be.

Use Mason's Level

Follow the procedure described above except in the following particulars. Instead of line level and mason's line, use a mason's (or carpenter's) level and a straightedge. The latter may be a board six to twelve feet long. One edge must be perfectly straight and the center portion of the opposite edge, for at least two feet, absolutely parallel with it. Set the stakes slightly nearer together than the length of the straightedge. To check their relative heights, rest the long straight edge of the straightedge across the tops of both stakes, set the level on the parallel portion of the upper edge. Raise or lower one end of the straightedge until the bubble is centered. Measure the differences in levels (if any) and adjust the stakes so that the pencil marks on them indicate where the finish

1886

LAWNS

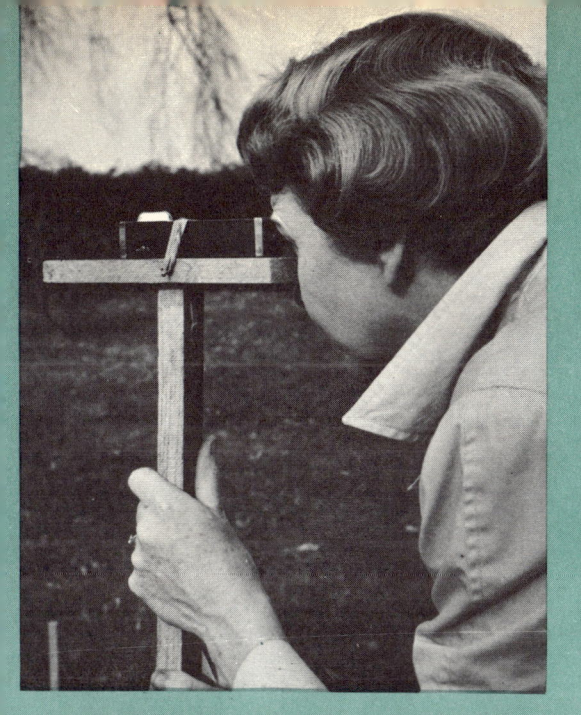

A sighting level makes it easy to determine grades over considerable distances and costs very little.

A surveyor's level, on the other hand, is a more costly and extremely accurate method of leveling.

grade is to be. Do measuring job carefully.

A hand sighting level is an inexpensive instrument that enables levels to be determined over a considerable distance with little effort. Use it with two simple, homemade gadgets: one, a measuring rod, eight to ten feet long, clearly marked in feet and inches (lesser gradations if close work is to be done); the other a stake about an inch and a half square with a six-inch piece of board nailed squarely across its top to form a platform. The length of the stake, plus the thickness of the platform, plus the distance from the bottom of the sighting level to its center line of sight (about half an inch) should be a specific length; four and a half is convenient when leveling grade stakes that stick six inches out of the ground.

Tie the level to the top of the platform with a string fastened to a couple of nails driven on opposite sides into its edges or loop a stout rubber band around level and platform. Have an assistant hold the measuring rod vertically with its end touching the top of one grade stake. Place the bottom end of the stake attached to the platform on top of another grade stake. Hold the platform stake vertically and look through the eyepiece of the level toward the measuring stake. Move the stake you are holding until the bubble you see centers exactly on the center line of the scale that is visible at the same time. The point on the measuring rod held by the assistant that coincides with the center line of the scale you see is then level with it. By reading the height of that point on the measuring rod the difference in levels, if any, between the tops of the two grade stakes is apparent.

Your grading of the subsoil need not be as exact as the finished surface of the lawn but it should approximate it closely. Make sure that no water-collecting hollows are left because these may result in wet swales where it will be difficult to grow good grass. When you are grading provide for good under-drainage. It is relatively easy to do then, more difficult and costly after the lawn is established.

If the subsoil is porous and the water table is low, there will be no difficulties on this score. But if free water stands near the surface or if the subsoil is clayey and more or less impervious you may have problems. In the latter case make sure that all surfaces slope so that water drains from them.

If water stands on or near surface install agricultural tile drains, making sure they rest on a firm well-packed bottom so there is no danger of their sinking or getting out of line after they are installed. These drains will normally be set a foot or more below the top of the rough grade, 18 to 24 inches below the finish grade.

On small plots, grading may be done with a shovel and wheelbarrow; for larger areas

1887

GRADING PROFILES FOR LAWNS

This type of grading requires more soil, provides for nearly level area near house, then long slope.

This provides for nearly flat area near house by creating a terrace supported by masonry wall. Excess soil from below terrace is used above wall.

This provides for a nearly level area near house, then two slopes. New grade is made by cutting and filling, using earth from high area to fill in.

This provides for nearly level area near house, then gently rolling hill which gives lawn feeling of spaciousness. Soil moved from high to low areas.

- - - - - - - original grade
━━━━━━━ new grade

When land slopes toward house, regrade so that a nearly level area slopes from house for drainage.

a bulldozer, scoop or other suitable implement is most practical. Whatever means is employed, if the ground is clayey avoid working on it when it is wet and sticky if at all possible. Unfortunately, this plan of action cannot always be followed if arrangements must be made beforehand for bulldozers, etc., or when such implements have to be used when it is convenient for them to be spared from other jobs. During the grading of the subsoil remove any large stones and builders' debris.

After the rough grading is finished to a predetermined height beneath the finish grade, do whatever you can to improve the subsoil before placing the topsoil over it. Grasses root deeply in agreeable undersoil and deeply rooted lawns survive droughts and other hardships much better than turf with its roots in the upper few inches only. If possible add organic matter such as compost (it need not be well decayed for this purpose) in quantity and, if the soil is acid, a heavy application of ground limestone. A three- or four-inch layer of coarse coal cinders worked into really heavy clay

GRADING PROCEDURE

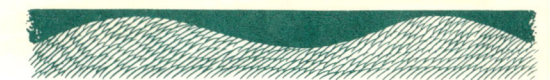

(Drawing left) Original grade. (Right) If surface is merely leveled, topsoil is unevenly distributed, leaving thin or bare areas where grass will not grow well, and deep soil areas.

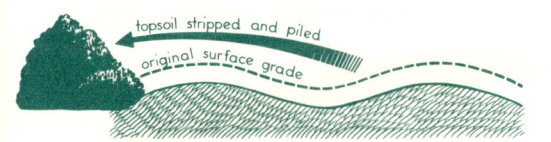

(Left) Correct way to grade is to first strip off the topsoil and pile it nearby or where no change of grade is to be made. (Right) Then grade subsoil so it is leveled off.

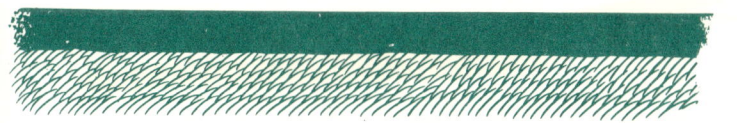

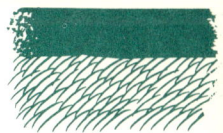

(Left) After subsoil has been graded and made level, replace the topsoil in even layers. (Right) Key to these drawings.

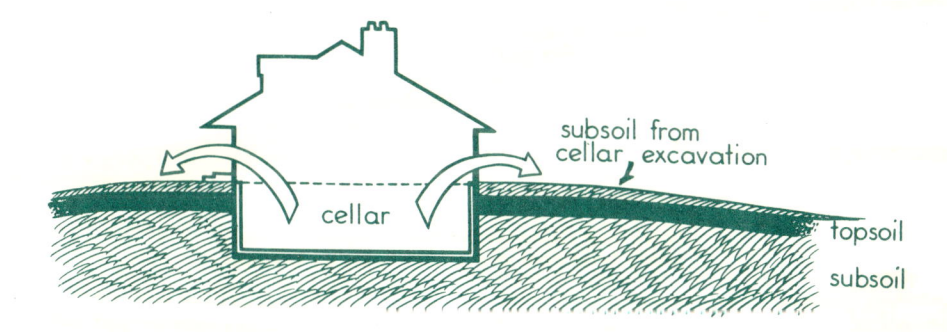

Builders often distribute subsoil over topsoil. Prevent this if possible; if not, correct this before making a lawn.

is highly beneficial in opening it up, improving aeration and drainage. Remember, this is the last time you will have opportunity to improve the subsoil. Then spade, or plow or rototill the upper surface to a depth of six inches, mixing thoroughly with the soil the added ingredients and taking care, of course, not to disturb any drains.

Final surface grading is done when the area is raked smooth just before the seeds are sown or the turf is laid, but that consists of very minor adjustments. For all practical purposes the rough grade that results from the spreading and smoothing out of the topsoil is that of the finished lawn.

First firm the sub-grade by treading it or rolling it, but do not pack it hard. Then rough-rake its surface so that a good bond will be established between subsoil and topsoil. Spread the topsoil to such a depth that after settling it will be at the level you want. Figure a six-inch layer of loose topsoil will sink from one to two inches when compacted, therefore to end with a six-inch depth of topsoil, you must spread a seven- to eight-inch layer of loose soil.

Bulldozers and other heavy mechanical equipment are vital to building activities but pack down soil.

Where heavy machinery has packed down subsoil, it should be loosened before topsoil is spread.

This requires 22 or 23 cubic feet of topsoil for each 1,000 square feet of surface. When you price good topsoil you will understand why I stressed the wisdom of saving all topsoil present on the site. If you don't have sufficient topsoil to insure a good lawn, bring it in from elsewhere or undertake a program of soil improvement and conditioning.

This will take a little time but to attempt lawn making where the topsoil is too poor or too shallow is courting failure.

Where slopes are too steep for the particular garden effect wanted, terracing is necessary. Terraces need not be perfectly level. It is better if they have at least a slight fall and in many places the gradient may, with advantage, be considerable.

Terraces may be supported by solid masonry walls, dry walls (walls built without cement) or by steeply-sloped banks appropriately planted with creeping junipers, cotoneasters, creeping roses, English ivy or other suitable plants. Grass banks are sometimes used but are difficult to maintain if the slope is more than one foot in height for each three feet horizontally.

When grading for terraces try to establish main levels between high and low ground. If this is done the material excavated from the high ground will be available to fill the low places and purchase of fill made unnecessary or reduced. Preserve all topsoil and grade in such a way that when the job is finished there is an even layer over the whole area.

So far as humanly possible preserve all valuable trees. Consider this when deciding what contours the ground shall have. Place substantial guards around endangered specimens during bulldozer and trucking operations. Instruct contractors and operators to exercise all possible care. Then pray for the best.

Scraping soil from over roots and cutting substantial portions off root systems, seriously injures trees and may result in their death. Cutting roots too deeply and too close to the trunk on one side of a tree may weaken its hold so that it is likely to blow down in a storm.

Adding fill over tree roots should be done with caution. They need air to live. A comparatively thin layer of clayey soil, packed tight, can cut off the supply to the extent that the trees slowly suffocate. It may take a few years for them to die but they surely will if the air supply is seriously reduced. Changes of grade that result in flooding the soil in which tree roots ramify with water is also disastrous; avoid it.

Use Porous Fill

A fill of loose, porous soil (of a sandy or gravelly character) can be put over roots to a depth of about a foot without harm, provided the soil is not heaped around the trunk. To prevent this, build a well wall of stone or brick around the trunk and about 12 inches from it. If you must fill over roots to a depth of more than eight inches with heavy soil or 12 inches with porous soil, take the following precautions. If the depth of fill exceeds those mentioned by no more than three or four inches, cover the area containing the roots and some little distance beyond with a layer of largish stones; over these place smaller stones, gravel or coal cinders to within eight inches of the finish grade, then add the topsoil.

Should you be forced to fill to a depth of 18 inches or more over roots, take spe-

LAWNS

Where fill is placed over roots of tree to be saved, a protective well is built around the trunk.

Trees to be saved should be protected from damage by machinery. Use wood frame, corrugated metal.

cial precautions. Bare the surface roots from the trunk to their farthest extent, usually just beyond the spread of the branches. If the soil is heavy and packed, loosen it slightly with the prongs of a fork but don't spade it over because that breaks too many roots. Apply a dressing of organic fertilizer to the loosened soil.

From close to the trunk to the outer circumference of the roots, lay six (in the case of a very large tree, eight) lines of four-inch agricultural drain tiles. These should radiate from the trunk like the spokes of a wheel. Make sure the drains slope downward as they spread from the trunk at the rate of about one eighth of an inch to the foot. Now connect the ends of these spokes with a circle of drain tiles to form, as it were, the rim of the wheel. This rim encircles the tree at the outermost limit of its roots, ordinarily just beyond the drip line of the outer branches. If there is any danger of the soil being waterlogged, lay another row of agricultural tile from a spot on the rim where one of the spokes join it in a downward sloping direction to some outlet away from the tree.

Where the spokes connect with the rim, set six-inch glazed tile drainpipes vertically with their tops level with the ground surface and their lower ends opening into the agricultural tiles. Unlike the agricultural tiles, the glazed pipes should have sockets so that the end of one fits snugly into that of the next, and the joints should be cemented. The ends of the agricultural tiles are butted together and are not cemented. The vertical pipes may be filled with rough stones or left open. In either case their upper ends are covered with grids.

The chief purpose of the tiles is to carry air to the roots, but they also serve to drain away any superfluous water and also provide (through the gridded surface openings) a ready means of watering and fertilizing the tree. Watering in droughts, and annual fertilization are helpful, too. •

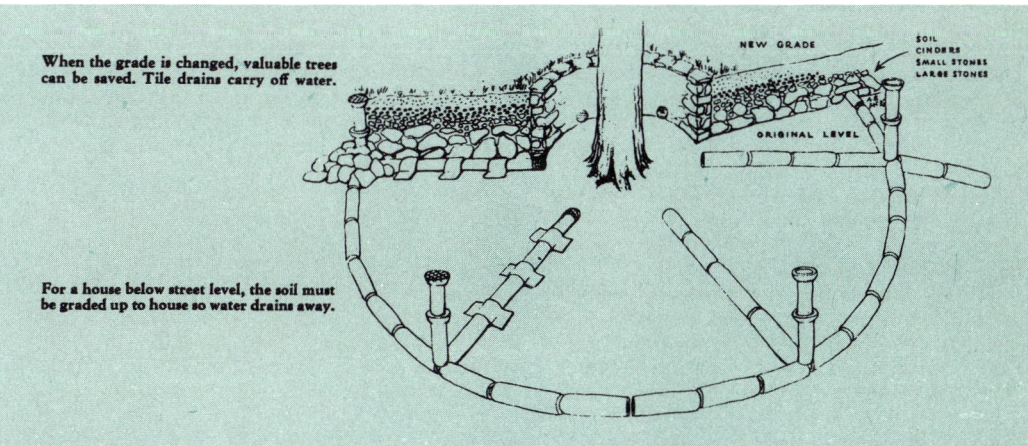

When the grade is changed, valuable trees can be saved. Tile drains carry off water.

For a house below street level, the soil must be graded up to house so water drains away.

1891

LAWNS

New York Botanical Garden
Drains in position before cinders or gravel cover them. Depth of trench is adjusted to the white line placed directly above the trench.

DRAINING
... the way to handle wet soil

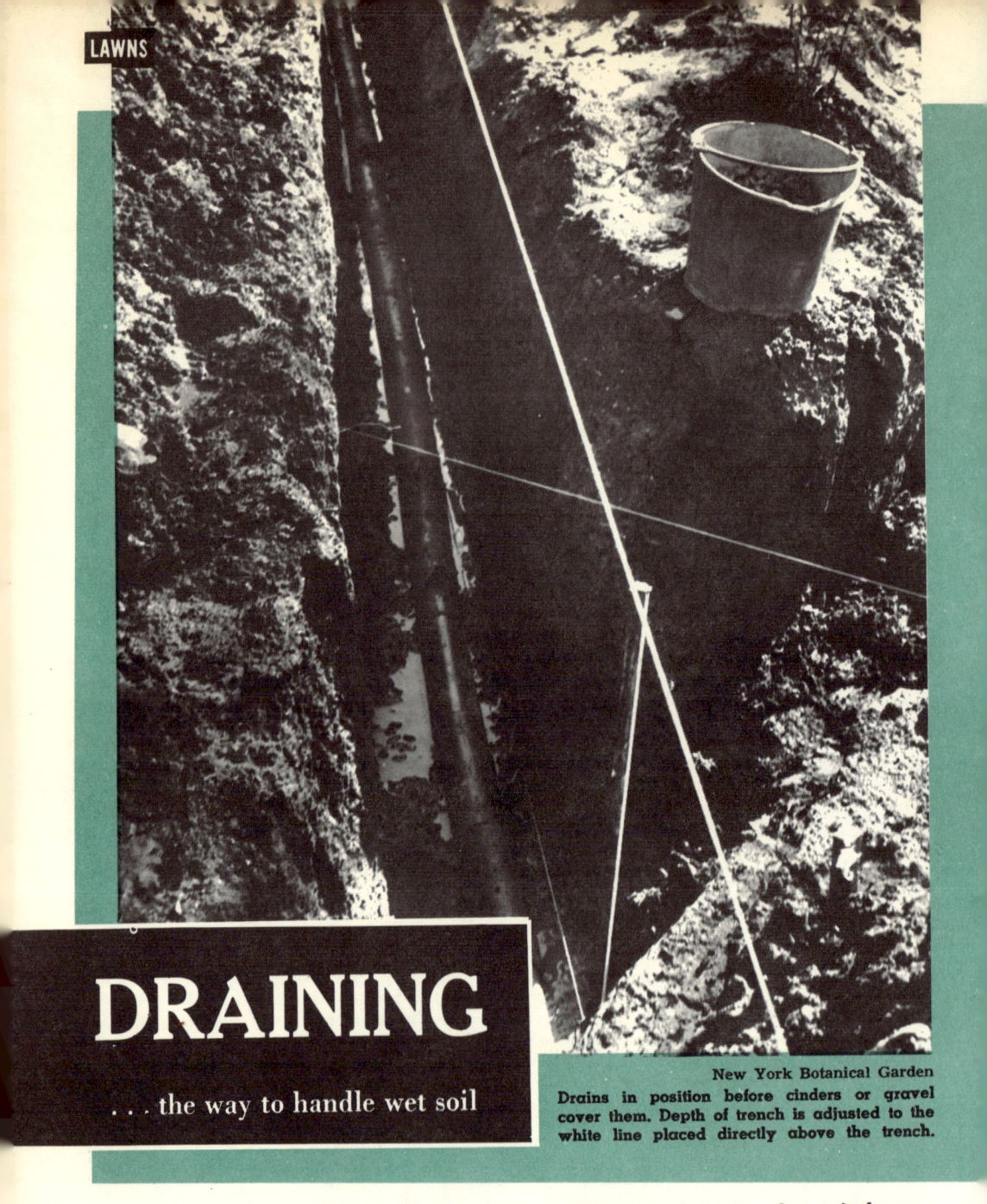

GRASS will not grow well in waterlogged soil. Its roots need air as well as moisture. The ideal is a film of water surrounding each soil particle and air in the spaces between. It is as though you dipped a bunch of grapes in oil or molasses, lifted it out and held it to drain. Around each grape a film of the liquid clings, even after draining, but there are considerable air spaces between the individual grapes.

Except in swamps and bogs where free-standing water is at (or close to) the surface, this is the condition that normally exists in the upper soil. But if you dig down deep enough you will, unless you hit bed-rock first, come to a level below which the spaces between the soil particles are filled with water. The top of this free standing water—its surface, is the water table. Holes you dig fill with water to this level.

In some places you have to go down

LAWNS

Areas where water lies in shallow pools for hours or days after rain need sub-surface drainage.

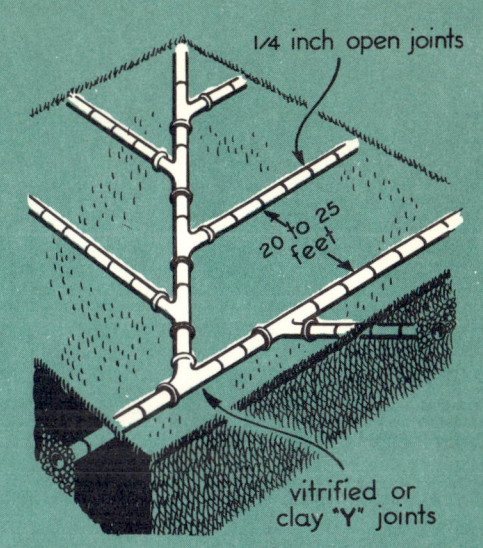

This drawing shows an effective lawn drainage plan. Laterals may be closer or farther apart.

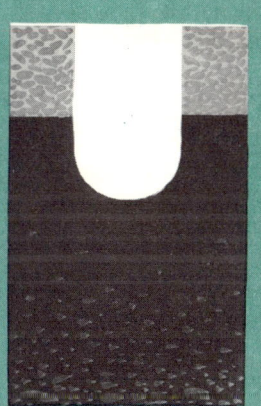

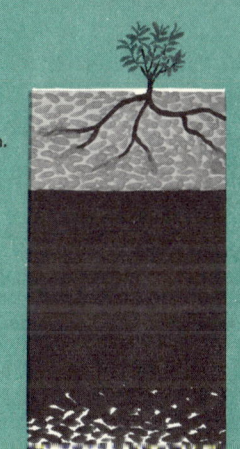

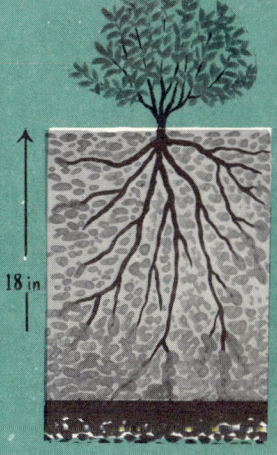

Dark areas in drawings above show soil underlayer. Do not plant where underlayer is waterlogged and impervious as in Figure 1. Hole may be dug deeper, filled with stones to reach porous underlayer, as in Figure 2. Poor root development (Figure 3) is result of only six inches between ground level and water table. For healthy plant, soil should drain to 18 inches as shown in Figure 4.

many feet to reach the water table; in others it is closer to the ground surface. Provided it is not nearer than a foot, you can maintain a very fine lawn without artificially draining the soil; but for most trees, shrubs, perennials and vegetables it is better that the water table be not closer than one and a half or two feet to the surface.

If the water table is too high, make sure of the cause before going to the expense of installing drains. Perhaps a thin, impermeable layer of clay or hardpan overlying porous subsoil is responsible. Breaking through this with a subsoil plow or by deep digging will relieve the situation. In extreme cases such thin layers can be made permeable to water by dynamiting, but this should be done only by professionals.

Another possibility is that the water table

LAWNS

New York Botanical Garden
Tools for draining: spades for digging out dirt, wire hook on pole for lowering drains into trench.

Tile drainpipes are lowered into position, then are covered with cinder and gravel, topped by soil.

is high because the land lies low along the bank of a pond, lake or stream. If this is the case no good can come from installing drains at a level lower than the surface of the water. Other methods of overcoming the difficulty must be followed. The two most practicable are raising the level of the ground by filling and digging open ditches, 15 to 20 feet apart, leading to the pond, lake or stream. These ditches do not lower the permanent water table, but they prevent its rising temporarily above the level of the nearby water following heavy rains and they help to aerate the soil.

The latter is important. One of the reasons that grasses and many other plants fail in waterlogged soil is because it becomes sour as a result of the accumulation of poisonous substances coming from organic matter that decays without sufficient air. Fortunately there is usually enough movement of underground water near the banks of lakes, ponds and streams to prevent its becoming stagnant and sour from accumulated poisons. Because of this, for some few feet back from the bank, you are likely to be able to have healthy lawn even though the water table is closer to the surface than 12 inches. This is fortunate, for it permits the maintenance of gently sloping banks even to the water's edge.

If the water table cannot be lowered by other means, and an outlet can be found into which to drain the surplus, an installed drainage system is a certain answer to waterlogged ground. Provided the job is properly done, it is sure to work and continue effective for many decades. It is a cure, not a palliative.

Finding an Outlet

The outlet, which must be the lowest point of the drainage system, may be a pond, lake, stream, ditch or sewer. In small areas it is sometimes possible to use a dry well as an outlet, provided the dry well is located in porous ground, but before doing this you must be very sure that the well is capable of disposing of the amount of water the drains will bring to it, and you can be easily deceived about this. Dry wells as outlets for drainage systems cannot be generally recommended.

It is possible to make drains of stones, brushwood and other materials, but by far the best are agricultural tiles of unglazed earthenware. Each is a foot long. Those having three-inch or four-inch bores are satisfactory. If the area to be drained is

LAWNS

With drainpipe segments partially covered, one is shown removed to illustrate how water flows.

Main drains need not necessarily be made of tile. Here is drain built of stones, carefully graded.

large, a number of lateral drains may be connected with a main drain having a six-inch bore.

Having located an outlet into which you can drain the superfluous water make a plan of the drainage system-to-be. Do this accurately, bearing in mind the following facts. All drains must slope gradually upward away from the outlet. The fall should be from four to six inches or more in each 100 feet (if you are in a tight spot and are mighty careful, you can get away with three inches in a hundred). The drains should be spaced 18 to 30 feet apart and run in straight lines. Where they connect with a main drain they should do so at an acute angle in the direction of the flow of the main drain, never at right angles. Side drains should never be brought into a main drain directly opposite each other. Stagger them so that the flow of water from one lateral doesn't interfere with that of another. Avoid, whenever possible, running drains where the roots of trees are likely to get into and clog them.

Because grades can be very deceiving to the eye you must check carefully the amount of fall (slope) given the bottoms of the trenches in which the drains are laid. It will not do to merely measure downward from the surface because the ground itself is likely to be irregular. Go about it in this way:

Stretch a line (string) taut where each drain is to go and fasten its ends to stakes. Next, at the lowest point of the drain (its outlet) drive a stake into the ground on each side of the line and about two feet from it. Let these project about one foot. Make sure that the tops of the two stakes are perfectly level by placing a straightedge from one to the other and checking with a level. At distances of 10 or 20 feet along the line, place similar pairs of stakes, always checking that the tops of each pair are level.

But each successive pair must be slightly higher than the pair before. The amount of this rise must be the same as the amount of fall the drain is to have. To illustrate: suppose you have decided upon a fall of six inches in every 100 feet. That is equivalent to six tenths of an inch every 10 feet or one and two tenths inches every 20 feet. If your stakes are 10 feet apart, each successive pair must be six tenths of an inch higher than last pair; if 20 feet apart, one-and-two-tenths inches higher.

You may establish the correct height of successive pairs of stakes in various ways:

LAWNS

with a surveyor's level or a transit if one is available, with a straightedge and level, or with a line level. There are other methods. The important thing is that the measurements be accurate.

If you use a straightedge, 10-foot spacing between pairs of stakes is ample. Beginning at the outlet end, place it with one end resting on top of a stake and the other on top of a stake of the next pair. Now insert between the stake that should be lowest and the straightedge a small block of wood of the exact thickness that the difference in levels should be (six-tenths of an inch of the fall is to be six inches in 100 feet and the pairs of stakes are 10 feet apart). Check the top of the straightedge with a level. It should be perfectly horizontal. If it is not adjust the height of the stake that should be highest until it is. Repeat the procedure between the second and third pair of stakes, the third and fourth and so on to the end of the drain.

Make certain that the tops of each pair of stakes are perfectly level.

If you use a line level, the pairs of stakes may be 20 feet apart. On top of the stake that should be lowest place a block of a thickness equal to the difference in heights between successive pairs of stakes (one and two tenths inches if the fall is to be six inches per 100 feet). Stretch a thin line with line level hooked at about its center between the top of the block and the top of a stake of the next pair farther up the line. Read the level. It should indicate that the top of the block and the top of the stake are level. If it does not, adjust the upper pair of stakes until they are level.

Locating Trench Bottom

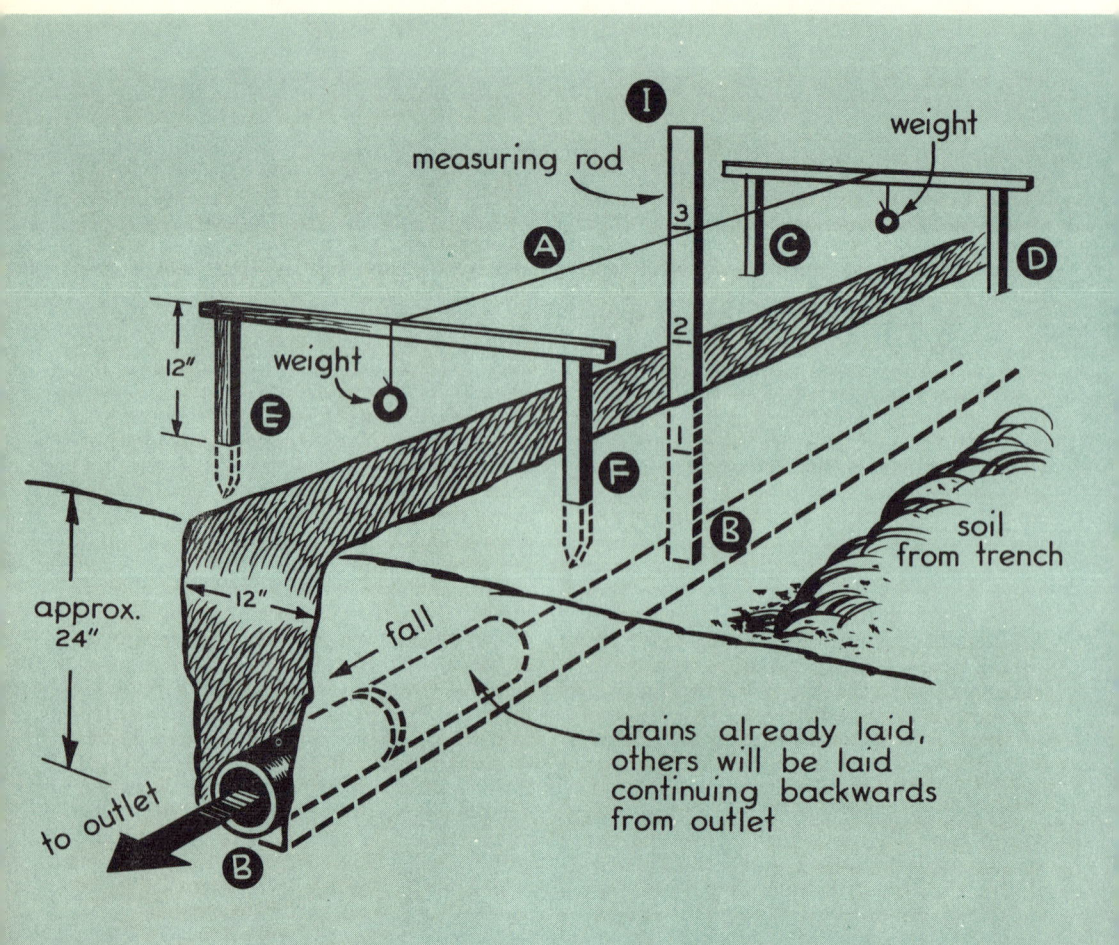

Use the stakes to establish the bottom of the trench as follows: Lay a stiff (non-bending) cross bar across the tops of one pair of stakes, and a cross bar of exactly the same thickness across the tops of the next pair.

Stretch a line, a foot or two longer than the distance between pairs of stakes and with a weight attached at each end, from cross bar to cross bar directly over the trench. The weighted ends of the line should hang over the cross bars and draw the line taut. At all points the bottom of the trench should be an equal distance below the line. Determine the distance below the line at the outlet. Mark a measuring rod appropriately and use this to check the trench depth at all points.

For draining large areas, machines are available that cut the trenches in which pipes are laid. Hand digging is used for smaller scale operations. If the latter is employed use narrow spades for taking out the lower part of each trench; this reduces the total amount of soil to be moved. And the more you take out the more must be put back.

Begin at the outlet and work backward. This allows water, which would otherwise collect in the trenches, to escape. Don't dig deeper than the exact level at which the drains are to be placed. The maintenance of a hard bottom under the pipes is important. If you dig deeper than they are to be set then back-fill under them; subsidence is likely to occur later and interfere with the water flow. A scoop is useful for clearing out the bottoms of the trenches.

Butt the ends of the drains together. Don't cement them. You may cover the joints with tar paper to prevent fine clay or silt finding its way in, but this is not necessary provided a three- or four-inch layer of cinders, crushed stone or gravel is placed around and over the drains, and this should be done for best results. Next fill in with soil taking care that the subsoil is placed underneath and the topsoil on top. •

(Drawing right) Drain outlet is shown here. If outlet is exposed, cover it with a grid or wire netting to prevent entry of insects or vermin, keep the drain clean.

(Drawing left) Construction of the bottom of a trench with even fall. Key to drawing: (A) white line for measuring depth of trench (B) bottom of trench (C, D, E, F) opposite pairs of stakes, all level. E and F are slightly lower than C and D to permit fall (G, H) movable cross bars of same thickness (I) measuring rod to check distance of bottom of trench from the white line.

LAWNS

GETTING READY FOR PLANTING

...it means getting the soil into condition

(Photo below) Deep spading plus liberal addition of organic matter prepares soil for good lawn. (Photo across page) Top soil is spread if necessary.

New York Botanical Garden

LET'S ASSUME that the area where you plan to make your new lawn does not need draining or that drains have been installed, that the grade is satisfactory, and that you are not going to bring in additional soil. What needs doing before the seed is sown or turf is planted? The answer depends upon the kind of soil and its condition.

If what you have is obviously topsoil and reasonably good to the depth of six inches or more, read on.

Nearly all soils (the exceptions are peaty soils and mucks) benefit from mixing them with liberal amounts of decayed organic matter. The presence of this in generous amounts is of tremendous importance in the cultivation of good turf. As this is the last chance you will have to put organic matter beneath the surface take advantage of the opportunity. If you can possibly get rotted manure, compost, sedge peat (commercial humus), leaf mold or peat moss in quantities sufficient to spread a three-inch layer over the whole surface, do so. Unless your soil is humus-rich don't try to get away with less than two inches, especially if your soil is sandy. Well in advance of

LAWNS

American Agricultural Chemical Co.

sowing turn the organic matter under with a plow, rototiller, spade or spading fork, mixing it thoroughly with the upper six inches of soil. If you can get organic matter in greater amounts than those suggested, mix it with the upper eight inches of soil.

If your soil is very clayey, mix in, together with the organic matter, a couple of inches of sifted coal cinders (not fine ash) of a size that pass through a half inch screen and consist of particles which feel gritty when rubbed between the fingers. If cinders are not available use coarse sand. Should the soil be very sandy, as it often is near seashores, mix in, in addition to organic matter, three or four inches of clayey soil if you can possibly obtain it. If you can get only a limited amount of clayey soil mix it with the top couple of inches.

Have a soil test made (your County Agricultural Agent will do this or advise you where you may have it done). If it shows lime is needed (and in most areas where rainfall exceeds 40 inches a year it will be), spread ground limestone or hydrated lime in amounts necessary to bring the pH of the soil to between 6 and 7.

Personally, I prefer limestone to hydrated lime because it is effective longer. Mix it very thoroughly with the

LAWNS

O. M. Scott and Sons Co.
A garden tractor, like the one being used above, facilitates the soil for sowing a green manure crop. The tractor does not mix the soil as deeply as a plow, spade or rototiller but does the job nicely.

upper four to six inches. Don't feel that this second mixing is a waste of labor. Working and reworking the soil in preparation for lawn making is highly beneficial. It brings the layer in which most roots will be into a fine uniform condition conducive to even growth. Nothing is more likely to result in spotty development of grass than lack of uniformity of the soil. Don't tolerate clods or patches of clayey soil, wads or masses of nearly pure organic matter, areas of unmixed sand or subsoil, or large stones and rocks within a few inches of the surface. Remove builder's debris as well as dead stumps, tree roots, etc. Rotting wood develops fungi (not usually kinds harmful to living plants) that give rise to toadstools which may mar the surface of the lawn periodically for many years.

Some heavy soils benefit from treating with synthetic soil conditioners such as Krillium, but worth while results are not always obtained. Krillium is not a fertilizer. Improvement from its use comes from its ability to "glue" together extremely fine soil particles into larger granules. When this occurs the soil behaves like coarser soil. It permits the passage of air and water and is less likely to become pasty and excessively sticky from walking on it. The manufacturers recommend that for garden use these conditioners be applied after the soil has been brought to a granulated, friable condition suitable for sowing grass seed, not to unimproved sticky clays and other soils in poor condition. The chief advantages claimed are that they stabilize and make longer lasting the desirable granular structure of the soil. Clearly, they are not needed on sandy and similar soils.

Synthetic soil conditioners are not inexpensive nor are they miracle workers that make organic matter, lime, fertilizer and work unnecessary When conditions are favorable to their use they are certainly worth considering. They may help, for example, in stopping surface soil from washing off steep slopes before the grass seedlings take hold, but investigate by small-scale trial on your own ground before investing in them heavily.

If you decide to use a synthetic soil conditioner follow the manufacturer's directions. It should be very thoroughly mixed with the upper few inches of soil.

Fertilizer will be necessary. Theoretically it is possible to determine from a soil analysis exactly which nutrients are lacking and in precisely what amounts each should be given. Practically, it doesn't work that way. In the first place, a soil test, which is simple and inexpensive to make, is not a complete analysis. A complete analysis is costly. And secondly, even a complete

LAWNS

Whitney Seed Co., Inc.
All large stones, rocks, rubble and builder's debris should be removed before the soil is fixed.

After subsoil grading is completed, at least six inches of top soil should be spread over the ground.

One to four weeks before the seed is to be sown or the grass planted, spread the fertilizer evenly.

Thoroughly mix the fertilizer with the top three or four inches of soil by raking over it vigorously.

1901

LAWNS

American Agricultural Chemical Co.
If the area to be planted is large, a good-sized spreader provides even distribution of fertilizer.

The fertilizer is then raked thoroughly and evenly into the top three or four inches of the soil.

analysis does not completely reveal the availability of the nutrients in the soil. Common sense and judgment based on experience and empirical knowledge must still play a large part in determining which fertilizers to use and in what quantities.

Nitrogen, phosphorus and potash are the elements most essential to add, and it is important that at least one half of the nitrogen be in "organic" form so that it is released comparatively slowly. Some of it may, often with advantage, be in more quickly available form, although excellent results are had from organics alone.

If you favor organics, a good treatment is 200 pounds of pulverized sheep manure and 100 pounds of bonemeal to each 1,000 square feet. If, in addition, you can spread unleached wood ashes at the rate of 35 to 50 pounds to each 1,000 square feet it is all to the good. For each 100 pounds of bonemeal you may substitute at a considerable saving in cost, 50 pounds of 48 percent superphosphate, or proportionately greater amounts of superphosphate containing less phosphorus.

If you favor mixed commercial fertilizers, and most are excellent, for each 1,000 square feet use 40 to 60 pounds of one with a 4-8-4 analysis, 30 to 50 pounds of a 5-10-5, 20 to 30 pounds of 10-6-4, and proportionate amounts of those having other analyses, basing the amounts used on the amount of nitrogen (indicated by the first figure of the analysis) that they contain.

Apply the fertilizer a week or two before sowing or planting, and rake it into the top two or three inches. Be sure to spread it evenly because although the nutrients it contains sink in the soil they move laterally scarcely at all. Uneven distribution results in some spots being underfertilized and others getting too much. Result: a patchy lawn.

About a week before or a week after spreading the fertilizer is a good time to grub-proof the lawn by mixing with its top three inches arsenate of lead at the rate of 15 to 20 pounds every 1,000 square feet. This treatment is effective for several years.

Soil Preparation Vital

You may feel that the above recommendations involve a lot of work. They do, but I know of no less thorough method of establishing a foundation for a really good lawn. Turfmen and other experts agree that thorough soil preparation, done before the lawn is sown or planted, is the cornerstone upon which good turf culture is based. If you are not prepared to go to this trouble you'll never have a first class lawn.

Actually, the preparation does not involve as much as it sounds in the telling. If you get an early start so that operations are well spaced and proceed methodically from one to the other, if you have the supplies you need at hand, and if you take every advantage the weather offers you

Rotary tillers are excellent for turning soil over deeply in preparation of lawn making, landscaping.

Unless six inches of good top soil is brought in, thin soil (such as this) benefits from green manuring.

will be surprised at the progress you make. Succeeding operations become progressively lighter as the soil gradually assumes that friendly crumbly, well-tilled state so favorable to root growth.

Scheduling operations for making the soil ready for planting, calls for thought. Here are the considerations. Early fall is by far the best time to sow seeds. Turf may be laid, plugs planted and sprigs set in spring. If green manure is to be turned under do it not later than six weeks before sowing or planting. Rotted manure, compost, humus, peat moss and other decomposed organic matter may be incorporated any time in advance of planting. Lime may be added any time before planting but not together with manure or fertilizer. Add fertilizer one to four weeks before planting but not at the same time as lime or arsenate of lead. Arsenate of lead may be added any time provided the soil is not turned over deeply afterward. By preparing the soil, except for the spreading and incorporation of fertilizer, a month or more in advance of the fall sowing date weed seeds (including crab grass) have an opportunity to germinate and you can destroy the seedlings by cultivation or chemicals. This assures a clean seed bed.

A good timetable for fall lawn making is: early August, mix in organic matter, cinders, sand and clay according to needs of soil. One week later incorporate lime and arsenate of lead if needed, and a week after that mix in synthetic soil conditioner if you are using it. Late August or early September mix in fertilizer. Mid-September sow grass.

If the lawn is to be completed in spring mix in organic matter, cinders, sand and clay, according to needs, as early as possible, preferably the fall before and lime, if needed, a week later. Mix in arsenate of lead, if needed, two to three weeks before sowing or planting, fertilizer a week later. If a synthetic soil conditioner is to be used mix it in just before sowing or planting.

Beginning From Scratch

If your soil is deep enough (at least eight inches) to carry a lawn, but of such poor quality that the addition of decayed organic matter, in amounts you can afford, fertilizer and lime will not make it suitable for growing turf, you can remedy the situation without buying topsoil. It takes time but it can be done. Even subsoil can be converted to excellent topsoil within a year or two. And subsoil, or subsoil covered with a thin layer of passably good topsoil, is what many homeowners inherit from builders. This is particularly likely to be true in "development" type houses where extensive grading operations have taken place. Rascally builders have actually been known to strip off good topsoil, sell most of it or use it elsewhere, and spread a thin layer back on the original site. Others simply bury topsoil or hopelessly mix it

LAWNS

Monsanto Chemical Co.
Heavy soils tend to remain in lumps when spaded, benefit from organic matter and gritty materials.

Light soils tend to fall apart and crumble when spaded, also benefit greatly from organic matter.

with poor undersoil. On other sites little or no good topsoil exists when the builder begins. Whatever the cause, if your topsoil is thin or non-existent correct this.

Grading and drainage need first consideration. Handle these as described earlier in this book. Lack of sufficient organic matter is the next hurdle. Scale it by using all compost, leaf mold, peat moss, manure, etc. you can possibly get and supplement it by a concentrated program of green manuring.

Green manuring means growing cover crops especially for the purpose of turning them under and converting them in the soil into humus. The humus is formed by the decay of the extensive root systems as well as the tops. To induce cover crops to make maximum growth, add fertilizer before each crop and lime if a soil test indicates its need.

Begin your soil improvement program at any time. Lime if necessary and spread a complete fertilizer at the rate of about 50 pounds to each 1,000 square feet if it is a 5-10-5, or if it is of some other analysis at rates proportionate to the amount of nitrogen contained.

Mix this with the top three or four inches of soil then sow the cover crop. If it is late summer or fall use winter rye (two quarts per 1,000 square feet). If spring use spring rye (two quarts per 1,000 square feet) or Canada field peas (two quarts per 1,000 square feet). If it is summer use soy beans (two quarts per 1,000 square feet), crimson clover (one pound per 1,000 square feet) or buckwheat (two quarts per 1,000 square feet).

It isn't necessary to rake the surface perfectly smooth before or after sowing any of these crops but rake them in so that most of the seeds are covered. When top growth is six to twelve inches tall, spade the cover crop under or bury it with plow or rototiller and immediately refertilize and sow another cover crop. Don't turn the last of the cover crops under later than six weeks before sowing the permanent grass seed.

If you begin in late summer or early fall, you should be able to grow and turn under three or four cover crops by the following August. Each will add a great quantity of humus to the soil and improve its texture and granulation tremendously. You will be utterly surprised at the evident improvement that occurs in less than a year. You must, of course, add fertilizer before each green manure crop is sown. This is not waste. It stimulates the growth of the green manure, and the nutrient elements the ferilitzer contains are stored in the tissues of the cover crop and are returned slowly to the soil as the plant remains decay, to later nourish the lawn grass.

Continue Manuring Program

Most poor soils will be sufficiently improved after one full year of green manuring to be in condition for sowing permanent lawn grass on them, but if yours isn't you can, with advantage, continue the green manuring program for a second year. An alternative plan, if the soil does not seem good enough to support a permanent turf at the end of the year and you do not feel you can wait longer before having a respectable looking lawn, is to sow in early spring a crop of Italian or domestic ryegrass (not rye). These are inexpensive and

Best soil is medium loam which breaks apart readily when pushed to and fro by the teeth of a rake.

Chemical soil conditioners, such as Krillium are employed to preserve granular structure of soil.

quickly produce a beautiful temporary lawn which you can mow and use just like any other lawn. In early August turn it under (it, too, will add considerably to the humus content of the soil) and you are then ready for sowing your permanent lawn.

If you can't tolerate even one summer with a coarse cover crop occupying the land, follow the following two-year plan of improvement. Grow alternate crops of winter rye, sown in fall and turned under in spring when six to eight inches tall, and crops of Italian ryegrass or domestic ryegrass, sown in spring and kept neatly mowed all summer and turned under in fall. Fertilize before each crop is sown and give the ryegrass two or three light applications of fertilizer during the summer. If you begin this schedule in the fall, you will turn under two crops of winter rye and two of ryegrass before you sow your permanent lawn two years later. If you begin in spring, you will turn under one crop of winter rye and two of ryegrass before you sow your permanent lawn about a year and a half later. These three or four crops will benefit your soil almost beyond recognition. They will give it a new look.

A green manuring program operated over a year or two brings other benefits besides adding humus and improving soil texture. Bacteria and other soil organisms are encouraged and given time to propogate and to change what was dead and comparatively inert earth into beautiful "living" topsoil. Not even manure and compost can do that in a hurry. If mixed with sterile subsoil even they need some time for their leavening action to work. •

After Krillium is spread evenly over surface, it is mixed in top soil with rototiller, rake or fork.

LAWNS

LAWNS FROM SEED

... it's the most common method of starting grass

1906

LAWNS

THE MOST usual method of starting a lawn is from seed. It is least costly and, given reasonable care, very satisfactory. After the soil has been made suitable for receiving the seed, the most important considerations are the kind to sow, the time to do it, how to do it and the after care required. Let me explain these matters.

There are many kinds (species and varieties) of grasses that can be raised from seeds and are useful in lawns.

Some are special purpose grasses that have only limited usefulness, others are of great significance and interest to lawn makers almost everywhere.

It is quite possible to make a lawn of one kind of grass only, and this is sometimes done. You will find advocated by some people lawns made exclusively of creeping bent, of Merion bluegrass and of other special types. When perfectly kept such greenswards can be magnificent but they need considerable upkeep and demand special knowledge on the part of their caretakers. In a one-grass lawn any other grass is a weed and must be eliminated (not always an easy task). Should a disease or insect to which the particular grass is especially susceptible gain a hold you have real trouble on your hands. The whole lawn is likely to be affected quickly, perhaps with disastrous results. In a lawn composed of several kinds of grasses the less susceptible make a brave stand against the enemy and hold out; their weaker relatives succumb.

Except for very special purposes (making a putting green for example) it is always better to sow a grass seed mixture than just one kind. In a way it is insurance. Different grasses, even different varieties of the same kind, prefer different soil conditions and often these preferences are for

After grading, fertilizing and conditioning, the new lawn area is ready for compacting by rolling or treading. Do this when earth is dry.

After compacting, surface is made smooth by pulling a harrow over it. As finished a surface as possible should be obtained. Seeding follows.

O. M. Scott and Sons Co.

LAWNS

minor variations not easy to recognize by simple soil tests. If you sow several kinds in mixture those best adapted to your soil flourish; the others expire or become minor elements in the turf. It often happens that soil and other environmental conditions, such as shade and moisture, vary from place to place in the same lawn. By sowing a mixture of grasses the varying needs of these different situations are provided for.

There are other advantages. In most cases a mixture gives more uniform greenery throughout the season than a single type of grass. This because of seasonal growth and temperature preferences. Bluegrasses thrive in the cool weather of spring and fall and go partially dormant during hot weather. Bent grasses generally make their best growth in hot weather. In dry weather fescues prosper better than other grasses. There are grasses more resistant to being walked upon than others. There are grasses valuable because they germinate and grow quickly, act as "nurses" to the slower-to-get-going kinds and then gradually die out. In the meantime they prevent erosion and help to keep weeds

O. M. Scott and Sons Co.
On small areas, a rake replaces a harrow. When raking, level surface, free soil of lumps, stones.

If you are dealing with sizable areas, a seed sowing implement saves a good deal of work. Make sure that it is adjusted so that the seed is distributed as thickly as you want, neither heavier nor lighter.

out. Almost surely a mixture of grass seeds is your best bet when making a new lawn.

Not any mixture will do. Don't buy cheap ones. Of necessity those are largely composed of the less permanent grasses, kinds least costly for the seedsmen or packager to buy. It has to be that way. Good seeds of desirable varieties are comparatively expensive. They cannot be sold to compete with cheaper types. Percentages count, even cheap seed mixtures usually contain some bluegrass and perhaps some bents and fescues. The point is in what proportions are they compared to ryegrass, timothy and fescue? A total of more than 30 percent of these and other temporary grasses is usually the maximum permissable in satisfactory lawn seed mixtures although the distinguished turf specialist Dr. Howard B. Sprague recommends a "standard mixture for soils of average to good fertility and sunny exposure" that includes 40 percent temporary grasses. This mixture consists of 45 percent Kentucky bluegrass, 10 percent colonial bent grass, 25 percent redtop, 5 percent white clover and 15 percent perennial ryegrass.

Ferry-Morse Seed Co.
For small plots of ground, hand sowing is satisfactory. Done skillfully, it is highly satisfactory.

After sowing, a light raking over to cover the seeds, then a rolling with a medium weight roller.
Ferry-Morse Seed Co.

Only if soil is dry should it be watered immediately after sowing. It's better to seed while soil's moist.
American Agricultural Chemical Co.

LAWNS

Ferry-Morse Seed Co.
In late winter this lawn has been made ready for fertilizing and sowing in the very early spring.

By sowing early in spring and by weeding and watering carefully, a good turf is grown by fall.

In most parts of the country, everywhere except the subtropical South, Kentucky bluegrass (Merion bluegrass is a variety of it) should be the foundation of mixed-seed lawns in sunny or predominantly sunny locations. It is generally the most satisfactory and permanent of general purpose lawn grass for everywhere except where considerable shade exists. For shaded lawns Chewings fescue and Illahee fescue are the real standbys. Mixtures should contain adequate amounts of these basic grasses to insure good stands.

Beware of mixtures that are advertised and offered on the basis of "quick" results. They usually contain much too high proportions of ryegrass, timothy and other quick growers of a temporary nature.

In many states the law requires that lawn seed mixtures be labeled with the names and percentages of the grasses they contain and also the percentages of germination that may be expected. These are protections for the buyer. Study them carefully when comparing prices.

There is no doubt that by far the most favorable time to sow a new lawn is early fall. Then the soil is still warm enough to stimulate growth, and the grasses make good roots before called upon to face the rigors of winter. A great advantage of fall sowing is that the young plants do not have to compete with as many different kinds of seedling weeds. Warm weather weeds, such as crab grass, do not germinate then. Another great advantage is that the grasses are established and ready to grow in earliest spring. They gain a great start on spring sown grasses and, incidentally, on weeds that begin their natural period of growth in spring. And, of course, there is usually ample time to prepare the ground for a fall sown lawn, whereas in spring the season is so rushed that all too often preparatory work must be skimped.

Spring Sowing

Don't mistake me, it is quite possible to get a good lawn from a spring sowing. But the care and attention needed to do so is greater than from a fall sowing. Two special problems that must be faced are the rapid growth of weeds and the need for more abundant watering during dry periods throughout the first summer, this latter because the roots have not penetrated as deeply as those of grasses sown the previous fall. Weeds are likely to be especially abundant if such plants flourished in the topsoil the previous year, and there is really no practical way of getting rid of them in spring before the lawn grass is sown. In preparation for fall sowing, a few weeks' repeated shallow cultivation before the grass seed is sown will clear the surface soil of most weeds.

After plowing, digging or working with a rototiller the soil will be loose to a depth

LAWNS

Warm weather weeds (such as the "pussley" weed above) mean trouble for lawns sown in late spring.

Lawn sown too late on ground infested with weed seeds is solid with "pussley" by mid-summer.

of six to ten inches. It must be compacted moderately. The best way to do this is to tread all over the surface with a sort of dancing motion in which the ball of the foot firms the ground not only at the surface but underneath. This is more effective than rolling, which tends to firm the surface only. Compacting must be done only when the soil is fairly dry. After you have trodden the soil (if the area is really large roll it instead) work the surface over with a rake until it is perfectly smooth and fine. This should be done shortly before sowing so that rain does not "cake" the ground surface after you have finally prepared it and before the seeds are sown. If rain does come after you have given this final raking and before you sow, rake the surface again to loosen it.

Let's suppose that your seed bed is in perfect condition and the seed is at hand. Now comes the business of sowing. Choose a calm day. It is impossible to sow evenly if it is breezy. Divide the seed to be sown in half, then walking in parallel paths in one direction (say north and south) sow one half as evenly as you possibly can over the whole area. When this has been accomplished sow the remaining seed over the same area walking in parallel paths at right angles to the original direction. In this way you will get the most even distribution. The sowing may be done by hand or with a mechanical seeder adjusted to let the seed fall at the density required.

If you sow by hand this is the technique. Bend your back. Take a handful of seeds. Hold them with the fingers somewhat cupped and very slightly separated. Then with your hand moving parallel with the ground and about 18 inches above it, swing your arm freely in a semi-circular motion and allow the seeds to scatter in an even, fine cloud from the upper part of the hand. Don't close your fist so tightly that the seed leaves your hand in a heavy stream from between forefinger and thumb. To secure even distribution you may find it advantageous to stretch parallel strings, six to ten feet apart (to suit your convenience) across the ground surface and to walk slowly down the center of each marked off strip as you sow, scattering the seeds from string to string. With a little practice you will have no difficulty in perfecting this technique so that you sow evenly.

After the seed has been scattered, rake it into the surface so that the seeds are covered to a depth of half an inch or so. When the whole area is sown roll it slowly with a medium weight roller.

Within a reasonable period, longer or shorter according to the temperature, but usually in 10 days to three weeks, the young grass will appear above the ground. Don't make the mistake of sprinkling it daily but if the upper inch or so of soil becomes obviously dry then water it freely

LAWNS

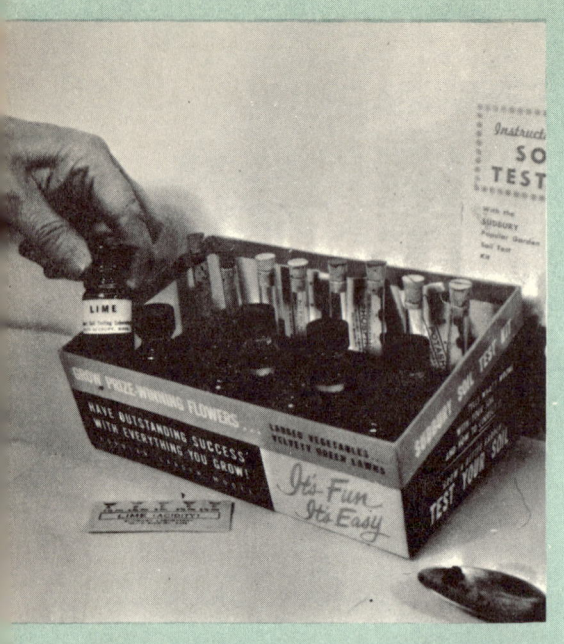

The bottle needed to determine if soil needs lime added to it or not - is taken from soil testing kit.

Then a quarter teaspoonful of dried air soil is put in the test tube. Test determines soil acidity.

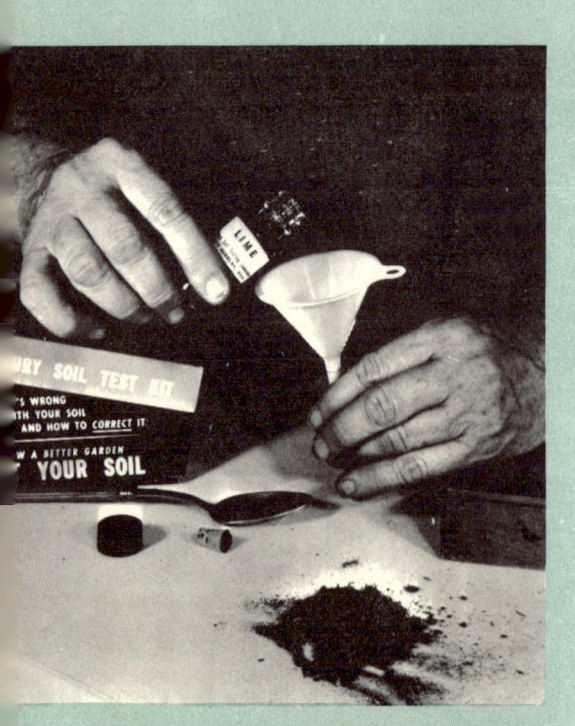

Test tube is then partly filled with some of the liquid from the bottle and thoroughly shaken.

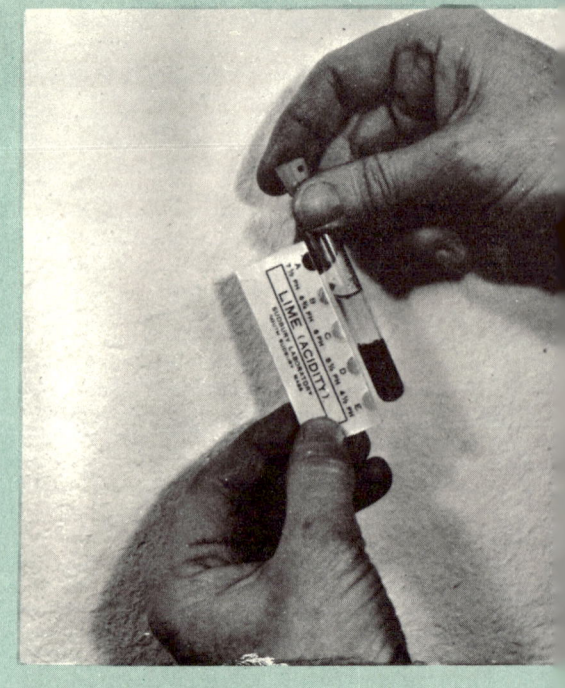

Liquid sets for several hours, then is checked with color chart for degree of acidity, alkalinity.

with a fine sprinkler adjusted so that it will not wash the surface soil away. Once the seed has started to germinate the young plants must not be permitted to suffer from lack of water. In the very young stages of the grass, the surface soil must never be allowed to get really dry but as the grass gets taller and stronger and as its roots strike deeper, watering can be less frequent but more water should be given at each application. Watering is only needed, of course, during dry periods.

When the grass is two inches tall or very slightly more cut it with a very sharp mower with the blades set at a height of one and three quarter inches. A mower with dull cutting knives will pull the plants out of the ground and cause much damage. Even with the best care there may be some bare spots in a lawn sown with seeds (particularly if sowing is done in the spring). These should be reseeded immediately they become apparent.

Best Lawn Making Season

Each year thousands of homeowners, either from ignorance of the fact that fall is the best lawn making season, or because of a determination to get their lawn started in the spring in spite of that, begin then. If you intend to make a new lawn in spring above all else get started early. The earlier you start the more likely your lawn is to succeed and the less work you will have in establishing it. By early I mean as soon as the ground is dry enough to work and well before the last frost. Under no circumstances, however, walk upon your soil and work it when it is a wet condition.

Having decided to make your lawn in spring be prepared to give it most excellent care during its first summer. If you can nurse it along through this period the probabilities are that you will establish good turf by the fall. If the soil is well prepared no further fertilizing during the first summer will be necessary but attention to watering and to mowing are of first importance. The rules are simple. Do not cut the grass too short. Permit it to grow to a height of about two and one half inches. Each time it does this cut it to two inches. Use a sharp mower. During dry weather water the lawn regularly and thoroughly at about weekly intervals; don't give nightly sprinklings. Exercise persistent care to eradicate weeds. If you do all these things faithfully, by September you will have a good lawn which, with a little additional feeding then and perhaps a little reseeding, will get a splendid start the following spring.

Weeds in spring-sown lawn often grow at greater speed than the grass. If many weed seeds were present in the soil you will soon see obnoxious plants developing and perhaps towering above the surrounding grasses. Eradicate them immediately. With a young, newly-seeded lawn hand weeding is the best method. It may be tedious but is effective if persisted in, and it gives the real gardener a certain sense of satisfaction to tug out pestiferous weeds and destroy them. When weeding a new lawn lay down boards to stand on so that the young grass is not unduly injured.

If you are not able to get your soil into good condition in time for sowing early don't make your permanent lawn in the spring. Instead, start planting a temporary spring lawn. With very little soil preparation you can do this. Simply attend to the grading, add whatever humus you can and a little fertilizer and lime if needed and sow the ground with Italian or domestic ryegrass. Rake it lightly into the surface but don't go to the same trouble you will when you make your permanent lawn. The ryegrass soon germinates and makes a fine looking lawn through summer. You may mow it, walk on it and use it just as you would an ordinary lawn but it will not be permanent and if you do nothing to replace it, will die out within a year or so. But this temporary lawn will crowd out weeds, and when you dig or plow it under before you sow your new lawn in mid-September, the tops and the roots of the ryegrass will add valuable humus to the soil and improve it tremendously in preparation for the permanent lawn. •

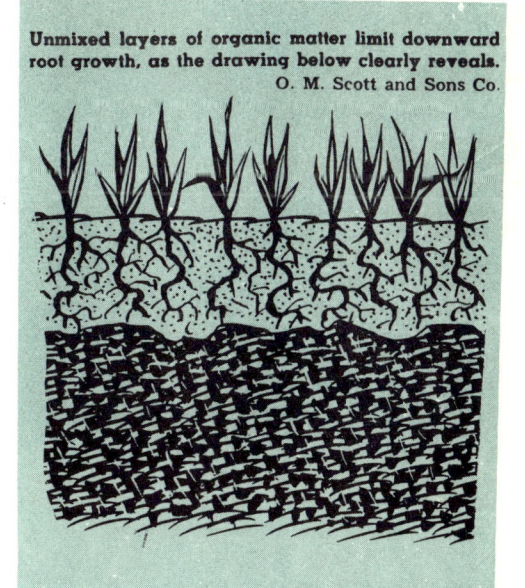

Unmixed layers of organic matter limit downward root growth, as the drawing below clearly reveals.
O. M. Scott and Sons Co.

LAWNS

TURF LAYING
... the quickest way to a lawn

Brown Brothers
Lawn like that shown above was built by setting in turfs of grass as shown in photo across page. Lay turfs on moderately firm ground with even surface.

THE QUICKEST way of making a lawn is by laying turf. If you have to buy it, it is also the most expensive. But sometimes turf can be obtained from another part of the garden. Possibly a building, a paved terrace or a path is to be put where lawn exists and the grass sod can be removed and used elsewhere. New beds and borders cut in lawns also provide supplies.

A lawn made of turfs looks well from the beginning and is usable almost immediately. If properly installed and given adequate care it may be put down successfully any time from spring to fall.

For clothing slopes, a lawn made of turfs has the advantage of checking erosion immediately. A border of turf provides excellent well-defined margins to a lawn, the major center part of which is sown from seed after the turfs are laid.

Turf is easy to cut and install once the best techniques are mastered. The sod should be at least three years old. Choose a time when the soil is moist. Mow the grass closely. Then with an edger (a tool with a long handle and a crescent shaped blade) slice the sod into squares of appropriate size (12-inch sides are generally suitable). Use a garden line stretched tightly across the grass or the edge of a plank lying flat on the turf as a guide for cutting the lines straight. If you have no edger you can make do with a spade for slicing the sod into squares.

For cutting beneath the sods so that each square may be lifted cleanly and intact, you may use a spade, too, but if you have any considerable amount to lift it will pay to obtain a sod or turf cutter. This is a sort of long handled spade with a sharp cutting blade and a shaft set at such an angle that the blade can be easily pushed horizontally beneath the sod by an operator who bends over and pushes the handle at about knee level or slightly higher. Before cutting, the thickness of the finished turfs should be decided upon. One and a half to two inches is suitable. Cut the turfs slightly thicker than the finished dimension.

As each turf is lifted, place it grass side down in a tray as deep as the finished sod is to be thick. This tray should have three sides only, the fourth being left open to permit the sod to be slipped in and out.

Let the side of the tray opposite the open side rest against a "stop" of some kind to prevent the tray from slipping, then with an old scythe blade or a two-handled knife having a blade longer than the width of the tray, cut off all surplus soil and roots by

LAWNS

Before cutting and lifting of turf sections, mow grass closely so that turf becomes compact unit.

Using edge of a board or a garden line, cut the turf into 12-inch squares with an edging tool.

Use sod cutter to slice under each turf. Cutter's blade permits turfs to be cut evenly, effortlessly.

standing in front of the closed end of the tray and drawing the blade toward you while it rests across the tray's edges. In this way all turfs are cut to a uniform thickness, and laying them evenly is greatly facilitated.

Prepare the soil on which turf is to be laid exactly as for seeding but with its surface as much lower than the finish grade as the sods are thick. Make sure that the soil is moderately compacted and then loosened slightly on its surface by raking. This helps to assure a better bond between sods and soil.

Lay the sods in rows with the joints staggered like joints between bricks in a wall. If the sods have been well cut and carefully handled little or no packing of soil beneath them will be needed, but should they have lost some of their soil and be thinner in spots than the required thickness, pack sufficient soil beneath them as the work proceeds to bring them perfectly level. Butt the sods closely together and set them firmly in position by giving each several blows with the back of the spade. When several square yards have been laid give them an additional firming by beating them with a wooden tamper. Then water thoroughly with a

LAWNS

Lift the turfs as they are cut and transfer each, grass side down, to a shallow, three-sided tray.

Using a long knife or an old scythe blade, carefully slice off all the excess soil and roots.

Tip the turfs, now of even thickness, out of the tray. Handle gently when transferring to ground.

Place turf on well-packed, even-surface ground. In the process, tap turf lightly against others.

sprinkler giving a fine spray. The following day, or as soon as the grass has dried, sprinkle enough sifted soil over the surface so that when brushed down it fills any crevices or openings that show between the turfs. Next spread a little grass seed along the joints and in any spots where the grass is not too thick and brush it in.

Care of a turf-laid lawn is simple. It must never be permitted to dry out during its first season. During its first month, if the weather is dry, it should be soaked every second or third day. It may need rolling once or twice in its early weeks. On heavy soil newly laid turfs tend to heave out of position during winter. It is better to turf such soils in spring or late summer rather than fall. On steep slopes it is a good plan to drive pegs into some of the turfs. These will hold all the turfs in position until they have rooted firmly into the soil beneath them. If this is not done they may slide down the slope under the influence of rain or frost. •

LAWNS

Turfs are packed into place by smacking tops of them soundly with the back of a spade or shovel.

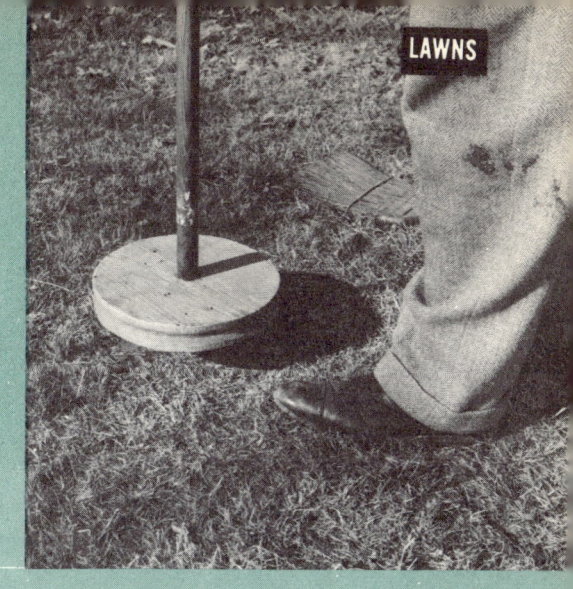

When a reasonable area has been covered with turf, ram it down with wood tamper, then water.

After grass is dry, spread enough sifted top soil to fill in crevices between turfs, then work it in with a broom. A little grass seed may also be added.

Here a steep bank is undergoing a job of turf laying. Banks made of turfs are not subject to the erosion which often results if new grass is sown.

LAWNS

STOLONS, SPRIGS AND PLUGS

... plant them for new grass

SOME GRASSES spread rapidly by creeping stems or stolons. It is quite practicable to establish good turf by planting small pieces of them. These take root and, if planted closely enough together, give rise to plants that soon touch and form unbroken turf. Grasses that may be propagated in this manner are chiefly subtropical kinds such as Zoysia, St. Augustine, Centipede and Bermuda. In addition there is the cool-climate creeping bent.

Creeping bent grass grows readily if the stems it forms so plentifully at or below

LAWNS

(Photo across page) Meyer Z-52 Zoysia is often used as strips of sod, can be cut into plugs by knife or pruning shears. (Photo above) Zoysia set into holes made by trowel.

the soil surface are cut into small pieces and planted. This is the method used by many golf course superintendents to produce perfect turf for putting greens. The turf so formed is extremely uniform. Here's how to go about getting it.

Chop the stolons into pieces half an inch to an inch long and scatter them over soil that has been prepared as thoroughly as it should be for seed sowing. Make sure it is firm and raked smooth before you distribute the stolons. Sow them as you would seed, but not as thickly. The pieces should be spaced about half an inch apart. One and a half bushels of chopped stolons are sufficient for 1,000 square feet. Make sure they are distributed evenly and press them into the surface by rolling. Spread a covering of fine soil, one quarter to one half inch thick, over the stolons and roll again. An easy way of doing this is to lay a flexible steel door mat over the newly distributed stolons, heap fine soil on it, then, with the back of a rake, spread it level with the tops of the treads of the mat. Remove any surplus soil, lift the mat carefully (a two

1919

LAWNS

Lawn Grass Development Co.
Lawn is plugged by setting up guide lines 12 inches apart, putting plugs along line at one-foot intervals.

person job) and treat the adjoining area in the same way. Repeat this until the whole planted surface is covered with soil. Then roll lightly.

It is very important to water a lawn newly planted in this manner often enough to keep the soil moist.

Where a lawn of a kind exists, and the soil is known to be good to a depth of six or eight inches, it is possible to establish a turf of creeping bent without spading or turning it over. Simply destroy the grass already there. This you may do by skimming it off very thinly with a spade or by applying a very heavy dressing of sulphate of ammonia. Scratch the surface with a rake then sow the stolons and treat as advised above.

Important Considerations

Before beginning a creeping bent lawn consider these facts. It is more costly in labor than making other type lawns from seed. If you have to buy the stolons (possibly you can obtain them from an established lawn without cost) they are more expensive than seed. Lawns of creeping bent require a tremendous amount of upkeep—frequent mowing, watering, fertilizing, top-dressing, etc. They are really for specialists.

One other point. Seaside bent is a kind of bent grass that creeps and can be easily raised from seeds. It produces a turf almost as good as the Washington and Metropolitan strains of true creeping bent which can only be increased by the use of stolons.

Sprigs are young rooted shoots—pieces of stolon with leaves and roots attached. Lawns of subtropical grasses, Bermuda, Carpet, St. Augustine and Centipede, may be established by planting such shoots at distances of six to nine inches apart. This is called sprigging.

In preparation for sprigging, the soil is made ready as for sowing seed. It is then well watered and the sprigs (each consisting of several joints and shoots) are planted with a dibber (pointed stick) and are firmed in place. After planting, the area is again well watered.

Plugs are pieces of sod, one and a half or two inches or so in diameter, of creeping grasses. When planted, they quickly grow together and cover the ground. They differ from sprigs in that each consists of many rather than few of shoots and includes the soil in which the roots grow (sprigs carry little or no soil with them). Zoysia grasses are the ones chiefly propagated by plugs. They make good turf sooner when grown in this way rather than from sprigs.

Make the soil ready as you would for seeding. Plant the plugs with a trowel, six to twelve inches apart, setting the surface of each level with or very slightly below the soil surface. Make the soil about the roots firm. Water thoroughly after planting. Old lawns may be plugged with Zoysia which will gradually intermingle with established grasses and may take over entirely eventually. •